Official EFT™ from A to Z

Official EFT™ from A to Z

How to Use Both Forms of

Emotional Freedom Techniques

for Self-Healing

Gabriëlle Rutten
Author

Gary Craig
Co-author

Zion Publishing

a boutique publisher

English Translation: Alison Brock & Gabriëlle Rutten

English Editor: Helle Gylling

Cover Design: Taco Claas

Why the Dandelion? The humble dandelion is a symbol of hope, love and happiness. The bright yellow color represents the sun shining on all the good deeds in your life. The black seeds are said to carry wishes for prosperity and new beginnings as they fly into the sky. They can even be seen as a symbol of a free-spirited soul, of innocence and playfulness. Dandelions offer a symbol of hope and resilience. They are able to survive just about anything, including harsh winters, pollution, drought, being stepped on or run over by cars. They can quickly bounce back from adversity and continue to grow.

Credit background photo: Johannes Plenio / Unsplash

Library of Congress Control Number:
2023906011

ISBN: 979-8-9856705-5-4

Published by
Zion Publishing
Des Moines, Iowa, USA

There is only one word that frees us from the weight and pain of life.
That word is love.

Sophocles, Greek poet, 496 BCE – 406 BCE

Contents

Disclaimer

EFT is achieving remarkable clinical results and the scientific evidence base is growing steadily. All over the world, professionals are using EFT as an intervention, and lay people are using it as a self-help tool. EFT has been an effective technique ever since it was first introduced in 1995. There are, however, natural reactions that may occur when stressful events are processed. This is explained in Chapter 2.

This book provides an alternative explanation of the root cause of psychological issues and physical illnesses and the way these issues and the symptoms of such illnesses can be managed. The information in this book is provided for educational and informational purposes only. It is not in any way intended as a substitute for medical advice or therapy or the legal equivalent thereof (including diagnosis or treatment).

Neither Gary Craig nor Gabriëlle Rutten is a licensed health professional, and the information given in this book is not advice of any kind; in particular it is not medical or clinical advice. If you have or believe you have any medical condition, seek the advice of a qualified physician or health provider. Never delay seeking professional medical advice because of something you have read in this book.

Each person (layperson and professional) must take complete responsibility for their use of EFT and any information in this book. The authors make no representations or warranties of any kind, expressed or implied, as to the information in this book and disclaim all liability for any loss and/or damages in connection with its use. If results or progress is not forthcoming, you may need the assistance of an experienced EFT professional who is certified in Official EFT. For all information regarding Official EFT, including a list of certified EFT professionals, please refer to the websites of Gary Craig (emofree.com) and Gabriëlle Rutten (official-eft.nl).

Foreword

As the founder of EFT, I am pleased and grateful not only for the interest and enthusiasm with which EFT has been received but also for the fact that EFT has been used successfully as a method of healing by many people around the world since its inception in 1995. The results speak for themselves.

Until 2014, only the tapping form of EFT was available. Instead of writing a book, I created an EFT Tapping manual in 1995 that I made available for free on my website (www.emofree.com), and that has been downloaded over a million times. You can now find this in the section titled Gold Standard EFT Tapping Tutorial on my website.[1] For a long time, I believed that this manual was sufficient. However, EFT Tapping has been imitated many times since its inception by people who have not been trained by me and who have given it their own interpretation. There are now over 1000 books published on EFT Tapping, none of which are mine. Nor has there been any consultation with me about the content of these books. This has, unfortunately, created a lot of confusion because the numerous interpretations of EFT Tapping are different from the original EFT Tapping I teach and from each other. There is no consistency nor any regulation as to its use. More often than not, EFT is not explained and taught with the depth that is necessary to achieve real and lasting results, leading some people to dismiss this valuable self help tool simply because they were not instructed properly.

Of course, I am happy that there is so much enthusiasm about EFT, but there is a growing need for clarity. I also want to use this opportunity to formally introduce my most recent advancement in EFT, namely Optimal EFT and working with The Unseen Therapist™, which I have been using and teaching since 2014. I have written an introductory book called *The Unseen Therapist*, which can be downloaded for free from my website.[2] The results that can be achieved with The Unseen Therapist are even more

---

1   https://emofree.com/english/eft-tapping-tutorial-en.html
2   https://emofree.com/unseen-therapist/read-this-first.html

impressive than with EFT Tapping. Unfortunately, it appears that even this form of EFT is already being imitated by people who have not obtained the requisite training in Official EFT™, which is a term I now use to encompass both Gold Standard EFT (EFT Tapping) and Optimal EFT.

In short, I believe that clarity is urgently needed to ensure that those interested in EFT are provided with the necessary information and guidance needed to use it successfully and achieve long-lasting results. To this end, I have designated a number of centers that may use the name Official EFT and provide education in it. You can find them on my website (www.emofree.com). People can contact these centers if they wish to learn the official form of EFT in English and various other languages. Nowadays, I personally focus primarily on Optimal EFT, but all my centers offer, or will offer in the near future, training and/or certification in both forms of Official EFT so that none of the knowledge and practice of EFT will be lost.

This book is the first official manual for both forms of EFT, written in consultation with me. I am thrilled with the results and heartily recommend it as part of your EFT library. Gabriëlle Rutten is the director of the Gary Craig Official EFT Training Center in the Dutch Language. She has combined her sound knowledge of EFT with a unique perspective on the emotional root causes of physical and psychological problems, which adds new insights to the EFT process. Gabriëlle was previously a medical doctor but decided to stop practicing conventional medicine and now uses only Official EFT to assist clients to resolve the underlying root causes of emotional issues and physical illnesses. I hope this book will help you and I express the wish that Official EFT may continue to contribute to the healing of the world.

Gary Craig
Sea Ranch, California, October 2022

Preface

My story

My journey into medicine started with my love of biology in school. I was fascinated with how the human body works and, at some point, I decided to become a doctor. I never imagined, however, that after spending years studying and practicing medicine, I would end up abandoning conventional medicine altogether and adopting a radically new approach to healing using EFT.

My studies in medical school were interesting enough, but I soon realized that, apart from studying anatomy and how the body works, the majority of our training involved matching the correct medication with bodily symptoms, as opposed to trying to identify the root cause and taking steps to resolve that. Still, when I graduated cum laude from medical school in 1988, I was eager to put everything I had learned into practice. However, I quickly became dissatisfied with my work as a doctor because of the tendency towards over-medicalization of illness (more medical care is applied to a health problem than is required). Also, I became disillusioned by the fact that the medical practice is divided into so many specialties, each one focusing on ever smaller parts of the whole person. This fragmented way of doing medicine did not make sense to me.

After 4 years of clinical research in internal medicine, I decided to practice occupational medicine, which I preferred as I was able to look at what a person (as a whole) could still do, instead of focusing on disease and disability. Doing this work helped me really understand first-hand how significant a role stress plays in our lives. After a while, I began to see a connection between certain types of stress and emotionally charged situations on the one hand and the resulting physical and emotional symptoms on the other hand. Yet, like other fields of medicine, occupational medicine focuses primarily on the solutions offered by conventional medicine, namely medication and surgery. I was more interested in finding a holistic approach to healing, so after ten years in occupational medicine, I became determined to find a better way to target the negative emotions that have such a huge impact on our health. Over the years, I have been inspired by the work of Joe Dispenza, Bruce Lipton, Eckhart Tolle, Bessel van der Kolk, Peter Levine, Anita Moorjani, Pim van Lommel, Rupert Sheldrake, Milton Erickson, Ryke Geerd Hamer and others. They have helped me shift from the old paradigm of conventional medicine to a whole new way of looking at health and disease, and cause and effect.

In 2002, I discovered EFT Tapping (now called Gold Standard EFT), developed by Gary Craig, who had begun his education in engineering at Stanford, but who went on to develop EFT. It was so very different from what I had learned as a medical doctor. Intrigued, I began to study all of Gary Craig's videos on EFT that were available at the time. I began to focus on my own issues and the results were quite remarkable. For example, I used to take strong medication for my frequent migraine headaches, but after using EFT for only 3 months, I stopped getting migraines altogether. A few months later, I was free of lower back pain that had plagued me for over 20 years. All this in a matter of months! These remarkable results for my own issues really piqued my interest as a medical doctor and inspired me to dive into EFT in earnest. I became certified in EFT, and over time, I completely abandoned conventional medicine. I deregistered as an MD and shifted my entire practice to using only EFT with my patients (whom I now call my clients). I help my clients resolve their stress and negative emotions with EFT and teach them how to use EFT by themselves. The results are much better than what I could get with pharmaceutical drugs and I have never used my prescription pad again. It is such a relief for me to be able to help clients find the real cause of their problems instead of just treating their symptoms.

In 2008, I began training other professionals in the use of EFT because of the obvious benefits of this approach. Over the years, I have stayed in touch with Gary Craig and kept my training in line with his developments.

My first book, *EFT – Emotional Freedom Techniques – From A to Z*, was published in 2009. In this (Dutch) book, co-author Henk van der Veen and I described the original tapping form of EFT.

In 2011, Gary Craig began referring to EFT Tapping as Gold Standard EFT to distinguish it from the many other forms of EFT that have proliferated since its inception. Then, in 2014, Gary introduced Optimal EFT, a new advancement of EFT that is a meditative process and spiritual in nature. Gold Standard EFT and Optimal EFT are the two forms of EFT developed by Gary Craig, the founder of EFT, and together, they are now known as Official EFT™.

In 2015 and 2016, I trained with Gary Craig to master Optimal EFT. This close working relationship culminated in Gary Craig appointing my center as one of the Gary Craig Official EFT Training Centers in 2016. That same year, I was also introduced to the work of Dr. Ryke Geerd Hamer, a German doctor of internal medicine. Hamer discovered the connection between emotionally shocking events and certain reactions in the body and found that many of the symptoms we have been taught to think of as disease symptoms are actually healing symptoms. Using Hamer's discoveries, it is possible to determine the type of emotional conflict that is at the root of various symptoms and diseases, and that can then help you identify the specific, negatively charged events you need to resolve with EFT. – They provide me with additional insights that I use to guide my clients in the direction of healing.

I am more convinced than ever that it is mind over matter and that our negative emotions not only contribute to our ill health – they are the central cause of illness! In the 35 years or so that I have been helping people heal, I have found ample evidence to show that the body does not do anything on its own. It is the mind that directs the body. The body itself is neutral. This is very different from the conventional view, but bear with me as I explain it further in this book. This new view is backed by science. All I ask is that you keep an open mind and try it out for yourself. Humans evolve because a few individuals are brave enough to see things differently, regardless of what mainstream tries to dictate.

This journey has led me to work with clients using EFT exclusively and to offer training and certification in Gold Standard EFT Tapping since 2008, and in Optimal EFT since 2018. I also offer numerous EFT training courses with a particular focus on chronic physical issues, trauma and how to use Hamer's insights in combination with EFT. I teach not only EFT practitioners but also doctors, psychotherapists, psychiatrists, psychologists and other healers who want to integrate EFT into their practice, as well as people who simply want to use EFT for their own issues.

This Book

In this new book, I describe both forms of EFT. We will look at the background of each form, give more insight into the working mechanisms and explain how the basic protocols work. I have written this book in consultation with Gary Craig, the founder of EFT, gratefully making use of everything I have learned from him, including all the material on his website, the Optimal EFT webinars and our many conversations. Even though I wrote the book, I will often use the terms we and us, because my views and explanations are largely based on his ideas. In this sense, the book is written by both of us and I consider Gary Craig to be my co-author. It is an honor to introduce you to Official EFT™ in collaboration with the founder of EFT.

Gary Craig and I have completely different backgrounds and complement each other well. He is an engineer trained at Stanford University. I have a medical background as a physician, and I am now the director of the Dutch Gary Craig Official EFT Training Center. We both have many years of experience in providing EFT sessions to individuals and groups and also providing EFT training to laypeople and professionals.

The Outline of this Book

This book shows how effective EFT is in addressing emotional problems and chronic stress so that you – literally – can achieve emotional freedom. The body and mind are closely interrelated. If you are doing well mentally, it is likely that you will also have fewer, if any, physical symptoms and vice versa. EFT is now making a significant impact in the world, and it is our desire to give you the opportunity to learn the basic protocols of both forms of Official EFT™ because they have been proven to be effective. We hope that you too will benefit from them. We have written this book in such a way that a layperson can learn how to use the techniques as a self-help tool. But this book can also be used as a reference book by EFT professionals.

In Part 1, we explain the causes of stress-related issues, how EFT works and how to apply both forms of EFT, so that you will know exactly how to use it. In explaining the causes of stress-related problems, I refer to the Five Biological Laws of Nature founded by Ryke Geerd Hamer, because I consider his findings to be some of the most well-documented medical discoveries that explain the mind-body connection.

In Part 2 of the book, I provide many examples and tips from my EFT practice, based on my 20+ years of experience with clients. I also provide additional explanations derived from Hamer's work. Part 2 will help inspire you to learn how to identify the underlying emotional causes of your issues and how to address them with EFT. Even if your specific issue is not in this book, you will find many examples and explanations of other problems that you can simply adapt and apply to your own issue.

If you apply EFT properly, you will soon see and feel the results. If you use EFT daily and muster the discipline to clear out old negative events and traumas, the results can be permanent. In the near future, a workbook will follow in which we will offer you even more support. However, we encourage you to start with this book as it provides you with the foundation that you need. We would also like to point out that everything described in this book is based on real-life cases.

Reader's Guide

We recommend that you first read Part 1 all the way through. Once you have studied Part 1, you will understand how to apply EFT to your problems, and you can then use Part 2 for additional inspiration. In Appendix 3, you will find the diseases and symptoms covered in this book from A to Z. It is best to study Part 2 in its entirety to gain a good understanding of how to approach problems by looking for the underlying emotional cause.

I wish you an abundance of emotional freedom and hope you can resolve your blocks to the essence of life: giving and receiving love.

Gabriëlle Rutten
Härnösand, Sweden, October 2022

Acknowledgments

It was a great honor for me to work with Gary Craig to bring this book to fruition, and I hope I have done justice to his EFT legacy. I dedicate this book to him.

The only reason this book is available in English is because of two angels who descended from the Heavens and offered their help: Alison Brock and Helle Gylling. I initially used a translation program to convert my first draft of the Dutch book into English. However, the result was such illegible gibberish, that even I had to keep going back to my original Dutch text to make sense of what I was reading. After I reworked it into at least a readable, coarse version of English, Alison performed miracles in rewriting it with proper verbiage and syntax, adding a degree of clarity to the text that made it better and stronger than the original. Then, Helle carefully reviewed it, polishing the text and ensuring that it spoke to the desired audience. Her countless hours of editing resulted in a smooth and easy-to-read manuscript. My gratitude to both of you has no end. Everything that reads well in this book is their accomplishment, and the remaining bloopers are my own.

As always, Taco Claas is my rock in the background, and his help with all the technical aspects and the illustrations was indispensable. Without his support, this book would not have been possible.

I thank Karin van Baelen and Mies Kloos for sharing their knowledge about Hamer's work with me.

Finally, another miracle happened: my good friend Robbie Dunlap, author of *Dogfish Island*, helped me find the perfect publisher: Mary Nilsen of Zion Publishing. She helped me create the interior design, with great patience, precision and wisdom. Mary's and Solveig Nilsen-Goodin's critical reading helped me strengthen my message. Thank you.

Part 1

1 | INTRODUCTION

The more original a discovery, the more obvious it seems afterwards.

Arthur Koestler, Hungarian-born British author, 1905 – 1983

What Is EFT and What Is it Used for?

EFT (Emotional Freedom Techniques) is a technique for releasing negative emotions and limiting beliefs. EFT is an easy self-help tool, and, in the hands of a skilled professional, it can be used to successfully resolve the most intense traumas and stress-related problems. This book describes the application of both forms of Official EFT™ founded by Gary Craig, Gold Standard EFT (or EFT Tapping) and Optimal EFT, the latest advancement of EFT.

This book focuses on using both forms of EFT as a self-help tool. We believe that EFT deserves a place alongside other available techniques because EFT is radically different and surprisingly effective. Many self-help tools (and therapies) focus on behavior, positive thinking and/or gaining insight into your issues. EFT focuses directly on resolving the root cause of the problem, i.e., the negative emotions (or stress) underlying the problem. Properly applied, EFT can be used to permanently sever the connection between a stress trigger and the conditioned stress response. In other words, EFT ensures that stressful past events no longer have a negative impact on your experience and behavior in the here and now. Your normal emotional response remains, but you will no longer experience the excessive, over-the-top (and unnecessary) negative emotional reactions.

With EFT, gaining insight into your problem is not a goal in itself, but it is nevertheless a significant additional benefit. However, understanding where your issues and problematic behaviors originated does not resolve the issues. This is where EFT dives deeper than other techniques, as EFT can be used to sever the link between a stressful event that you have experienced in the past and the negative emotion that is (automatically) activated when you are (sub)consciously confronted with something that reminds you of that past event. By severing that link and clearing the stuck negative emotions, a space opens up in which you can respond more appropriately to what you are encountering in the present moment, enabling you to have a completely different experience. With EFT, you can free yourself emotionally, so that old stressors and negative emotions from past events no longer have a hold over you.

In short, EFT helps you to resolve the negative emotions from previous experiences that are stuck in your subconscious mind, so that you can respond to what is happening in the present moment, rather than being involuntarily carried away by these unresolved negative emotions from the past that aggravate your current experience. This does not mean that you will no longer experience anger or sadness or other negative emotions. The key is that once you have cleared the negative emotions from the past, there is no longer a connection to all the previous similar situations and negative emotions that tend to compound your anger or sadness and make your emotional reaction to the current trigger worse, bigger or more intense, than it would be otherwise. You clear out your emotional storehouse so that you can simply deal with what is going on in this moment. And that is very liberating!

Frequently Asked Questions

Is EFT for me?

EFT works for all problems in which stress plays a role. Do you have any negative emotions or limiting beliefs? For instance:

- I am not worthy, I do not count, I am not good enough.
- I am not attractive, I am too fat, I am too thin.
- I am too shy for that, I am easily intimidated.
- I cannot control my emotions, I am easily irritated, I am impatient.
- I am too stupid for that, I cannot do that, I would not dare do that.

Or do you suffer from (subconscious) memories of unpleasant events, such as:

- Child abuse (physical or emotional), sexual abuse;
- Domestic violence, quarrels, fights, divorce;
- Accidents, operations, war traumas;
- Labor or employment disputes;
- Witnessing or experiencing violence.

Or are you suffering from (chronic) symptoms, illnesses or problematic behaviors, such as:

- Headaches, migraines;
- Chronic fatigue, burnout;
- Depressive symptoms;
- Anxiety disorders, PTSD, phobias;
- Back pain, rheumatism, neck pain, or other skeletal pains;
- Addictions (smoking, alcohol, other drugs, food addictions or any out-of-control behavior).

If you are dealing with any of the issues above, then it would definitely be beneficial for you to start using EFT. These are all beliefs, emotions and issues that can block you from being your true self and being able to respond to situations in a calm and appropriate manner. Perhaps you feel limited, inhibited or unable to change certain behaviors. Maybe you cannot stop smoking, or you are eating too much, or you are too scared to speak in public. You may be stuck in a vicious circle of limiting beliefs and/or physical issues and pains. These are all very good reasons to learn EFT so that you can overcome them!

What makes EFT so different?

What makes EFT unique is that you can use this simple technique to address the root cause of your problem. The main benefit is that your past negative experiences will no longer play a role in your life.

Let us look at an example of an emotional issue: a woman got divorced a few years ago and it was a bitter separation with many emotional arguments. Every time she thinks about the divorce (for example because of her children, birthdays, alimony or child support) it evokes unpleasant emotions, such as anger, sadness, a sense of powerlessness or a feeling of abandonment. While it is helpful to gain a deep understanding as to why she feels these emotions, such insights do not make the negative emotions go away. It may also be helpful to talk about the divorce and get support, but that does not make the emotions disappear either. She may feel better if she manages to pick herself up and start to enjoy her life again, but she will still experience negative emotions when confronted with any situation or thought that reminds her of the divorce. Using EFT, it is possible to neutralize those past experiences by clearing out the underlying negative emotions. Sometimes, the emotions resolve quickly or immediately, other times more slowly and only after applying EFT for an extended period of time. But success is almost always assured, provided that EFT is applied properly. Once the negative emotions around the divorce have been released with EFT, this woman will find that when a thought comes up about the divorce or she runs into her ex-partner again, she will feel free, neutral or sometimes even positive or forgiving. That then becomes her natural automatic reaction. It has nothing to do with pretending, being above it or being more mature. She is able to remain relaxed and calm because she is simply no longer triggered.

Let us also look at an example of a physical issue. Perhaps you often suffer from headaches. If you take the time to identify the situations that cause you stress and worry and result in a headache and then use EFT to release the stuck negative emotions you feel in these situations, you will soon notice an improvement in your headaches. You may also need to look at the circumstances and perhaps make some changes (like changing jobs or ending a relationship) before you can reduce the stress permanently. However, properly applying EFT enables you to resolve the stress faster and more effectively. It helps you identify and address the emotional causes of your headaches, which enables you to think clearly and calmly about the situation and make appropriate decisions, instead of making rash decisions in a state of stress that may make the situation and your symptoms even worse. Most people completely underestimate how much they suffer from their own unresolved, chronic stress. When you resolve this stress, a whole new world opens up for you.

Will I stop feeling emotions if I do a lot of EFT?

If you use EFT, you will not stop feeling emotions. Your ability to feel remains fully intact. Emotions are part of our human intelligence, and they are meant to help us navigate our way through life. Notice how you feel in any given situation. Are you having a positive emotional reaction? Do you feel happy, joyful, cheerful and/or peaceful? Excellent! Continue to do whatever you are doing and do it as often as possible. However, if you do not feel right or good, then you need to work out what is going on. Is there a real external threat? Or is your reaction caused by your own internal thoughts?

Suppose the external threat is a car coming at you at great speed while you are crossing the street. In such a situation, your fight, flight or freeze response turns on in less than a split second so you can get off the road to safety. If this was a very intense experience, then the details of that event are stored in your long-term memory for next time. Suppose you had an earlier experience of a near-fatal crossing, prior to this event. In that case, your fight, flight or freeze response might already be turned on before crossing the road and your reaction to the approaching car may be more intense. However, there is no need to immediately go into a full fight, flight or freeze mode or a blind panic whenever you need to cross a road. That reaction is over the top, because, with your normal level of awareness, you can cross the road safely. With EFT, you can neutralize this and previous experiences, so that you can cross the road calmly, without unnecessary stress. You may think: *But is it not useful that I remain afraid so that I can react quickly if something comes at me suddenly?* No. This is a big misunderstanding. You can learn from previous experiences and be sufficiently alert to cross roads safely without having to experience an intense feeling of stress whenever you do so. EFT can play a big role in resolving this kind of unnecessary stress.

In addition to feeling stressed about an actual physical threat, it is also possible to experience an intense negative emotional reaction whenever you feel threatened psychologically, even when you are not actually threatened. For example, say that someone is strongly critical of you. That may trigger your fight, flight or freeze response, even though you are not in any danger. Here, EFT plays just as important a role. If you use EFT to deal with these kinds of situations, you will be able to listen calmly to the criticism, determine whether there is any truth in it or whether it has more to do with the other person and respond appropriately, instead of taking offense, losing your temper and reacting in a way that you may later regret.

How do I use EFT?

How to use EFT will be explained in detail in Chapters 2 and 5. By way of illustration, and to give you an idea, suppose you had a rather unpleasant conversation with a friend. When you return home, you may still feel upset or irritated. While you are immersed in this feeling, you can immediately apply the basic EFT protocol (either EFT Tapping or Optimal EFT) to release that negative emotion. After doing so, you can test to see if the conversation still triggers you by pretending to be back in the conversation and noticing how you feel. You need to relive the moment as vividly as possible and determine what negative emotion (if any) is still present. You then use EFT again to resolve any remaining emotion and test again. Continue this process until you no longer feel anything when you relive the moment, which brings this issue to a conclusion.

By applying EFT, your experience of this unpleasant conversation has become neutral. Of course, this does not mean that you will not have any negative reactions the next time you see that friend. You will likely need to do more EFT, to address not only the emotional response to this one interaction but also the underlying reasons that caused you to react emotionally. If you have been in the same situation with this friend previously, you will also need to address some of those other interactions with him or her using the same process. It is extremely effective when you use EFT immediately after an unpleasant experience, as you then resolve the emotional charge of that moment, often within a few minutes, instead of storing it in your subconscious mind. Moreover, if you train yourself to deal with these kinds of experiences as soon as possible, you will find that EFT will work increasingly faster and more easily.

The example given above is a relatively minor unpleasant event that is easy to address on your own. In this book, we provide many examples that help you learn how to apply EFT to your own smaller issues. We do not recommend that you use EFT to work on intense and complex traumas with only the knowledge of the basic protocols of EFT in this book. If you have experienced major traumatic events or suffer from complex chronic symptoms, it is advisable to seek the support of a well-trained EFT professional.[1]

Are the effects of EFT permanent?

The effects of EFT can be permanent if you apply it properly and thoroughly. If you successfully use EFT to sever the connection between your negative emotions and the related past events from which they arose, then you will certainly feel a great sense of emotional freedom. It does not change what happened, but you will no longer feel those negative emotions when you think about a past event, or when something else in your current environment reminds you of that event. If you use EFT consistently on all of the

---

1 https://emofree.com/practitioners.html | https://official-eft.nl/eft-behandelaars

significant past events that give rise to negative emotions, then you will permanently dissolve a huge collection of conditioned negative responses and stuck emotions. As a result, you will no longer be bound by those conditioned behavioral responses, but instead, you will be able to react to what is happening in the present moment, without being carried away by the negative emotions stored in your subconscious from your past experiences.

After applying EFT, you may notice that you are less easily angered or irritated, or you do not feel annoyed so quickly anymore, or perhaps you no longer easily feel criticized. In other words, your behavior may change from aggressive or passive to assertive. As you resolve more negative experiences and dissolve more negative, limiting beliefs with EFT, you will likely start to feel increasingly liberated, so that you can be your true self. You will have a better understanding of yourself and others and be more able to interact with others in a more loving and forgiving way. Imagine what the world would be like if we had all cleaned out our negative emotions and negative beliefs. We could, then, interact freely and openly with each other.

When it comes to physical issues and diseases, EFT is also extremely effective. Negative emotions and chronic stress play a major role in diseases in many ways. Mainstream medicine is increasingly recognizing the significant role that chronic stress plays. It is a major contributing factor (and oftentimes the cause) of many medical problems and ailments, and the connection between negative emotions and physical problems is receiving more and more attention. One impacts the other, and vice versa. That influence applies to everything from the common cold to bronchitis, from headaches to heart disease, from cancer to diabetes, from arthritis to rheumatism. EFT is a unique technique that you can use to make your issues become less of a problem and oftentimes completely disappear.

> **Whether you are dealing with psychological issues or physical problems, you may be able to obtain lasting results in a surprisingly large number of situations if you apply EFT properly and thoroughly.**

Does EFT work for everyone?

EFT works well for most people and is easy to learn if you have both an open mind and a curious mind. However, if you are unable to access your feelings and emotions, then it may not work as well as a self-help tool. In such a case, it would be advisable to consult a well-trained EFT profession-al. Similarly, if you have negative beliefs regarding the effectiveness of EFT or a conviction that EFT cannot work for you or your problem, or that it is simply too weird, then you would benefit from seeking the support of an EFT professional, who can help you overcome those beliefs.

Does EFT work for everything?

Gary Craig has said from the beginning: *Try it on everything.* You will nev-er know until you try. There is a Dutch saying: *No is what you have, yes is what you can get.* And it certainly cannot hurt to try EFT, because it has no side effects. You cannot do it too often or do it wrong in a way that could make something worse. At most, it simply does not work to resolve the issue or it does not work right away because you do not yet have a good enough grasp of exactly how to apply it. However, EFT, properly applied, does work for every stress-related issue. Of course, we are not claiming here that you can solve every problem and issue with EFT. But it is possible to significantly reduce your stress level with EFT and, in so doing, solve any number of physical and psychological issues, which can lead to a more loving, energetic, and fulfilled life.

Does EFT work immediately?

Usually, EFT does not work immediately. Based on the information available on the Internet about EFT, you may have received the false impression that EFT always works very quickly. Although we have personally experienced 'One-Minute Wonders' and witnessed the resolution of severe trauma within one to three sessions of EFT, it usually takes longer to achieve long-lasting results. Although EFT can be extremely fast and effective, that does not mean that a long-held issue will disappear entirely within one session. Some problems are complex and require skill, patience and perseverance to resolve permanently. Also, people frequently make a number of mistakes when applying EFT, mistakes that will hinder the ability to obtain quick and lasting results. We will identify and explain these mistakes in Chapters 2 and 5 so that you do not fall into the same traps.

Furthermore, while we have received many reports from people who have solved major problems by themselves using EFT as a self-help tool, we are also aware that not everyone can (or wants to) do this healing work on their own. In fact, we advise you not to work on severe trauma with only the knowledge of this book. When it comes to serious symptoms, major life issues, or traumas, it may be more beneficial to consult a well-trained EFT professional. EFT professionals can guide you through the entire process and provide you with the personalized support you need. They are better able to prioritize what needs to be dealt with first and what can be left untill later, enabling you to dive deep without causing additional trauma. In this way, you can obtain lasting results and truly overcome your issues, once and for all.

In Conclusion

With the help of the instructions and examples given in this book, you will learn to apply the basic protocols of both forms of Official EFT in a thorough manner. It is not difficult, but simply a matter of practicing and doing it as often as possible. Let us get started!

2 | THE FOUNDATION

Happy is he who has learned to see the causes of things,
the necessary interdependence of everything.

Vergilius, Roman poet, 70 BCE – 19 BCE

In this chapter, we will be examining the root causes of psychological issues and physical problems. This will pave the way for identifying the most
effective way of addressing such issues with EFT. We will also introduce a
number of foundational techniques that are key to properly applying both
forms of Official EFT. We recommend that you study this chapter thoroughly before moving on.

The Root Cause of Your Problem: Stress Is Learned Behavior

Experiencing any kind of problem (physical or psychological) in certain
situations indicates that your stress response has been activated and that
these situations are related to your problem.

Your problem may be a relationship issue, such as a dispute with a
friend, a family member, your employer, or even a stranger. It may be
low self-esteem, anxiety, depression or an eating disorder, or you may have
a phobia, such as a fear of spiders or public speaking. Or, your problem
may be physical, such as a headache or a backache, tinnitus or tonsilitis,
stomach ache or joint ache.

The correlation between a trigger and your stress response is often subconscious, so you may not even be aware that you have been triggered. Whether or not you are triggered depends on events in your past and the way you were conditioned to respond. For example, you may have seen your parent react in a frightened way to spiders, so you learned to be afraid of spiders. Once you are triggered, your stress response turns on automatically. The more often you experience certain situations that trigger the stress response, the stronger the link becomes between the triggering details of those experiences and your conditioned reaction to them.

This way of learning serves a useful purpose. It helps us learn how to behave appropriately and how to stay safe and avoid danger. For example, we learn from a young age not to touch a hot stove, how to behave politely, and so on and these experiences become a 'subconscious database.' We consult this subconscious database all day long to determine how to behave in any given situation, mostly on auto-pilot. This is a subconscious process that happens at lightning speed. Most situations are actually neutral and only take on meaning after we consult our individual databases, where our experiences, judgments and beliefs are stored. In other words, our emotional reactions and behaviors are not so much determined by external events but mostly by what is stored inside us, in our subconscious mind.

To understand this better, we will now look at how the brain processes information. The right hemisphere of the brain is analog and creates images. It has no sense of time. It cannot make a distinction between yourself and your surroundings, but instead, it perceives a continuum between yourself and everything else.[1] The left hemisphere of the brain, on the other hand, is digital and abstract, with logical reasoning and an awareness of past, present and future.

The right hemisphere creates images based on all the information you perceive with your senses: what you see, hear, feel, taste and smell. Not everyone creates visual images. Some people may have a rather vague visual picture of a past situation or may not be able to visualize anything. Instead, they compose a 'picture' of the memory based on the sounds, smells or tactile sensations that they experienced. It does not matter which senses you rely on to form these images or sensory memories. Once such an image (visual

---

1   Jill Bolte Taylor: My stroke of insight. TED talk: http://www.ted.com/talks/jill_bolte_taylor_my_stroke_of_insight.

or otherwise) of a situation is formed, it is stored in your subconscious. When you are later reminded of that situation by something you are experiencing in the present moment, the right hemisphere of your brain recalls that stored image of the prior situation and experiences it as if it is happening right now. The corresponding conditioned response is automatically activated through numerous relays in your brain. When experiencing images of happy memories, your relaxation response is activated, so you may feel calm, happy or joyful. For instance, hearing a song that you associate with a good memory may activate a happy nostalgic feeling. On the other hand, if you experience something negative that reminds you of a stressful past event, images stored in the right hemisphere of your brain from such past events will come up (usually subconsciously) and your corresponding conditioned stress reaction will be activated automatically.

These conditioned automatic responses culminate in stress patterns that may lead to unnecessary and over-the-top reactions in present-time situations. It is these ongoing stress patterns that may ultimately lead to chronic stress and manifest as a physical or psychological problem.

Research shows that chronic stress has a negative impact on human health and causes many physical problems.[2][3][4][5][6] As far as physical problems are concerned, we go one step further than conventional medicine as we take the view that *the cause of all physical problems is unresolved chronic stress* unless proven otherwise. We invite you to determine the validity of this claim by using Official EFT to resolve your major stress patterns and witnessing the results for yourself. We hope this book will inspire you to do just that.

2 Yaribeygi, H., Panahi, Y., Sahraei, H., Johnston, T.P., Sahebkar, A. (2017). The impact of stress on body function: A review. *EXCLI journal, 2017;16, 1057-1072.* doi:10.17179/excli2017-480.

3 Sarkodie, E.K., Zhou, S., Baidoo, S.A., Chu, W. (2019). Influences of stress hormones on microbial infections. *Microbial Pathogenesis, 2019; 131, 270-276.* doi: 10.1016/j.micpath.2019.04.013.

4 How stress affects your health. (2016). *American Psychological Association.* http://www.apa.org/helpcenter/stress.aspx.

5 Morey, J.N., Boggero, I.A., Scott, A.B., Segerstrom, S.C. (2015). Current Directions in Stress and Human Immune Function. *Current Opinion in Psychology, 2015; 5, 13-17.* doi:10.1016/j.copsyc.2015.03.007.

6 V.L., Caruso, D., Palagini, L., Zoccoli, G., Bastianini, S. (2019). Stress & sleep: A relationship lasting a lifetime. *Neuroscience & Biobehavioral Reviews. 2019;* doi: 10.1016/j.neubiorev.2019.08.024.

How Do You Get Rid of Stress?

Now that you understand how we have learned our conditioned automatic responses from the events in our past, we will explain why talking about the problem and understanding why we have it does not actually help us to resolve it. The key point is that your past experiences have produced an automatic link between certain triggers and your stress response, so your stress response will be activated as soon as you find yourself in a situation that is similar (or even slightly similar) to a prior negative experience. You have subconsciously trained yourself to turn on the stress response in this type of situation.

To resolve this, it is necessary to start at the origin of the problem: the specific moments in which the stress reaction was first activated and subsequently programmed in as an automatic response. Then, you need to sever the link between those experiences and this automatic stress response. Thus, it is important to identify the specific events in which the link was first established. You can then use EFT to neutralize these moments by severing and disabling the link so that the stress reaction is no longer activated automatically. Once you start using Official EFT, you will be able to experience how this works in practice. If you properly apply EFT to a specific negative moment, you will feel that the stress response simply cannot be activated anymore when you relive that moment, either as part of the EFT process or in later situations. Please note that neutralizing one specific event most probably will not solve your entire issue. It usually takes more than that, because a stress pattern is always based on a series of specific events. You will need to neutralize enough of these events to resolve the whole stress pattern, and thus the entire issue. This is not complicated, but it does require a plan of action and, most likely, some perseverance. We will explain this further in Chapter 5.

Stress Response and Relaxation Response Explained

The essence of EFT is to substitute the relaxation response for the stress response so that you are no longer stuck – against your will – in the automatic stress response. To understand this better, we want to dive a little deeper into stress physiology. You can skip this part, but this little excursion will give you a better understanding of the underlying mechanisms of EFT.

Stress Response

The stress response is also called the fight or flight response, or sympathetic stress response. Its counterpart is called the relaxation response. This latter term is relatively new and was first coined by Herbert Benson.[7]

Let us begin with the sympathetic stress response. In any situation that is perceived as threatening or dangerous, your body responds by fighting or fleeing. This fight or flight response is initiated by the amygdala nuclei in the limbic system (the part of the brain where emotions are generated and regulated). The amygdala nuclei are also called your emotional brain. They process the information coming in from your senses and they connect it to the emotional meaning the event has for you, based on similar past experiences. So, if a situation is perceived as threatening in some way, your fight or flight response kicks in.

When the sympathetic stress response is activated, you may experience symptoms (in all sorts of combinations and degrees): heart palpitations, rapid breathing, dry mouth, trembling, sweating, tunnel vision, nausea, an uncomfortable feeling in your stomach. This is a perfectly normal physiological reaction to enable your body to fight or flee, which increases your chance of survival.

Freeze Response

All mammals, including humans, react to a perceived threat by either fighting or fleeing, but if neither of those is possible, then the freeze response occurs. This may result in feeling like you are nailed to the ground or paralyzed by fear. Most prey animals start with fleeing and most predators with fighting. In the wild, the freeze response provides animals with an opportunity to escape. Many hunting animals respond mainly to movement and

---

7 Benson, H., Klipper, M. (2000). *The Relaxation Response. Updated and Expanded.* (Press: Revised edition). New York (USA): William Morrow Paperbacks (HarperCollins Publishers Inc).

do not like a 'dead' animal, and most predators are not scavengers. This is why the freeze reaction is also an effective way to survive a life-threatening situation.

During the freeze response, both the sympathetic and the parasympathetic nervous systems are activated to the maximum, like driving full speed and slamming the brakes on without taking your foot off the gas. A huge flood of endorphins causes the body to stiffen and possibly fall. When you are having a freeze response, you may feel numb and detached with no physical sensations (pain) or emotions. Your heart rate and breathing slow down and you may even hold your breath. You may be staring into space, and it may be difficult for others to get your attention. The freeze response creates distance between a traumatic event and the experience of it, numbing the feelings and helping a person to get through it.[8]

Animals also react in this way, but they are usually better able to move out of the stress response back into the relaxation response because unlike us, they do not dwell on the past and they do not stay stuck in the freeze response. You can witness the way wild animals do this if you observe them after they have fallen down and pretended to play dead. If they have a chance to get up and run away, they almost always tremble and shake violently, which indicates that they have come out of the freeze response and are now discharging the part of the fight or flight response that was disrupted by the freeze response. This enables them to move into the relaxation response and continue without any residual stress symptoms (although they may have to recover from non-lethal injuries). We humans are also wired this way, so we may experience discharges such as shaking, trembling, or other involuntary movements. If you are able to make full use of the stress response to get through a situation, or if you go into the freeze response and then completely discharge any residual stress and move into the relaxation response, it is unlikely that you will experience any further issues related to that situation. However, if you are not able to do so, your stress response may either remain (slightly) activated, or you will be triggered very easily, or (part of) the freeze response remains activated.

---

8 The part of the parasympathetic nervous system that puts the brake on the sympathetic reaction is the dorsal vagus nerve. It can shut down the entire system and we go into freeze. To better understand what happens, we need to go into the polyvagal theory, introduced in 1994 by Stephen Porges, but that is beyond the scope of this book. You may want to visit: https://www.stephenporges.com/.

The freeze response itself may be imperceptibly brief but it is often remembered more consciously. You realize that you were paralyzed with fear and that you could not move or do anything. Additionally, there is another mechanism at work: even if the freeze response is discharged, all of the details of the situation as well as the stress symptoms that you experienced are stored in your long-term memory for future use. This is part of our learning process. Thus, if a situation (even partly) resembles a previous stressful experience, then your stress response will immediately and automatically be turned on. Positive reactions to situations are fine, as it is beneficial to generate a good feeling. But these automatic negative reactions contribute to chronic stress. The purpose of EFT is to address the negative reactions that are over the top, unnecessary and happen involuntarily. When something happens that triggers you, you are not consulted by your subconscious as to whether you need or want the stress response to be turned on. It is simply activated. That is why situations that cause ongoing stress will eventually lead to all kinds of physical symptoms and diseases. Accordingly, it is crucial to understand what makes you stressed and to resolve these stress patterns with EFT.

Relaxation Response

The relaxation response is the counterpart to the stress response. It is a necessary reaction to recover from stress and return to a balanced state. The physical characteristics of the relaxation response include: heart rate and blood pressure dropping, breathing slowing down, muscles relaxing, cortisol levels declining, memory improving, your ability to think clearly increasing. You also experience a restoration of the blood supply to the digestive system thus starting up digestion again. You may also notice that your hands and feet are warm again, and that your skin tone, saliva and tear flow have returned to normal.

The first step when using EFT is to activate the stress response that is associated with a particular situation by reliving the moment as if it is happening right now. This is called exposure. Then, you stimulate the relaxation response by tapping or doing Optimal EFT, which deactivates the stress response. If you do this correctly, the link between the specific trigger and the stress response is severed and that particular trigger will no longer automatically trigger your stress response. Does this mean you can no longer fight or run away when you are in a threatening situation? Of course not. Your survival mechanism is still intact. Only the unnecessary and over-the-top emotional stress response, associated with past experiences, is resolved. You will still be able to respond with appropriate stress to what is happening right now.

> Properly applied, EFT results in permanently severing the link between the trigger and the conditioned stress response, resolving the unnecessary and excessive negative emotional reaction. Hence the term: "Emotional Freedom Techniques."

The Essence of a Successful Approach

When something 'bad' happens, we almost always want to talk about it. We want to share our story with others, and we hope they will understand and comfort us, or maybe offer us some advice. While this may give us a temporary sense of relief, it does not help us to process and resolve the negative emotions of the event. Rather, we relive what happened by talking about it and experience the negative emotional charge over and over again, every time we recall the event. This does not resolve anything, otherwise, once we are finished telling our story, we would feel fine again and chronic stress would be impossible.

Scientific research has long shown that more needs to be done to effectively process trauma and resolve it. Unfortunately, conventional therapies still involve a lot of talking and medication. The former increases the chances of re-traumatization, and the latter, at best, reduces the symptoms without resolving the cause. Understanding why your past has caused you so much stress does not resolve the long-lasting effects it has on you. Researchers agree that a good approach to resolving trauma consists of a form of exposure (to what happened), combined with a form of cognitive therapy.[1][2][3][4][5][6][7]

EFT offers this and more: in addition to this two-pronged approach, it offers an additional technique to actively disconnect the link between the trigger

1   Kolk, van der, B. (2016). *Trauma traces: The recovery of body, brain and mind after overwhelming experiences.* Eeserveen: Human!; ISBN 978946316031.

2   Levine, P. (2011). *In an Unspoken Voice: How the Body Releases Trauma and Restores Goodness.* Berkeley, California: North Atlantic Books; ISBN 9781556439438.

3   Watkins, L.E., Sprang, K.R., Rothbaum, B.O. (2018). Treating PTSD: A Review of Evidence-Based Psychotherapy Interventions. *Front Behav Neurosci. 2018;12:258.* Published 2018 Nov 2. doi:10.3389/fnbeh.2018.00258.

4   Foa, E.B., McLean, C.P., Zang, Y., et al. (2018). *Effect of Prolonged Exposure Therapy Delivered Over 2 Weeks vs 8 Weeks vs Present-Centered Therapy on PTSD Symptom Severity in Military Personnel: A Randomized Clinical Trial* [published correction appears in JAMA. 2018 Aug 21;320(7):724]. *JAMA. 2018;319(4):354-364. doi:10.1001/jama.2017.21242.*

5   Hendriks, L., Kleine, de, R.A., Broekman, T.G., Hendriks, G.J. & Minnen, van, A. (2018). Intensive prolonged exposure therapy for chronic PTSD patients following multiple trauma and multiple treatment attempts, *European Journal of Psychotraumatology, 2018;* 9:1, DOI: 10.1080/20008198.2018.1425574.

6   Church, D., Hawk, C., Brooks, A.J., Toukolehto, O., Wren, M., Dinter, I., et al. (2013). Psychological trauma symptom improvement in veterans using emotional freedom techniques: a randomized controlled trial. *J Nerv Ment Dis 2013 Feb;201(2):153-60.*

7   Powers, M.B., Halpern, J.M., Ferenschak, M.P., Gillihan, S.J., Foa, E.B.(2010). A meta-analytic review of prolonged exposure for post-traumatic stress disorder. *Clin Psychol Rev. 2010 Aug;30(6):635-41.* doi:10.1016/j.cpr.2010.04.007. Epub 2010 May 2. PMID: 20546985.

and the stress response. Applied properly, EFT provides lasting results so that the traumatic experience can become a neutral memory.

What applies to significant traumatic events also applies to smaller events with a negative charge, because the underlying stress physiology is the same. While relatively minor negative experiences may not have dramatic effects in the moment they are experienced, a buildup of these minor effects can have serious and long-lasting consequences. For example, consider a situation where you grow up with parents who constantly criticize you and your behavior. Each moment may be too small to be considered traumatic, but the repetition consistently and completely undermines your self-esteem and self-confidence. The approach to resolving these smaller but frequently occurring negative situations is the same as the one used for a one-time highly traumatic event, because, as stated above, the underlying mechanism is exactly the same. Both forms of Official EFT offer a well-structured technique that properly activates the stress response without overwhelming you. They also permanently remove the link (which requires that you properly test and continue to apply EFT until the emotional charge is completely gone). We will show you how to do this below.

The Essential Step: From Problem to Specific Event

Most people formulate their problems in general terms, for instance: *I have low self-esteem; My relationship is not going well; I feel insecure at work; I have constant fights with my parents; I suffer from insomnia; I am dreading the presentation I have to give; I do not dare to open my mouth around other people; I cannot get my business off the ground; I have a fear of blushing; I often have headaches; I have bowel problems;* or *I have fibromyalgia.* These seem to be fairly specific descriptions of the problem, but if we look at what is being described here, it is either the circumstance in which a person experiences stress (for example a fight) or it is the stress symptoms themselves (for example headaches), without a description of the underlying root cause (the specific events).

With EFT, we use a metaphor that helps you to identify the root cause of the problem, by breaking down the overall problem into specific events that you need to address individually to solve the overall problem. We call this the Table Top with the Table Legs metaphor.

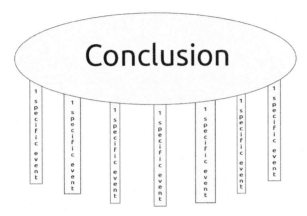

Figure 1. Metaphor of Table Top with Table Legs

The Table Top describes the problem (the conclusion or the negative belief) and is the title of one of your stress patterns. Examples include: *I always fall for the wrong partner, I am a bad mother, I have a fear of public speaking, I am a failure,....* Underneath the Table Top are all the Table Legs or experiences that underlie the problem and make this conclusion 'true.' Each Table Leg is one specific event. There are many more Table Legs under this Table Top than under a real table. There may be dozens or hundreds, depending on how often a particular type of event, leading to the conclusion, has occurred. To select the right specific events for the problem, you can ask yourself the following two questions:

1. What is a good example of a specific moment in which this happens?
2. What specific moments have I experienced that make this conclusion true for me?

If all goes well, you will end up with numerous examples of moments from your past where the problem plays out. It is these specific events that start and maintain the stress pattern. The best wording to describe these specific events or moments is:

The moment when X happens and I feel Y.

It is important to describe the moment in the present tense because it is necessary to relive each specific moment that contributes to your problem as if it were happening right **Now**. This wording helps you to avoid thinking in the past tense. This is a trap many of us fall into because we are used to thinking and talking about events in the past tense. When we do so, our right brain (which does not understand time) will immediately start generating images of that event and experiencing it as if it is happening right now. That is why we can get triggered by something that happened 20 years ago. However, the left brain (which is aware of time and knows there is a past, present and future) interrupts and points out that the event is over, it is no longer happening now, so we are fine. That is how we fool ourselves into thinking that we have processed negative emotions from past events and that they no longer trigger us.

To properly sever the connection between a past event and your conditioned stress response, you need to fully activate the stress response by engaging your right brain and then discharge that response using EFT. In order to do so, you need to relive the event in an associated way, rather than in a dissociated way. Association involves fully reliving a past experience by looking into the situation through your own eyes and engaging all of your senses. It requires you to step into the moment as though it is happening right now, so that you see what you saw, hear what you heard, feel what you felt and so on. By contrast, if you think about a past event or talk about it in the past tense, you are dissociated. You may still feel emotions about the situation, but you are not fully connected to it or to those emotions.

Rather than thinking and talking about the moment in the past tense (which will distance you from the event), we need the opposite to happen. To fully activate the stress response, you need to use the present tense and pretend that the specific moment is happening right NOW and that you are in the event, rather than looking at yourself in the event from a distance. By reliving the moment in this way, you are helping the right hemisphere of your brain to completely believe that it is indeed happening right now. At the same time, you are temporarily deactivating the left hemisphere, which logically knows that it is not happening now. While staying as connected as possible to the negative emotions and reactions, you then apply the rest of the protocol of Official EFT (either Gold Standard EFT or Optimal EFT).

In practice, this means that you can immediately start tapping or doing Optimal EFT when something is happening and you are experiencing a negative reaction because you are in the middle of your specific moment so your stress response is fully activated (provided of course that it is appropriate and convenient to apply EFT on the spot). If you keep focused on what you feel and keep tapping or doing Optimal EFT until the stress reaction is neutralized, you can sever the link between that moment and your stress response, while the exposure is ongoing. Obviously, however, this will not always be possible because there may be other people present or you may not be able to stop what you are doing. Fortunately, you can achieve the same results by doing EFT at a later, more convenient time, provided that you relive the specific moment properly.

Note: As mentioned previously, we do not recommend that you relive a specific event that you anticipate could be traumatic and evoke a lot of emotion unless you have first used various techniques to take the edge off (discussed later on in this chapter) and feel that you are able to address it yourself. Otherwise, it is best to consult a well-trained EFT professional to help you with this particular issue.

Reliving the Specific Event in the Right Way

In practice, it is more likely that you will use EFT to resolve events from the past, as opposed to using EFT to address an event occurring in the moment, which may not be practical. Accordingly, it is important to learn how to relive specific events properly. Before we go any further, there are three key points that we need to look at:

1. Dividing the specific moment into emotional peaks (crescendos). Most stressful specific events need to be divided into shorter segments with only one crescendo each. Compare this with a TV commercial: some are 120 seconds long, but quite often they are only 30 seconds or even 5 seconds! Just realize how much is happening in that short period of time. You cannot resolve a two-hour argument in one round of EFT. You need to identify and separate each specific moment within that two-hour period that has an emotional charge, and then resolve each of these emotionally charged crescendos one by one until you have resolved the whole event.

2. Scoring the emotional intensity between 0 and 10. A unique feature of EFT is that you assess the intensity of your negative emotional and/or physical reaction before you start. Then you do a round of EFT, and after that, you assess the intensity again, so that you can determine whether the intensity of the emotional or physical reaction has decreased. You continue applying the protocol until your reaction (to this particular moment) has disappeared completely. To assess the intensity, we give it a score between 0 (where you feel nothing, no negative reaction) and 10 (your maximum negative reaction). It is a subjective measure of what you feel, so you need not worry about the accuracy of your score. If you do not know what the number is right away, then simply guess what it may be approximately. It is best not to overthink it. You are just using it as a benchmark so that you can determine whether your negative reaction has been resolved completely, in which case you have finished processing that moment.

3. Feelings and emotions. How do we use these terms within EFT? If you have a negative reaction, then your sympathetic stress response is activated. You may experience bodily sensations (such as heart palpitations, a dry mouth, or an uncomfortable feeling in your stomach). We call these sensations feelings. If you label what you are feeling in your body, you might come to the conclusion that you are angry, sad or anxious. This label is what we call an emotion.

There are three main groups of negative emotions, namely anger, sadness and fear. A lot of what we may call emotions are more of a conclusion, such as feeling lonely, misunderstood, resentful, offended, etc. If you come to such a conclusion about how you feel, then try to dig a little deeper to identify what emotion goes with this conclusion. Does it belong to the 'anger group,' the 'sadness group,' or the 'fear group'? This makes it more specific. For instance, you may experience loneliness as a sad kind of loneliness or an angry kind of loneliness. Sometimes you may feel only one emotion at first (for example, anger) and after it has subsided you may realize that you are sad as well. If you notice two emotions of approximately equal intensity at the same time, you may name both of them and work on them together, in the same round of EFT. However, if one is much higher, then it is better to work on that one first and do the less intense one after you have resolved the higher one.

If an emotion comes up a little later and that emotion is higher than the one you started with, then switch to resolving that emotion first and then return to the first one. This is also applicable to bodily sensations: if you first notice your mouth is dry and when that has subsided, you feel heart palpitations, then switch your focus to the latter. If possible, try to connect the emotion to the feeling (sensation) in your body. For instance, *I feel this anxious feeling in my stomach*, or, *I feel this angry feeling in my chest*. Do not worry if you cannot readily identify this combination yet. Work with what you do feel. With practice, you will develop the ability to do so. You will also get used to your emotions and feelings shifting as you work through each moment with EFT. Simply follow the emotions and feelings (body sensations) that you are experiencing in this one specific moment. Also, make sure that you work on one crescendo at a time and neutralize it before moving to the next crescendo. This will take some getting used to, because we naturally want to deal with or talk about the whole story and analyze the when, why, who, and how. You need to avoid retelling the whole story as much as possible, because this activates too much emotion all at once, making it very hard to resolve the emotional charge effectively.

Association in Two Steps

Properly reliving the individual crescendos of a specific event is called exposure. We recommend that you choose a specific moment with a relatively small negative emotional charge that happened today or yesterday, rather than anything traumatic, when practicing the two steps outlined below. We will only practice reliving the moment in this section. A more detailed explanation of the protocols is given in the following chapters. Here are the steps:

1. Close your eyes and step into the first crescendo. Pretend this moment is happening right **Now** and make sure that you are IN it: you are looking through your own eyes and using all sensory information to make it as vivid as possible. Do not look at the scene or think about this moment, but really be in it. Relive what is happening in this moment. This step should be short, 5-20 seconds at most, otherwise you are likely to start thinking about it instead of feeling it.

Tip #1: If you start thinking, analyzing, and asking yourself questions, you need to shorten the reliving step. Simply let whatever is going on in this moment happen in the present tense. For example, you do not think back to a moment yesterday when you were sitting in your office chair in your office and someone came in and stood in front of you and pointed an accusing finger at you, looking irritated and saying that you made a big mistake. Instead, you feel the seat and the back of the chair you are sitting on now. From this lower position (you are sitting, and the other person is standing), look up a little and see this person standing in front of you and pointing a finger at you while looking irritated, and hear them say, "You made a big mistake."

To help you do this, you may pretend you are a movie director, and that your head is the camera you are looking through, so you decide on the position of the camera. However, you are not limited to what you see and hear, like in a regular movie. You can also engage your other senses: what you feel, smell and possibly taste. It is especially helpful to do this if you find it difficult to really relive the crescendo. Take your time to realize where you are, what it looks like here, if there are others present and where they sit, stand or walk, what sounds you hear, what smells you smell and whether this location is warm, cold or neutral. If you use all the sensory information, then it is easier to really be in the moment. If you see nothing or only vague shapes, but primarily hear sounds and voices, then focus on that information as much as you can: notice where the sound is coming from, how far away it is, and whether the sound or voice is loud or soft, shrill or muffled, and so on.

2. Identify what you feel (emotion and/or bodily sensation), choose a word that best describes it, and assess the intensity, giving it a score between 0 and 10. Keep it simple. You just need to choose a word or two that describe what you are feeling, whatever comes to mind first. Do not start thinking and analyzing. Beginners often report that they do not know

what to say. This confusion may have its source on the Internet where one can find many demonstrations of EFT with the use of elaborate language, clever wording, or long lists of possible emotions. However, the words you use when doing EFT are not important. The key is to ensure that you fully activate the stress response to feel the negative emotion. Focus on the feeling and then just pick a word that best describes what you are feeling – in as short a time as possible. If you spend too much time on this, you run the risk, again, of reverting to thinking, and, equally problematic, the risk that the activated stress response will fizzle out and therefore will not be effectively deactivated in the subsequent round of tapping or Optimal EFT.

Tip #2: Identify the group of emotions your reaction belongs to: the fear group, the sadness group, or the anger group. Any variation in wording that points to fear, sadness, or anger is fine. For example, fright belongs to the fear group, whereas irritation may belong to the anger group. Try to avoid using conclusions such as, *I feel misunderstood*, or, *That should not have happened*. They are too general. By specifically identifying the underlying emotion and the group it belongs to, you are able to target and resolve the emotion with EFT more effectively. It also allows you to test more precisely whether the intensity of that specific emotion has been completely resolved. It is best to keep the description of your negative emotional reaction short, but it may be more than one word. As stated before, the combination of a conclusion and the feeling and possibly where you feel it in your body is the most effective. For example, *The fearful anxiety in my stomach; This sad misunderstood feeling; My frustrated rage*. Remember it is common for your emotions and feelings to shift, so continue to follow and describe what you feel as you go through the process.

Tip #3: If you want to work on an argument with someone that lasted half an hour or longer, you need to split the event into several crescendos and work on each one individually. Start at the first crescendo, use EFT until the emotional intensity comes down to zero and then move on to the next one. Sometimes, however, it is not possible to start at the beginning because a big crescendo further down the line is already triggering you and thus asking for attention. If that is the case, do that one first and then come back to work on the smaller crescendos before it, as well as the later ones. Make sure you limit yourself to one specific moment at a time! Also, remember to use all sensory input, which means paying attention not only to what was said but also to the facial expressions and the body language of those involved, as well as to other details; for example, doors slamming, something being thrown, others being present and their reactions. Work through the whole event in this way until there is no detail left that triggers any reaction.

We advise you to practice the steps outlined above several times, so that you know what to do. In this way, the process becomes automatic to you. You can avoid thinking about it, when using EFT to address a problem. Practice with small, annoying moments first, rather than with very upsetting or traumatic events.

There are four additional important issues regarding association:

1. Aspects of a specific moment. A specific event has many details, and these are called aspects. Aspects include all the triggering details of the event (that you perceive with your senses), your emotional reactions to them and your self-talk. You will often feel more than one emotion in one specific crescendo, but very rarely more than three. If you feel more than three, it is likely that you are thinking about it too much or possibly going back and forth from one crescendo to the next, within the same event. Or you may be shifting your focus onto other, similar situations. It is crucial to focus on one specific event at a time.

Not all aspects will be immediately apparent. Some may be hidden by others, or they may be hidden in our subconscious, outside our conscious awareness. As we process the specific event with EFT and release aspects, new aspects of the specific event may bubble up into our consciousness when we are ready to process them. This is an important reason why it is necessary to divide the specific event into shorter, specific crescendos and to relive everything in an associated way. Otherwise, you run the risk of skipping certain aspects and thus not neutralizing them, which means that you will not completely sever the link between the trigger and stress response. This produces partial and temporary results and can lead to the conclusion that EFT does not work. It is, therefore, important that you identify and resolve every aspect.

By way of example, say you have been in a car crash, and your car was hit by another car from behind. The aspects of that event may include the following:

- Characteristics of your environment: the car you are in, how the seat feels, your position in the car (as the driver or passenger), smells in the car, other people in the car, where you are driving, the motion of the car, and so on. Feeling the motion of the car is very useful to help you get INTO the situation.
- The moment just before the collision: What do you see, hear, taste, smell, feel, and think? What do you see in front of you? Do you look in the rear-view mirror? What do you hear?
- The moment itself: the impact of the collision, the sounds, any smells (from the brakes, rubber on the road, etc.), the muscle tension, suddenly shooting forward and being restrained by the seat belt, the airbags, any sounds you or others make, the feeling in your head, neck, shoulders, torso, legs, and the rest of your body, and so on.
- The moment right after the collision: What do you feel, see, hear, taste, smell? This includes everything that happens around you, everything you and others do.
- The outcome: What stressful things do you experience after that moment? This may include hospitalization, receiving medical treatment, disputes with others involved in the accident, car insurance and legal issues, or any continuing physical symptoms and pain. Identify your emotional reaction and really connect to the exact moment in which you experienced it.

Each of these specific moments has numerous aspects that may have triggered a stress reaction in you. There may also be other details in addition to those above. If you properly relive the moments as explained above, you will be able to identify each and every aspect that triggers the stress response. Every emotional reaction needs to be neutralized with EFT. This may take some time and involve quite a bit of work, but the good news is that the more thoroughly you address each crescendo and its aspects, the faster the whole event loses its hold over you. Furthermore, as you work through the aspects and fully resolve their emotional charge, the aspects that you have not yet dealt with become less intense, even before you start to work on them, because the emotional charge of the aspects you have cleared is no longer affecting them. Keep working until you have dealt with every aspect of all the crescendos, and once you have cleared them, relive the whole event again, step by step, to make sure that any remaining emotional intensity is identified and released.

2. Feeling emotions: the difference between association and dissociation. It usually takes practice to properly relive a specific moment instead of thinking about it, analyzing it, comparing it with other situations, shifting to other memories, etc. This is one of the most common reasons why you may not be feeling any emotion. It takes practice to restrain yourself from retelling the whole story (to yourself or someone else) and repeating the conclusions you have reached about the event. It is essential to stop following that little voice in your head, but it does take practice to do so. Instead of following that voice, simply close your eyes and imagine yourself in the specific moment, allowing whatever is happening to fill your awareness. A useful test to determine whether you are properly associated is to check if you are watching yourself like an actor in a movie (in which case you are dissociated) or if you are in the situation and looking through your own eyes (which means you are reliving the moment properly, in an associated way). When you are associated, you may see your own hands or your legs, but not your whole body. If you see yourself from head to toe, then you are dissociated, which means you are keeping yourself at a distance from the event and from your emotional response to it. This means that your stress reaction will not fully engage, so you will not be able to completely sever the link between the trigger and your emotional reaction. This is one of the most frequently made mistakes in EFT.

Note: Some people naturally dissociate so they need to practice more and work harder to properly associate themselves in the moment. It is even more important for such people to make use of all sensory input (from all five senses) and to take their time to place themselves in the surroundings of the specific moment, as described above in Tip # 1.

3. An important step: taking the edge off. When you suspect that the emotional intensity of a specific event is likely to be high because you are already feeling agitated or anxious by the mere thought of having to relive this event as if it is happening now, it is advisable to take the edge off with EFT. This means targeting your emotions about the event as a whole, before going into the details and reliving any specific moment. Use EFT to address those emotions and bring the intensity down as far as possible, ideally between 0 and 3. The key is to do this BEFORE you start the associated exposure and dive into reliving the event. Take your time to do this, to avoid getting overwhelmed by your emotions and potentially re-traumatizing yourself. We explain Symptom-Focused EFT further on in Chapter 5.

It may be helpful to 'reframe' the situation by reminding yourself that you somehow got through it, that you survived, that you are safe now, here in the present moment, and you are able to tell your story, because it is not happening now. This can help to neutralize any agitation or fear, which would otherwise make the situation more traumatic. We will discuss re-frames in more detail in Chapter 6. Once more, we want to point out that you should never try to work on any issue if it triggers panic or strong fear and you feel unable to handle whatever might come up if you were to go into it fully associated. Save it for a later date or consult a well-trained EFT professional.

4. Working until the emotional charge is zero. Testing after each round of EFT (by reliving the specific moment and assessing the intensity of your emotional reaction) helps you to monitor your progress and determine whether the emotional intensity has been completely resolved. If it has not, then you know that you need to continue doing EFT, until you have reached zero. It is this unique feature of EFT that makes the method so amazingly effective: you are constantly testing whether the stress response has been turned off completely because only then is the link between the trigger and stress response severed so that there is no longer any connection between them. If you do this correctly, the result is a definite and lasting disconnect, which makes the event a neutral memory.

To make sure that the memory is neutral, first work on all of the crescendos of the event (bringing the emotional intensity of each crescendo to zero while associated) and then go through the whole event again in an associated way, to check whether there is any remaining emotional intensity. Do your best to try to get upset or evoke any kind of reaction, both the original emotional reactions as well as any new negative reaction or any bodily sensations. This takes some getting used to, but it is very important. Testing is about trying to find any remaining emotional reaction, rather than to see if you are finished. The path to success is to continually work on an event until the link to your stress response is not working anymore.

Note: If you are dealing with an event that happened many times, you may not be able to bring the emotional reaction down to zero right away. We will give instructions as to how to handle these types of events in Chapter 5. But remember, most specific events are neutralized relatively easily, so keep going and aim for zero. A frequently made mistake is stopping too soon and not finishing the process. Often, when an intense reaction has subsided considerably, it is such a relief that we think it is good enough. For example, the intensity may drop from a 9 to a 3, and then we think *that's better,* so we stop. Well, yes and no. Of course, an intensity of 3 is better than a 9, but you need to continue using EFT until the emotional reaction of the whole specific event is a zero. Your problem will only be resolved if you completely neutralize the specific events that are contributing to your problem.

The only time when you do not need to continue until your emotional reaction is a zero is when you are applying EFT immediately in a current situation in which you are feeling stressed. In such a case, you can use EFT to simply bring your emotional reaction down as much as possible, so that you feel less stressed and are better able to cope in the situation. Then you can stop. This is a form of Symptom-Focused EFT: you aim at reducing the symptom that is bothering you (in this example feeling stress, but you can aim at a headache or another physical symptom in the same way). This works well, but almost always only temporarily. You will need to work on the specific moment again (at a later more convenient time) and completely bring all your emotional reactions down to a tested zero. We explain Symptom-Focused EFT further in Chapter 5.

You may ask whether it is possible to use EFT to bring the emotional re-action to every event down to a zero. Our answer is yes. All memories can be neutralized to a zero, including memories of traumatic events that may have been truly horrific. We have seen clients neutralize their stress responses to horrendous physical violence, war crimes, psychological abuse, and more, and become emotionally free in the process. However, before we explain further, we first want to emphasize again that we strongly recommend that you do not work on such traumas by yourself, using only the information in this book.

No matter how horrific and intense an experience may have been, the key point to remember is that you somehow got through it and survived it, that this experience is now in the past and that it is not happening now. This means that you no longer need the stress reaction that was activated back then. After all, the situation is no longer happening, so you do not need to fight, flee or freeze anymore. In addition, there is no need to fear that you will not survive because you are here now, telling your story, so you did survive. Therefore, it is possible to process the emotional reaction so that it becomes a neutral event. By neutral, we mean that the stress reaction about this experience, which happened in the past and is not going on now, is no longer activated. This does not mean, of course, that you are condoning what happened or that, if this was happening now, you would not feel any-thing. We are talking about the past event only. It is incredibly liberating to be free from the stress reaction related to this past experience. You are also only testing to see if this particular experience that occurred in the past is no longer triggering you in the present.

We may also need to remind ourselves that it is not necessary to hold onto the emotions from the past to protect ourselves from it happening again. This is a major misconception. Leaving your stress reaction on, staying angry, resentful, or afraid, being easily triggered and feeling like a vic-tim, takes a lot of energy, and it most certainly does not make you better equipped to prevent the same thing from happening again. It is not help-ing you in any way. Furthermore, this is not about not reacting to similar future situations. Of course, some experiences will always turn on your stress response. But these are not the right tests to determine whether the intense, specific experience in your past has a neutral emotional charge. You can only test that with the event as it happened, but which is now behind you. Truly letting go is the only way to stop letting the past have power over you. You use EFT to neutralize your emotional reaction to past negative events so that you are no longer affected by them, not to become desensitized to certain intense negative situations, now or in the future.

Note

If you are going through a very stressful experience, you will automatically dissociate to a greater or lesser degree. This is a natural protective mechanism. We all have memories of particularly upsetting events that we recall in a dissociated state. These are the memories we advise you not to work on alone, with only the knowledge in this book. In Chapter 6, we will outline a plan of action so that you can get started with the basic protocols. Start practicing these techniques with less intense situations. You will be surprised at how much you can achieve by resolving your smaller issues. Save the bigger, traumatic events for later, when you have more experience and a thorough knowledge of the basic protocols. For very severe traumas and PTSD (Post-Traumatic Stress Disorder), we advise you to seek the help of a well-trained EFT professional.

3 | GOLD STANDARD EFT (TAPPING)

Everything should be made as simple as possible, but not simpler.

Albert Einstein, German-American physicist, 1879 – 1955

Background of the First Form of Official EFT

EFT Tapping, the first form of Official EFT, was founded by Gary Craig and released in 1995. Since that time, it has been used by doctors, psychologists, psychiatrists and other therapists all over the world. EFT Tapping is also widely used as a self-help tool because it is effective and safe in the hands of a layperson. This is a major advantage it has over other therapies. The term Gold Standard EFT refers to the new and updated version of Gary Craig's EFT Tapping protocol, which became available in 2011.

Gold Standard EFT combines a specific form of exposure technique with tapping on a set series of acupressure points. This combination makes it a powerful and effective intervention. It involves gently tapping on easily accessible acupuncture points to stimulate the body's relaxation response, while simultaneously focusing on the negative emotion associated with a stressful experience using exposure, thereby extinguishing the stress response.

This process effectively severs the link between the trigger and the associated stress response. The proper use of the Gold Standard EFT protocol ensures that you are not exposed to your stressful experience in a way that may be too intense and overwhelming. In terms of trauma therapy, EFT is one of the gentlest ways to process traumatic experiences. As mentioned earlier, we recommend that you start using EFT on relatively minor issues. Leave the bigger traumas for later until you have a more thorough knowledge of the technique, as well as experience in successfully applying EFT to your smaller issues. For your biggest traumas, it may still be best to consult a well-trained EFT professional to help you with traumatic events.[1][2][3]

Gold Standard EFT was founded on wisdom and insights that came from Traditional Chinese Medicine (TCM),[4] particularly the principles of acupuncture,[5] and from developments made in a number of places over the last century concerning the mind-body connection. Notable contributors include Roger Callahan,[6] Robert Lovett and Henry and Florence Kendall,[7] Frank Chapman and Terrence Bennett,[8] George Goodheart,[9] John Thie,[10] Paul Dennison[11] and John Diamond,[12] among others. Appendix 1 contains a brief summary of these developments.

1 *Understanding the stress response.* Harvard Health Publishing. July 06, 2020. https://www.health.harvard.edu/staying-healthy/understanding-the-stress-response.

2 Borzou, S.R., Akbari, S., Fallahinia, G., Mahjub, H. (2018). The Effect of Acupressure at the Point of Hugo on Pain Severity of Needle Insertion in Arteriovenous Fistulas in Hemodialysis Patients, *Nephro-Urol Mon. 2018; 10(1):e14252.* doi: 10.5812/numonthly.14252.

3 Lee, E., Park, J.H. (2021). Effect of Acupressure on Pre-Exam Anxiety in Nursing Students. *Altern Ther Health Med. 2021 Jul 31;AT6370. Epub ahead of print.* PMID: 34331752.

4 Newman, D. (2020). Modern traditional Chinese medicine: Identifying, defining and usage of TCM components. *Adv Pharmacol. 2020;87:113-158. doi: 10.1016/bs.apha.2019.07.001. Epub 2019 Aug 24.* PMID: 32089231 DOI: 10.1016/bs.apha.2019.07.001.

5 Yang, F., Yao, L., Wang, S., Guo, Y., Xu, Z., Zhang, C., Zhang, K., Fang, Y., Liu, Y. (2020). Current Detective Work on Effectiveness and Mechanisms of Acupuncture Therapy: A Literature Review of High-Quality Studies. *Chin J Integr Med. 2020 Apr;26(4):310-320. doi:10.1007/s11655-019-3150-3. Epub 2019 Feb 1.* PMID: 30707414 DOI: 10.1007/s11655-019-3150-3.

6 Callahan, R., Trubo, R. (2002). Tapping the Healer Within: Using Thought-Field Therapy to Instantly Conquer Your Fears, Anxieties, and Emotional Distress. *McGraw-Hill Education. ISBN: 978-0-07-139492-5.*

7 https://www.kinesiology.com/kinesiology.php.

8 Seffinger, M. (2018). Foundations of Osteopathic Medicine: Philosophy, Science, Clinical Applications and Research. *Wolters Kluwer 4th Ed. ISBN: 978-1-49-636832-4.*

9 Gin, R.H., Green, B.N. Goodheart, G. Jr. (1997). D.C., and a history of applied kinesiology. *J Manipulative Physiol Ther. 1997 Jun; 20(5):331-7.PMID: 9200049.*

10 Thie, M. (2012) Touch for Health. *Devorss & Co. ISBN-10 087516871X.*

11 Dennison, P.E., Dennison, G.E. (1989) *Brain,* Gym Teacher's Edition; Edu Kinesthetics; *ISBN-13 : 978-0942143027.*

12 Diamond, J. (1977, 1980). The Collected Papers (Volumes 1&2). *Valley Cottage, NY: Archaeus Press; ISBN 1-890995-30-4.*

EFT Tapping Variants

You may already know EFT from other sources, and perhaps you have used it with varying degrees of success. Unfortunately, much of the information found on the Internet about EFT is either incomplete or too superficial to obtain lasting results. When Gary Craig first developed EFT, he posted an EFT manual on the Internet that has been downloaded over a million times. His enthusiasm for EFT prompted him to make it available for free so that as many people as possible would be able to discover its effectiveness and benefit from using it as a self-help tool. Gary Craig foresaw back then that EFT Tapping was only the beginning, noting in his manual that, "We are on the ground floor of a Healing High Rise." He expected people to use EFT and perhaps develop it further, while retaining its essence (identifying and working on relevant specific events, and testing thoroughly). Unfortunately, he did not realize until later that this was too naive an expectation.

Making EFT available for free has, on the one hand, enabled millions of people to benefit from using it. On the other hand, it has also caused a significant problem because, within a short period of time, all kinds of variants of EFT arose in which the essence of EFT was lost. For example, you can find many 'tap-along' videos and tapping scripts. Both are based on the erroneous assumption that tapping with generic sentences can help large groups of people resolve their problems. However, for EFT to be truly effective, it is always necessary to tune into the individual's needs, their personal experiences, and the specific root causes of their problems.

EFT is a customized process. General tapping on everything you could possibly be feeling with respect to a particular problem does not work. The essence of EFT entails addressing the root cause of negative feelings, limiting beliefs, and negative experiences. The key is to identify the specific events in your past that underlie your problem. These root causes are specific to you. Compare this with going to see your doctor for a stomachache. Adopting the approach of an EFT spin-off, the doctor may say, *Oh, that ache is often a stomach ulcer,* and proceed to treat you accordingly, without thoroughly investigating your problem and determining why you have a stomachache.

With Gold Standard EFT, we look into your issue – when it started and what was happening around that time – so we can identify and resolve the root cause. Tapping, while repeating general phrases and words, may make you feel better initially, as it may decrease the stress response at that moment to some extent, but the effect will be temporary, because that approach fails to properly address the root cause of the problem, namely the specific events and all of their related aspects that are unique to each individual. Accordingly, such generalized tapping fails to sever the link between the trigger and the stress response, which is the whole point of EFT. Therefore, as soon as the person encounters the same type of trigger, their stress response will be activated yet again.

In the same way, tapping while using positive language and tapping on positive feelings and thoughts may make you feel a little better, but it does not help to resolve the underlying link between the trigger and stress response. It is essential to focus on negative emotions (not positive ones) to fully activate the stress response and then use EFT to sever the link between the trigger and that response. EFT helps you to release negative emotions; it does not install positive ones. If you want to use EFT as a self-help tool, it is best to avoid all positive language. Keep focusing on the negative emotions and feelings in an associated way in a specific moment until you have neutralized them and brought their intensity down to zero.

In specific situations, an EFT professional may effectively use positive language in the EFT process, based on their professional training. But in most cases, positive language is to be avoided. For instance, positive language may be used as part of a reframe once most of the emotional intensity of a moment has been resolved, or if a client is feeling too emotional and needs to take a break.

Finally, there are EFT variants that claim to be faster and simpler than EFT Tapping. In our opinion, the basic protocol of EFT is already sufficiently fast and simple. Trying to make it even faster may jeopardize the ability to obtain permanent results. You can usually address and resolve a single experience amazingly quickly, but to obtain long-lasting results, a thorough approach is necessary, which generally requires perseverance and dedication. The root cause of the problem must be identified and resolved, which necessitates properly reliving each moment that triggers the stress response, then tapping until the emotional intensity is completely neutralized. The approach in EFT is simple once you understand how it works and how to apply it. Ultimately, your ability to successfully resolve your problems depends on your ability to persevere and properly apply EFT.

One-Minute Wonders?

In the early days of EFT, many success stories were shared, demonstrating extraordinary and impressive results. However, these stories tend to suggest that the results were obtained using a rather superficial, overly simplistic approach to the problems. They indicated that tapping, while repeating a few global words or phrases, would be sufficient to obtain such dramatic positive effects. In practice, however, this is rarely the case. While some people have experienced success with that superficial approach, most people have not, and have, therefore, come to the erroneous conclusion that EFT does not work. EFT does work, but it needs to be applied properly.

In summary, a lot of information about EFT is based on misconceptions about how it works and how to apply it in practice. The abbreviation EFT is used in the name of these spin-offs, adding to the confusion. You may have also come across another type of therapy, Emotionally-Focused Therapy, which originated at around the same time as Official EFT and uses the acronym EFT also. This is a relationship therapy that has nothing to do with Official EFT. If you want to find reliable information about EFT on the Internet, we recommend that you start by reviewing the vast amount of resources on Gary's website on Official EFT, including his Gold Standard EFT Tapping Tutorial and *The Unseen Therapist* e-book on Optimal EFT, that are both available for free.[13]

---

13 https://www.emofree.com.

How Does EFT Tapping Work?

EFT Tapping works by stimulating acupuncture points. According to Traditional Chinese Medicine (TCM), all negative emotions are caused by a disturbance in the energy system of the body.[14] This energy system consists of a network of meridians that connect over 2000 energy points in the body. The energy that flows through them is called Qi in TCM (this energy is given other names by other traditions, such as prana, life force and so on). Almost every meridian is related to a specific organ and named after it, such as the stomach meridian, the liver meridian and the small intestine meridian. An acupuncturist will insert needles in the acupuncture points situated along the meridians.[15] With Gold Standard EFT, we make use of only nine acupuncture points, which we gently tap on with our fingertips. No needles are involved; hence this tapping is a form of acupressure. Research, including studies with MRI (Magnetic Resonance Imaging),[16] shows that stimulating acupuncture points affects the central nervous system, resulting in increased neuronal activity of the thalamus (an important relay station in the brainstem) and the release of substances such as cytokines (which play a role in pain and inflammation), endorphins (our natural painkillers) and serotonin (which affects memory, mood, sleep, emotions and assists the processing of pain stimuli). The effect of stimulating acupuncture points can be compared to opiates, as it provides pain relief and stimulates feelings of happiness and well-being. As a result, EFT extinguishes the stress reaction. At the level of the meridians, acupuncture and acupressure restore the balance of Qi by removing disturbances and blockages in the meridians. When combined with the exposure technique of EFT, this effectively severs the link between the stress trigger and the resulting stress response. In other words, the link no longer works. The trigger may still be present, but your stress response no longer engages.

---

14 *Standard Acupuncture Nomenclature, part 1.* Rev. Ed. 1991 (https://apps.who.int/iris/handle/10665/207635).

15 Cabyoglu, M.T., Ergene, N., Tan, U. (2006, 2009). The Mechanism of Acupuncture and Clinical Applications. *Int. Journal of Neuroscience. (116), 2006 – issue 2:* 115-125. Jul 2009. https://doi.org/10.1080/00207450500341472.

16 Cai, R., Shen, G., Wang, H., Guan, Y. (2018). Brain functional connectivity network studies of acupuncture: a systematic review on resting-state *fMRI. J Integr Med. 2018 Jan;16(1):26-33.* doi:10.1016/j.joim.2017.12.002. Epub 2017 Dec 11.

The Basic Protocol of Gold Standard EFT Explained

In Chapter 2, we explained the importance of fully activating the stress response (that is linked to the memory of the specific event that you want to resolve) by reliving the moment in an associated way. This is called exposure. At the same time, you tap on the EFT acupuncture points, which turns off the stress response, bringing you into a relaxed state. In addition to using EFT to resolve your emotional response to past events, you can also apply EFT in the present moment when you are faced with a stressful situation. However, as it is usually not convenient to apply EFT in the moment, in practice you will be applying EFT to a memory of a stressful event (either recent or in the distant past). Even something that happened five minutes ago has become a memory.

Note

If your memory of an event is so traumatic that you suspect that closing your eyes and pretending it is happening right now may evoke a lot of emotion and potentially feel overwhelming, Then Do Not Do So. Only use this book to resolve smaller issues to start with and seek the assistance of a well-trained EFT professional if you wish to resolve significant traumas or any particularly intense experiences. Do not underestimate the effect of starting with smaller, daily issues. You will be surprised at how much better you feel after resolving these 'smaller' issues!

Step 1: Pick a moment with a negative charge

Identify a specific event that you want to work on and remember to use the present tense. Make this as specific as possible: you should be able to mark the specific event in your calendar. For example, *the moment last Monday when I come home late from work tired and my partner does not greet me. He angrily says that it is too late again to have dinner together, then he stomps out of the room and slams the door.*

Then, you need to identify the crescendos within this specific event, in which you feel any negative emotions. Perhaps the first crescendo is the moment when your partner fails to respond to your greeting and the second crescendo could be the moment when he angrily says: *So, you are finally home! I have already eaten. Do not expect me to wait for you to realize I am here too.* You may also identify a third crescendo as the moment when he stomps out of the room and slams the door. All of these details and all the emotions you feel are the aspects of this specific event.

Step 2: Association

Relive the first crescendo as vividly as possible by stepping into the moment and identifying your negative emotional reaction. Focus on this moment and score the emotions and/or any physical reaction you feel on a scale of 0 (nothing) to 10 (maximum). Do this intuitively, without thinking about this number. It is a subjective measure that we use to test whether there is any charge left after applying EFT. In this example, you may identify sadness at a 7. If you can also identify any bodily sensations, then combine them: a 7 sadness in my throat. Now you know what to tap on.

Step 3: Setup phrase and tapping sequence

Create a Setup phrase. The purpose of the Setup phrase is to keep you tuned into the negative emotion or bodily sensation that you are addressing and accepting that this is your reaction. Simply repeating a set phrase without tuning in does not create the disruption in the body or activate the stress response. This is why we instruct you to relive the moment and also use a Setup phrase so you remain tuned in. If the stress reaction is not activated, then we cannot use EFT to extinguish it. In this case, you may use: *Even though I feel this sadness, I accept myself.* Or (even better): *Even though I feel this 7 sadness in my throat, I accept myself.*

While saying this Setup phrase (preferably out loud), tap continually with the fingertips of one hand on the karate chop point of your other hand (KC, as illustrated below). This lets your system know what you are trying to address. The KC point is located at the fleshy part of the outside of either hand between the top of the wrist and the base of the baby finger, two-thirds up between your wrist and the baseline of your baby finger.

Figure 2: The Karate Chop point

Then, you do the tapping sequence, tapping 3-7 times on each tapping point. At each point, you repeat a word or short sentence that best expresses or summarizes what you feel. In this example, *my sadness* or (even better): *this sadness in my throat.* The tapping sequence involves tapping on the following points:

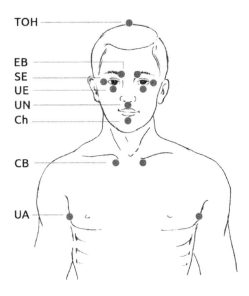

Figure 3. Tapping Points

TOH (Top of Head): Use a flat hand to tap on the top of the head. If you were to draw a line from one ear, over the head, to the other ear, and another line from your nose to the back of your neck, the TOH point is where those two lines would intersect. Do not tap in circles around this point, tap on the point.

EB (Beginning of Eyebrow): Tap with one or two fingers on the beginning of the eyebrow, where the hairs of your eyebrow start (not above the bridge of the nose).

SE (Side of Eye): Tap with one or two fingers on the bone bordering the outside corner of the eye, on the rim of the eye socket. Stay very close to the eye, not your temple.

UE (Under Eye): Tap with one or two fingers about one inch below the pupil, on the bottom rim of the eye socket.

UN (Under Nose): Tap with one or two fingers on the area between the bottom of your nose and the top of your upper lip, in the middle of the groove.

Ch (Chin): Tap with one or two fingers in the area halfway between the bottom of your lower lip and the point of your chin, in the groove.

CB (Collar Bone): Tap with your fist on the beginning of both collarbones, where you would knot a tie, making sure you are touching both sides.

UA (Under Arm): Tap with a flat hand on the side of the body under your arm (a hand width below your armpit).

Tapping Tips: While you can tap with either hand, most people use their dominant hand. Some of the tapping points have twin points on each side of the body. Years of experience have taught us that you only need to tap one of these twin points. However, if you have both hands free you can certainly tap on both sides for good measure.

Step 4: Test the crescendo

Relive the first crescendo of this specific event in an associated way and assess the intensity of the emotion. In the example above, this emotion was sadness and was first at a 7. Four things may have happened:

1. The intensity may have gone down, which is often the case. The sadness in this example may have dropped from a 7 to a 5. Use the same emotion with this lower score in the next round (Step 5).

2. The intensity of the sadness may not have changed. In that case, check again as to whether you are reliving the exact same moment, whether the emotion is exactly the same, and whether any bodily sensations are in the same location or have moved to another place. Every little change is significant, as it indicates there has been some effect. This takes some getting used to because we do not usually identify our emotional response so precisely. With some practice, this will become easier. Use what you feel with the same score and, if applicable, a different location in the next round (Step 5).

3. You may feel more sadness, which is fine because it means you are better connected to what you are feeling and have fully activated the stress response. Use the same emotion with this higher score in the next round (Step 5).

4. Your sadness may have diminished but now you may feel another emotion at a higher intensity. For example, your sadness may have dropped to a 5 or lower but now you feel anger at a 6. In that case, you can choose to tap either on anger and sadness combined (because they are almost equally intense) or switch to tapping on the anger. When that is reduced to zero, continue to resolve the remaining sadness. The order does not matter in itself, but tapping on the emotion with the most charge usually works best. Please note that in one crescendo, it is common to experience between one and three emotions, no more than that. If you feel more than three emotions, it is likely that you have already moved on to reliving the next moment, or that you have started to think about the problem more generally, asking yourself rhetorical questions like: *Why is this*

happening to me? Or, *Why does he always do this?* If this happens, focus again on reliving only the first crescendo and resolve the emotional intensity until it reaches zero before moving on. Use the new emotion with its score, or combine the emotions if the scores are similar, in the next round (Step 5).

Step 5: Repeat the setup phrase and tapping sequence until zero

Keep repeating the Setup phrase and the tapping sequence and keep testing this one crescendo (by reliving it). For each round, adjust the emotion and score according to what you have found during testing and work with the tapping sequence until all emotions are zero. Then you move on to the next crescendo. In the example above, the next crescendo is the moment when your partner is talking to you and expressing his anger. When that is neutralized, move on to the third crescendo. In other words, you repeat the cycle: relive (test) – Setup phrase – tapping sequence – relive (test), until all negative emotions of each crescendo are reduced to zero.

Step 6: The final test

The final test involves reliving the entire specific event once more, from beginning to end and doing your absolute best to get upset (for example, by exaggerating the sights and sounds and colors) to activate any remaining negative emotional reaction. If there is no emotional charge left, you have finished resolving this specific event. If you still get a reaction, then you need to do more tapping on any remaining emotions, until a final test on all crescendos is zero. We call this a tested zero. The most frequently made mistake with EFT is not being specific enough, closely followed by not working to a tested zero. The link between the stress trigger and conditioned emotional response is not severed when any intensity remains in any of the crescendos of a specific event. The remaining intensity can be smaller than 1, but not yet zero. It may be very subtle, like a little uneasiness somewhere in your body. When you test, focus on really trying to identify any remaining emotion or bodily sensation rather than testing to ascertain whether you are feeling sufficiently calm and therefore finished. The more thoroughly you do this, the quicker you will obtain permanent results.

Step 1

Choose a specific event with a negative emotional charge.

Step 2

Do an associated exposure of first crescendo.

Step 3

Apply Setup phrase & tapping sequence.

Step 4

Test the crescendo with associated exposure.

Step 5

Repeat Setup phrase & tapping sequence until the charge of each crescendo of this specific event is zero.

Step 6

Do a final test (the entire specific event must now be neutral).

Figure 4. Summary of Gold Standard EFT Steps

Is That All?

Yes, this is the basic Gold Standard EFT protocol. If you use it as instructed, you may be surprised at how much stress you can resolve by yourself.

A free download of the Gold Standard EFT Basic Protocol in English

is available at:

https://www.eftpraktijkactrom.nl/home-english/

Here is one more point of interest:

Variations of the Setup Phrase

The standard Setup phrase is: *Even though I feel [...], I still accept myself.* The first part of the Setup phrase describes your emotional reaction or your physical symptom in the moment and may also include the intensity. The second part is about accepting yourself regardless of what is going on. This makes it an affirmation. Many variations are possible, both in the first part in which you identify the problem and in the acceptance part. The key is to formulate a Setup phrase that accurately and specifically describes your problem and how you experience it (emotionally and/or physically) and, also, that it includes an acceptance of yourself and what has happened.

Variations include:

- Despite [...] I fully accept myself and all my feelings.
- Even though I have done [...], deep down I know I am totally okay.
- Even though [...] happened, there is nothing wrong with me.
- I feel [...] and I accept myself.

The Setup language of the original form of the EFT Tapping protocol included not only accepting yourself but also loving yourself. In the Gold

Standard EFT protocol, Gary Craig included only the acceptance language, as he has found that many people are resistant to expressing love for themselves, and also it is not necessary to include this language to receive the beneficial effects of EFT. Accepting oneself is sufficient. Of course, there is nothing wrong with expressing that you love yourself, so if that feels good, then please feel free to include it.

Some people even have difficulty saying they accept themselves. Our advice is to simply use these words anyway, to begin with. Often the resistance starts to diminish. However, if you experience too much resistance, then, instead of saying *I accept myself,* you may choose to use one of the following alternatives:

- … it may be possible to begin to accept myself.
- … I may be able to accept myself a little bit in time.
- … I would like to accept myself.
- … I am open to the possibility that I can begin to accept myself.
- … there is essentially nothing wrong with me.
- … I accept that I do not accept myself yet.

If you feel that you cannot use any of the above variations, you likely have a self-esteem issue that makes you feel insecure and rather critical of yourself. We all have negative self-limiting beliefs, and these beliefs can generally be boiled down to one main belief, which we call the Negative Core Belief. This could be: *I am not good enough, I am not worth it, I do not belong, I should not be here,* and so on. Over time, you will be able to weaken this belief with EFT, so for now, just choose one of the acceptance phrases above that you are least resistant to.

If you are doing EFT with children, you may want to adjust the Setup phrase so that it better suits their age and experience. A few examples:

- I am afraid, but I am safe now and there is nothing wrong with me.
- I just lied to Mom, but I am still a good kid.
- I am startled because Dad is angry with me, but he still loves me.
- Even though I feel angry, that is totally okay.

The general rule is: if there is too much resistance to a particular EFT Set-up phrase, or it is too threatening or just does not feel right, then create a phrase that approaches the goal of accepting yourself in smaller steps.

4 | OPTIMAL EFT (UNSEEN THERAPIST)

Those who do not carry Heaven within themselves seek it in vain in all the corners of the Universe.

Otto Ludwig, German playwright and critic, 1813 – 1865

Background of the Latest Form of Official EFT

Optimal EFT is a healing method that combines a specific form of exposure technique with a meditation in which you seek help from the spiritual dimension to release negative emotions and self-limiting beliefs. In Optimal EFT, we refer to this spiritual dimension or higher power as The Unseen Therapist™, so as not to conflict with anyone's spiritual or religious beliefs. To gain a better understanding of Optimal EFT, we recommend that you study Gary Craig's e-book on Optimal EFT titled *The Unseen Therapist*, which is available for free on his website, www.emofree.com.[1] For ease of reference, see the following brief summary.

What Is The Unseen Therapist?

The Unseen Therapist is our inner spiritual guide and healer. This inner spiritual guide is the breath of life in all human beings and is called many different names in the religions of the world. All spiritual paths describe a loving essence that is available to us all. It does not matter what name you

---

1 https://www.emofree.com/unseen-therapist/read-this-first.html

use. Gary Craig has chosen the term, 'The Unseen Therapist,' and has given it a female identity, because the female gender is generally perceived as softer and more compassionate. However, you may use any image, name and gender you wish when using this technique.

The Unseen Therapist is part of everyone's consciousness. Anyone can connect with this source and ask for help and guidance, but it usually takes practice and patience to hear it. This is because many of us have forgotten this loving essence within us, or were never taught that this belongs to us, and, therefore, we are not in the habit of using it. In this sense, working with The Unseen Therapist is more like rediscovering the power of love than learning a new methodology of healing. It is already there, within us.

It is our experience that this new form of EFT is more powerful and thus a significant advancement in EFT. We have found that it works more deeply and efficiently. Gold Standard EFT may already have provided you with much healing, but we invite you to try this new form of EFT as well. It is our firm belief that you will increasingly seek the help of The Unseen Therapist once you start doing so. Gold Standard EFT is still useful, of course, particularly in those moments when you are so upset that it is difficult to calm yourself down and move into a meditative state and connect with The Unseen Therapist. You may find it useful to alternate between the two forms of EFT, and over time, you will naturally discover which one is the most helpful in any given situation.

Optimal EFT has been available since 2014, but it originated much earlier. In 1988, Gary Craig had a spiritual experience that, in retrospect, was the beginning of a spiritual journey that ultimately led to the development of EFT. He has known from the inception of EFT Tapping that he wanted to bring Optimal EFT into the world, as he knew that healing through connecting with the spiritual dimension is the most effective way to heal and become emotionally free. However, in the early 1990s, he was aware that most people were not ready to connect with their higher power. Therefore, he was inspired to create and teach EFT Tapping at that time, but he also said, early on, and again later with the introduction of Optimal EFT, that we are in the basement of a healing high rise of a whole new healing paradigm and maybe, someday, we will meet at the penthouse.

With meeting at the penthouse he meant using Optimal EFT for healing, not EFT Tapping. With this in mind, he said in one of the earlier EFT videos that perhaps there would come a time when we would no longer need to tap on acupuncture points. Few people understood what he meant back then. They were simply excited to discover the impressive effectiveness of EFT Tapping, with its simplicity and extraordinary results.

Only now do we fully understand what Gary Craig meant by these words. He had decided at that time to make the acupressure technique part of the EFT protocol primarily because what is now called Optimal EFT was too big a step for most people to take. This was a wise decision, because it took a while even for EFT Tapping to become accepted and recognized as a valid method of healing, despite the fact that it is based on Traditional Chinese Medicine, one of the oldest forms of healing in the world. Those who were willing to try EFT Tapping were soon convinced of its effectiveness, but many in the medical and therapeutic establishments remained skeptical that such a simple technique could have such dramatic results, so it took some time for it to become more widely accepted. In 2010, Gary Craig took a sabbatical to explore how he wanted to move forward with EFT. In 2011, he came back and introduced the term Gold Standard EFT to distinguish the official protocol of EFT Tapping from the various EFT spin-offs. Then, in 2014, he launched Optimal EFT.

A Different Way of Thinking About Illness and Healing

The true cause of illness lies in the mind, not in the body or outside of it. This applies to physical issues as well as mental problems. It is mind over matter.[2] Your beliefs largely determine what happens to you, and your dominant (subconscious) thoughts create your reality. By mind, we do not mean the brain. The brain is a physical organ that simply receives and transmits information.[3] Nothing happens by itself in the brain, just as nothing happens by itself in the rest of the body. The mind, on the other

---

2 This is a large topic that is beyond the scope of this book and deals with quantum physics, the non-locality of the Mind and healing and spirituality, and also with the fact that the materialistic view in science is an unproven assumption. A good starting point is Rupert Sheldrake's website: https://www.sheldrake.org/about-rupert-sheldrake.
3 Lipton, B.H. (2008). *The biology of belief – how your thoughts shape your life*. Hay House; ISBN: 9781401923129.

hand, is not 'matter' but rather, it has a spiritual basis. One small aspect of the mind is what we call our consciousness. Our consciousness contains our daily thoughts, our beliefs and also our memories. It is our consciousness that determines our behavior. This is the home of our ego. It is also the origin of our physical and mental issues.

Gary Craig's 'NewThink'

In his e-book, Gary Craig introduces a new way of thinking that forms the basis of Optimal EFT and working with The Unseen Therapist. He refers to this new way of thinking as *NewThink* and describes the key points as follows:

1. NewThink 1: We do not understand the true cause of our ailments
2. NewThink 2: The true cause = negative emotions
3. NewThink 3: There is one natural remedy for everything
4. NewThink 4: Listening to what quantum physics has said for years
5. NewThink 5: Listening to spiritual evidence
6. NewThink 6: The Unseen Therapist is the only true healer
7. NewThink 7: We only have one challenge

NewThink 1: We do not understand the true cause of our ailments

Even professionals of conventional medicine admit they do not know the exact cause of the vast majority of diseases. They may provide a list of potential contributing factors, but rarely do they identify the cause. Tendencies, outside influences, and risk factors are not causes. Yet we rely on these physicians and, while our problem is sometimes solved, we are all too often subjected to unnecessary surgeries, misdiagnoses and side effects from prescribed medications.

If we understood the true cause of our disorders, our medical paradigm would look very different. The key question to consider when looking at any disorder is: what is the cause and what is the effect? To demonstrate, we will use depression as an example. It is generally assumed that depression is caused by a chemical imbalance in the brain. This is based on findings that depressed people have fewer neurotransmitters, such as serotonin and norepinephrine. However, no explanation is given as to why certain people have fewer neurotransmitters and what causes this chemical imbalance. It is well-documented in numerous research studies that negative childhood experiences and social and environmental factors, such as loss, trauma, isolation and feeling rejected, play a role in depression. However, only hereditary factors, chemical imbalances and hormonal changes are identified as causes of depression by the conventional medical profession, even though such findings are based only on laboratory tests conducted at the time the depression was diagnosed. Medication is usually prescribed to replenish the missing chemicals in the body. Those who rely on such medication to get well usually become dependent on it, often for the rest of their lives, because their symptoms return if they stop taking it. This is not surprising, given that the underlying cause of the depression has not been identified or addressed.

NewThink 2: The true cause = negative emotions

The true causes of diseases are negative emotions. Diseases show up in the body as manifestations of the unresolved fear, anger, guilt and other negative emotions that we accumulate over the course of our lives. It is now accepted by medical researchers that negative emotions are major contributors to our diseases, and a new field of medicine called psychoneuroimmunology has emerged, based on this discovery. However, doctors have not been trained to truly neutralize the damaging effects of negative emotions. Their education has been directed at the body. Matters of the mind are viewed as belonging to another field, namely psychiatry. Yet, psychiatrists also tend to treat the symptoms with medication rather than target the cause.

You have an incredible self-healing capability within you that is controlled by your mind. Once you take the time to use EFT to resolve any negative, underlying emotional problems, a healthy balance will restore itself automatically and this will often manifest physically in your body as well. Where the issue seems to be a permanent shortage of certain substances in the body (for example thyroid hormone, insulin or neurotransmitters), interestingly enough, no research has ever been done to determine whether the production of these substances will resume after the disturbing, underlying root emotional cause has been resolved. Diseases are the effect, while unresolved negative emotions in our subconscious mind are the root cause. When you resolve your emotional issues, you remove the root cause.

In Chapter 6, we provide a plan of action to enable you to address the root cause of your problems by helping you identify and resolve your emotional issues. If you have a physical issue that does not require urgent medical care, we invite you to try EFT first and use it to thoroughly resolve the related stresses. Then notice the effects of doing so, rather than taking medication to treat your symptoms and ignoring the cause. We are not suggesting that you should not seek medical help if you have severe, acute symptoms. But there are many issues and problems that do not require immediate medical treatment, so you could try Optimal EFT on these and discover first-hand what happens when you resolve your stress and negative emotions.

Whether you are willing and able to try this alternative healing approach depends on your personal circumstances, as well as your own beliefs and the views of those around you. If you are surrounded by people who are pushing you to follow conventional medicine, or if you yourself believe (consciously or subconsciously) that only conventional medicine will work, and you are fearful and simply cannot go against what everyone expects you to do (including the doctor), then you may choose to treat the symptoms in the usual way and use Optimal EFT to address other daily stresses and triggers for now. Or perhaps you are willing to try Optimal EFT for a short while before going to a doctor. Whatever the case, follow your intuition and do what feels best for you right now, rather than creating more stress for yourself.

NewThink 3: There is one natural remedy for everything

We have been conditioned to believe that every disease or ailment requires a specific remedy. One pill for a headache, another for anxiety. Radiation for some tumors, surgery for others. However, the true cause of our ailments is the same, regardless of the physical symptoms. The physical symptoms are echoes or manifestations of our unresolved negative emotions. The way physical symptoms manifest in our bodies is much less important than what causes them. Given that unresolved negative emotions and stress are the root cause of our ailments, it follows that one remedy (which resolves stress completely and permanently) is sufficient. Optimal EFT provides one natural remedy for everything, because The Unseen Therapist brings peace to the true cause of your ailments (negative emotions) and that peace can help to resolve the physical symptoms, or, in the event that they remain, enable you to enjoy a greater sense of peace even with such symptoms.

NewThink 4: Listening to what quantum physics has been saying for years

Our premiere scientists have been telling us for decades that the world is structured quite differently from how it appears. According to quantum physics, our physical world is an illusion. Even though our senses convincingly tell us that we are separate from each other and everything in the world, that is not possible on a quantum level. Our ego wants us to believe that we are individuals with our separate bodies and private thoughts. However, nothing is separate from anything else. There is only a grand Oneness, but we are not aware of it. If the world is not real, then we must question every belief we have about it. This includes our current beliefs about healing. If they are based on an illusion, then those beliefs are not to be trusted.

The more Optimal EFT you do, the more often you will enter a calm, peaceful state, where you will be able to feel connected to everything and everyone. This Oneness is our natural, loving state. This Oneness is also the centerpiece of the newest form of Official EFT. This is where The Unseen Therapist lets Her light shine, putting cause and effect in the right order and helping you to truly resolve the cause. She looks beyond our limiting beliefs and erroneous assumptions. As a result, you may achieve much greater results than with a conventional approach to healing.

NewThink 5: Listening to spiritual evidence

An inspiring collection of spiritual experiences has been accumulating proof of Oneness for decades, including spiritual epiphanies and near-death experiences. In his e-book, Gary Craig describes the epiphany he had in 1988. For him, it was the starting point for developing EFT and it inspired him to bring it to the world. A common feature of almost all of these spiritual epiphanies is the experience of an all-encompassing spiritual love – a healing love beyond description where everything is connected within that free-flowing Oneness of joy. Our fears, resentments and guilts dwindle into nothingness as this blissful state takes their place with a sense of complete protection and unconditional acceptance. Anxieties and physical ailments then become impossible because they cannot survive in an ocean of love where there are no negative emotions to cause them.

Working with The Unseen Therapist does not require you to experience an epiphany, but by practicing Optimal EFT, you can improve your communication with The Unseen Therapist and make use of this incredibly powerful state. Reaching and maintaining the ability to be aware of that state of pure loving presence, and calling upon it for help, lifts your life to new levels.

NewThink 6: The Unseen Therapist is the only true healer

The Unseen Therapist is the true healer. We learn to work by Her side and become Her valued assistants. She waits patiently and without judgment. All we need to do is open the door to Her presence. It is important to note that The Unseen Therapist will never interfere with our free will to believe whatever we wish. This explains why we are not helped automatically to resolve all our problems. Nor will She hinder our choice to retain, forget or hide, even from ourselves, the anger, grief, guilt, fear and other negative emotions that keep us stuck in the belief in separation. It might seem loving – at least on the surface – for The Unseen Therapist to wave Her spiritual magic wand and remove our erroneous beliefs and our retained, forgotten, or hidden issues. But that would violate our right to think and believe as we choose – and that would be an unloving act indeed! The limiting beliefs we hold may be completely subconscious, so we may not even understand why we have psychological problems or physical symptoms. Everyone wants to be healthy and happy, right? Yes, that is true, but we do not appreciate the connection between what we have experienced and our ailments, so we do not realize that we need to address the underlying emotional root causes to heal.

With this book, we want to help you learn to connect with The Unseen Therapist and use Optimal EFT properly so that you can achieve real and lasting results. The Unseen Therapist will help you access your issues and remove them from hiding, but She cannot take you further than your readiness allows. Your readiness will improve as you continue to practice Optimal EFT. Our healing journey is a process. You have so many beliefs that are contrary to the truth that it would be unrealistic to expect all your issues to vanish immediately. The key is to practice!

NewThink 7: We have only one challenge

What stops The Unseen Therapist from healing our bodies and instantly awakening[4] us? We do! We all share the same Oneness as The Unseen Therapist, so we have the same power, but we are not aware that we have it! We do not appreciate how powerful we really are. If we suddenly awakened and discovered what we really are, it would probably be too great a shock for most of us. This realization is therefore almost always a gradual process. The mistaken belief in separation is much easier to discuss academically than it is to own and truly internalize at the deepest level. To truly experience the Oneness that we are part of, we need to cultivate trust in The Unseen Therapist and in the process of Optimal EFT. Trust is an essential component of love. How do we cultivate that trust? Through experience. We can gain this experience by practicing Optimal EFT. This involves connecting to The Unseen Therapist, asking for Her help and, as we do so, reminding ourselves that She is always ready and willing to help. As we continue to practice and experience the benefits, we deepen our connection to The Unseen Therapist and build trust and confidence in Her and the process of Optimal EFT.

---

4 We use the term *awakening* to describe a spiritual shift in consciousness and reaching a state of greater awareness and presence.

The Basic Protocol of Optimal EFT Explained

The basic protocol of Optimal EFT is called the Personal Peace Procedure and it involves meditating with the help of The Unseen Therapist and connecting with the spiritual realm.

Meditation Works!

The beneficial effects of meditation are well established. Studies show that meditation has the following benefits:

- It reduces stress and decreases the reactivity of the amygdala (the fight or flight part of the brain).[5] Meditation and other mind-body techniques actually decrease the size of the amygdala.[6][7]
- Your brain function deteriorates less rapidly and your life expectancy increases.[8]
- You become calmer and your anxious thoughts highjack you less frequently.[9]
- Your concentration improves.[10]
- It reduces anxiety, stress, and depression and improves the quality of life.[11]

---

5   Bauer, C.C.C., Caballero, C., Scherer, E., West, M.R., Mrazek, M.D., Phillips, D.T., Whitfield-Gabrieli, S., Gabrieli, J.D.E. (2019). Mindfulness Training Reduces Stress and Amygdala Reactivity to Fearful Faces in Middle-School Children. *Behav Neurosci. 2019 Dec;133(6):569-585.* doi:10.1037/bne0000337. Epub 2019 Aug 26. PMID: 31448928.

6   Gotink, R.A., Vernooij, M.W., Ikram, M.A., Niessen, W.J., Krestin, G.P., Hofman, A., Tiemeier, H., Hunink, M.G.M. (2018). Meditation and Yoga Practice Are Associated with Smaller Right Amygdala Volume: the Rotterdam Study. *Brain Imaging Behav. 2018 Dec;12(6):1631-1639.* doi:10.1007/s11682-018-9826-z. PMID: 29417491; PMCID: PMC6302143.

7   Holzel, B.K., Carmody, J., Evans, K.C., Hoge, E.A., Dusek, J.A., Morgan, L., et al. (2010). Stress Reduction Correlates with Structural Changes in the Amygdala. *Social Cognitive and Affective Neuroscience. 2010;5(1):11-17.* doi: 10.1093/scan/nsp034.

8   Luders, E., Cherbuin, N., Kurth, F. (2015). Forever Young(er): Potential Age-Defying Effects of Long-Term Meditation on Gray Matter Atrophy. *Front. Psychol., 2015 Jan 21;5:1551.* https://doi.org/10.3389/fpsyg.2014.01551.

9   Brewer, J.A., Worhunsky, P.D., Gray, J.R., Tang, Y., Weber, J., Kober, H. (2011). Meditation Experience Is Associated with Differences in Default Mode Network Activity and Connectivity PNAS. *December 13, 2011 108 (50) 20254-20259;* https://doi.org/10.1073/pnas.1112029108.

10 Mrazek, M.D., Franklin, M.S., Phillips, D.T., Baird, B., Schooler, J.W. (2013). Mindfulness Training Improves Working Memory Capacity and GRE Performance While Reducing Mind Wandering. *Sage Jounals.2013. Research Article.* Find in PubMed https://doi.org/10.1177/0956797612459659.

11 Goyal, M., et al. Meditation programs for psychological stress and well-being: a systematic review and meta-analysis. *JAMA Intern Med. 2014 Mar;174(3):357-68.*

Conventional medicine is gradually becoming more open to the beneficial effects of meditation and some doctors even recommend meditation to certain patients suffering from chronic conditions. Hopefully, this will become more common. However, it is unfortunate that meditation is only given a supportive role when disease is already present, and it is not usually recommended as a preventative measure to maintain health and avoid disease. Conventional medicine once again often stops at treating only symptoms, instead of going further to address the cause of ailments. We believe that much more is possible with meditation. While the benefits of meditation are substantial, Optimal EFT and working with The Unseen Therapist go much further and help you address and resolve the root cause of your problems.

How is Optimal EFT Different From Meditation and Mindfulness?

Like regular meditation, Optimal EFT has a calming effect and improves your brain function over time. However, after spending time in meditation and leaving the room in a Zen state, feeling completely in the now and at peace, you may still experience the stress response as soon as you encounter a stressful situation later on. This is because regular meditation calms your mind and may even cause you to become less reactive over time, but it does not clear the unresolved negative emotions within your subconscious. The link between stressful situations and your stress response is not severed. The stress response (fight, flight, or freeze) is an automatic reaction by your subconscious mind that is more than 10 million times faster than your conscious thoughts. If we use computer language to explain this, your subconscious processes information at a rate of 11.2 million bits per second, whereas your conscious mind can only process information at 40-60 bits per second. So, it does not stand a chance to catch up and prevent the subconscious reaction from happening.[12] Accordingly, even though you may consciously feel calmer after meditating, your subconscious reaction to events in the external world has not changed.

---

12 https://sites.psu.edu/psych256sp14/2014/03/09/the-bandwidth-of-consciousness/ and https://www.britannica.com/science/information-theory/Physiology

Another difference between regular meditation and Optimal EFT is the intention with which you practice them. The aim of Optimal EFT is to completely sever the link between a trigger and your stress response. The protocol requires you to enter into a meditative state where you connect with The Unseen Therapist. Focus specifically on a triggering moment and continue working on it until your emotional reaction has been resolved completely. Make sure you keep testing your emotional intensity and do not stop until it is at a zero. Thus, Optimal EFT is a unique form of healing. No other technique or therapy requires you to keep testing to determine whether the negative emotional reaction to a trigger has completely disappeared.

Similarities with Gold Standard EFT

Both Gold Standard EFT and Optimal EFT require you to identify a specific moment when your stress reaction was activated. You then activate that stress reaction by reliving the moment in an associated way (after taking the edge off where necessary to avoid re-traumatization). You then either tap or enter into a meditative state and connect with The Unseen Therapist to resolve the stress response. Then, you test by reliving the moment again. You repeat this cycle until all negative emotions and/or physical reactions are neutralized. When you have reduced the reaction to zero, you test the zero by reliving the moment once more and doing your best to activate any negative emotions or physical sensations. In other words, you are testing to determine whether the link between the trigger and the stress response has been severed. The process is complete once you can remain calm or you no longer feel any reaction in your body when you relive the moment. After completing one or more sessions with Optimal EFT, people often report feeling a sense of immense peace and calm that they have never felt before. They also mention feeling like they finally understand and have compassion for those who they had considered had wronged them in some way.

What to Expect

Are you ready to use the Personal Peace Procedure and the love of The Unseen Therapist to address your own problems? Are you open to this new way of thinking and working? Will you join us in crossing the bridge, which will enable you to perceive yourself and the world from the loving perspective of The Unseen Therapist, who waits patiently on the other side of the bridge? Do you look forward to experiencing the loving oneness that we all share and receiving help from The Unseen Therapist simply by asking for it?

These are questions that only you can answer. We can assure you, however, that the process itself requires no prior training and consists of three simple steps that anyone can learn. But it is a process and something you need to practice. Your potential to heal is enormous, but we do not expect you to experience its full effects immediately. After all, you are entering uncharted territory, and so your results may initially range from fantastic to disappointing. They may even be completely lacking at first. What you get out of it depends on your level of readiness, your confidence, and your ability to communicate with The Unseen Therapist.

These criteria, and thus your results, are different from one situation to another and from one moment to the next. As with all skills, practice makes perfect. You will sometimes take three steps forward and then two steps back when crossing the bridge. Perseverance wins. Some newcomers have seen intense fears, severe depression, pains or physical limitations go away almost immediately in a miraculous way, while others shrugged their shoulders in disappointment because they did not perceive any change. Most beginners land somewhere between these two extremes. With consistent practice, anyone can achieve good results over time. However, more complex issues may require the assistance of an EFT professional who is certified in Optimal EFT.

Let us also realize that not all healings happen immediately and they may not even be recognizable. This is because The Unseen Therapist is aware of much more than we are. For example, She may know that an immediate healing is too threatening to your belief system, while you are not aware of this at all. In that case She will delay it or allow it to happen over a longer period. If your ailment covers a deeper, hidden problem that you are not yet ready to deal with, healing will be delayed until you are ready.

This, however, does not change the fact that Optimal EFT will exceed your expectations if you give it a chance and put time and effort into it. Anything is possible if we are committed to it. We only need a small amount of willingness to take the time to ask for help from The Unseen Therapist, and She will be there.

The Personal Peace Procedure Meditation

Gary Craig describes the Personal Peace Procedure meditation process briefly in his free e-book, as an introduction for beginners. Here, we will go into more detail about the technique and each step of the process.

The Personal Peace Procedure that underlies your personal healing could not be simpler. Here are the steps:

1. Identify a specific event with a negative charge.
2. Quiet your mind as best you can and enter a loving state by, for example, recalling a loving moment. Invite The Unseen Therapist to resolve the negativity.
3. Test the result and repeat until the negative charge is gone.

These steps form the foundation for all your sessions with The Unseen Therapist. Anyone can do this. You focus on a specific event, which is the emotional root cause of a psychological or physical problem. Addressing the true emotional root causes is similar to pulling out weeds, roots and all. How well you can get to these emotional root causes determines whether your problems will diminish or even disappear. It requires that you put all aspects of the problem on the table so that the Unseen Therapist understands that you are ready to resolve it completely.

For best results, we will explain each step of this protocol.

Step 1. Identify a specific event with a negative charge.

As with Gold Standard EFT, you look for a specific event where you have a negative emotional and/or physical reaction. Then, you identify what your negative stress reaction is and score it between 0 and 10. The correct associated way to relive the moment is the same as with Gold Standard EFT Tapping (described in Chapter 2). Please note that it will be necessary to break down your particular event into several, shorter pieces if it contains more than one emotional crescendo. Narrow the event down to shorter events with only one emotional crescendo each and do them one at a time. Again, we recommend that you limit yourself to events that you can relive in an associated way without help.

Step 2. Be quiet and loving. Invite The Unseen Therapist to resolve it.

We have broken down Step 2 into four phases. Eventually, these phases will automatically merge into one seamless routine that you can use for any specific event. The process may seem strange and even uncomfortable at first, but once you get some results, you have begun to cross the bridge to being aware and making use of this loving supportive power that is available to all of us. Your motivation determines how much progress you make and how successful you are.

Phase 1: Expecting Success

Expecting success will come naturally once you start to get results, but it can be harder in the beginning. The key is to be willing to try, which you no doubt are or you would not be reading this book. Fortunately, as a beginner, you do not need unwavering faith. Simply expecting a small degree of success is enough. No routine is needed for this. Do whatever comes to mind. Sometimes it works well to say, *Okay, Unseen Therapist, do your thing,* or *Come on,* or *I need your help,* or something else that suggests you are at least open to Her help. As you know by now, The Unseen Therapist is your spiritual inner guide and healer, and it is this power that you are trying to tap into. Therefore, it is important to expect success and let go of blocking thoughts, such as *This cannot possibly work.* If you do have such a block, do not struggle with it, but simply hand it over to The Unseen Therapist and ask Her to take it from you.

Phase 2: Achieving Stillness

This phase needs the most practice, as we all experience constant chatter in our heads that demands our attention and reminds us of things we need to do. While we cannot eliminate this chatter, we can, with practice, quiet our thoughts and still our minds. The quieter, the better, but you do not need to achieve perfect stillness to get results. If you are new to this process, it would be best if you start practicing when you are alone in a quiet environment, free of mobile phones and other distractions. As you become more proficient, you will be able to become quiet and peaceful even when you are in a noisy environment full of people. It is all about practice. Sit comfortably in a quiet space and take one or more deep breaths. You may want to count backward from 10 to 0 so that you do not get distracted by your thoughts. Do not expect perfection on your first attempts. Remember, you are learning a new important skill, and it will take time to master it.

Phase 3: Evoking a Loving Moment

Recall a loving moment – a time when you felt loved by someone or love for someone, a loving moment with a pet or a peaceful moment in nature. It could even be a loving moment from a book or movie. There are thousands of possibilities. If you cannot find one, then make up a moment or imagine yourself enjoying nature. It may help to smile gently.

Step into that moment and immerse yourself completely in that loving feeling. The Unseen Therapist is always present and instantly recognizes what you are doing. Thus, She sees the mere effort of getting quiet and recalling a loving moment as an invitation to be with you, even if it is not done 'perfectly.' By focusing your mind in this way, you not only turn on the healing power of love, but you are also taking your focus away from the chatter in your head.

Some beginners find this step challenging because they put pressure on themselves to find a perfect loving moment and feel that they have to get it right. Try your best to avoid that by reminding yourself that any simple attempt at recalling a loving moment is sufficient.

Phase 4: Ask the Unseen Therapist to Resolve the Specific Event

In practice, there is little time between step 1, in which you relive your particular moment in an associated way, and phase 4 of step 2. At this point, you know what you want to work on and you feel your emotional reaction. There are numerous ways in which you can ask The Unseen Therapist to solve the problem for you. Here are three approaches that you may try:

1. You become aware of your emotional reaction and how it feels in your body, and then ask The Unseen Therapist to resolve this feeling for you.
2. You ask The Unseen Therapist to solve this problem or the situation as a whole.
3. You relive the moment again and you ask The Unseen Therapist to resolve it.

In each of the above approaches, you do not need to do anything else, other than staying in your loving state as best as you can. You may find it helpful to use a metaphor, especially if you find it difficult to do nothing during the meditation itself or if you are new to the process. Simply let an image come to mind of what your emotional reaction looks like in your body and then imagine The Unseen Therapist resolving it with any metaphor that comes to mind, such as a beautiful white light, a cool breeze or a flowing waterfall. Or you may visualize The Unseen Therapist flooding the situation with love or helping it to float away and dissolve high in the sky. Allow it to happen as spontaneously as possible, without too much effort, remembering that nothing has to happen. If nothing comes to mind, that is okay too. We call this step a meditation, and if you notice your mind wandering off to other thoughts during this little meditation, gently bring yourself back to your loving state as best you can.

Experiment with each of these approaches and see what works for you and your specific event. As you become more experienced with the process, you may also spontaneously receive images or a message from The Unseen Therapist. It may be related to specific events that also need to be resolved, it may be an insight or deeper understanding of the situation, or it may be compassion for yourself and/or others involved.

The key point to remember is that nothing has to happen and you do not have to actively do anything during this Personal Peace Procedure. Some people remain in their loving moment for most of the meditation. For others, it is simply quiet and all may be black or white. Whatever happens is fine. It is best not to actively think about or analyze the problem. If such thoughts come up, just notice them and let them go, returning your attention to your loving moment.

The time you need for your meditation typically varies from two to ten minutes, but it may also be shorter or longer. Stay in the meditation until you feel that you have plateaued at a certain level or that you have reached a natural endpoint, without testing the result (that is the next step). If you are unsure if it is finished, stay in the meditation for a little while longer and then open your eyes. Again, do not worry about 'doing it right.' Just make a reasonable attempt. Eventually, everything will fall into place.

Step 3. Test the result.

Relive the specific event in an associated way and determine how it feels now, both physically and emotionally. If your reaction is not yet zero (for all aspects), then repeat the Personal Peace Procedure and test again. Continue doing this until the event has become neutral, with no negative emotional charge or physical reaction. In Chapter 6, we will explain what you can do if you do not seem to be able to resolve your emotional and/or physical reaction and get it down to zero for the specific event, even after several rounds.

A free download of the Optimal EFT Basic Protocol in English

is available at:

https://www.eftpraktijkactrom.nl/home-english/

Step 1

Identify a specific event with a negative charge.

Step 2

Be quiet and loving. Invite The Unseen Therapist to resolve it.

Step 3

Test your result and repeat until the event is neutral.

Figure 5. Summary of Optimal EFT Steps

Is It That Simple?

It is that simple, but this does not necessarily mean that success is guaranteed. Your success depends on a number of factors, most importantly being willing to fully commit to and trust the process. Like meditation, the first step is deciding that you want to try the process. Then you need to make the time to actually do it and finally, you need to fully accept whatever happens during the process (rather than judging yourself and trying too hard to do it properly, which can lead to you giving up). It is about surrendering and trusting the process. Your willingness to commit to the process on a regular basis and your readiness to put your issues on the table will determine how successful you are in seeking the help of The Unseen Therapist.

Here are two more points of interest to help you keep it simple:

I Cannot Quiet My Mind: Too Much Noise or Too Emotional

There may be times when you feel so upset, angry, sad, afraid or restless that you simply cannot bring yourself to close your eyes and try to quiet your thoughts and calm your mind. This is completely understandable. At such times, we recommend that you try tapping first, using the Gold Standard EFT protocol. While you are tapping, you can also ask The Unseen Therapist to help calm your mind and release your emotions and your attachment to your thoughts. Just notice the thoughts come and go and continue to tap until you feel calm enough to begin the Optimal EFT process. As you continue to practice calming your mind, it gets easier and easier. At some point, you may notice that you can effortlessly seek the help of The Unseen Therapist, even when you are extremely upset or in a noisy place full of people. When you are surrounded by noise and distractions, it may be helpful to call on The Unseen Therapist by saying silently: *I need Your help right now.* This may help you realize that, on some level, you are not alone and that She is always with you, even in these challenging circumstances.

I Am Not Able to Evoke a Loving Moment

We cannot emphasize enough that any simple attempt to recall a loving moment is sufficient. A loving moment can be anything, provided that it is uncomplicated and has the potential to put a smile on your face. For example, looking at your dog playing, or the moment you first held your child in your arms, or the beautiful sunset you saw last night. Even a hint of a peaceful feeling or a vaguely pleasant feeling will suffice. If that fails, you may think of something that you enjoyed when you experienced it, even though you are not able to feel that way now. Above all else, refrain from judging how well you manage to get into that loving feeling because that is not the point. Your best effort is good enough. The reason we recall a loving moment is to simply remind ourselves of what we really are (which is love, at one with The Unseen Therapist and each other) and to invite The Unseen Therapist to be with us so that we are better able to communicate with Her and seek Her help and guidance.

5 | INSTRUCTIONS FOR SELF-HELP

By helping yourself, you are helping humankind. By helping humankind, you are helping yourself. That is the law of all spiritual progress.

Christopher Isherwood, British-American author, 1904 – 1986

What Is Wrong with Me?

Hopefully, you understand by now that there is nothing inherently wrong with you. The only problem is that you have unresolved negative emotions stored in your subconscious mind from past events, that are affecting how you feel and react in the present moment. Whenever your emotional reaction seems to be more intense than the present situation warrants, those unresolved emotions are playing a role.

If, on the other hand, your emotional reaction is appropriate given the circumstances, then you are making good use of what you have learned from your past experiences. Unfortunately, this happens less often than we would like, although we are generally unaware of how often and how much our reaction is influenced by our past. Perhaps 80% to 90% of your reaction to current events is determined by your past conditioning and only 10% to 20% by what is actually happening now. Of course, the other way around is only 10% or less of your reaction caused by your previous experiences. The popular claim that 95% of our behavior is unconscious and only 5% is conscious cannot be backed up with scientific evidence. First, these numbers pertain to brain activity rather than behavior. Second, most research focuses on decision-making in relation to choosing, because that produces a measurable outcome, but there are no methods available to measure subconscious (or unconscious) behavior as such.[1] [2] No matter what the ratio is, it is undeniable that our behavior is influenced by what we have experienced in our past.

EFT allows us to process and release unresolved negative emotions, so we are no longer driven to repeat negative reactions and behaviors, resulting in emotional freedom and more peace in our lives. To achieve emotional freedom, you need to know how to use EFT properly. Simply deciding to behave differently in the future does not work, as you have no doubt realized by now. If it did, you would have overcome all your negative reactions, behaviors and habits a long time ago. This explains why so few people succeed with New Year's resolutions. It is not because you lack willpower or self-discipline and there is no hope for you. It is simply because your behavior is strongly influenced by your subconscious conditioning that continues to sabotage you, despite your best intentions.

In Chapter 4, we used the analogy of a computer: your subconscious mind works at a speed of 11.2 million bits per second whereas your conscious mind operates at a speed of only 40-60 bits per second. Therefore, before you consciously decide anything, your subconscious reaction is already underway, automatically making connections, judgments and decisions, and initiating the conditioned stress response. For this reason, it is essential to address and resolve the underlying cause of your behavior, namely the unresolved emotions and limiting beliefs in your subconscious mind, hidden in stored memories about past events. That is why EFT is such a powerful and effective technique, because, properly applied, it enables you to do exactly that!

---

1 Sutil-Martín DL, Rienda-Gómez JJ. The Influence of Unconscious Perceptual Processing on Decision-Making: A New Perspective From Cognitive Neuroscience Applied to Generation Z. *Front Psychol. 2020 Aug 11;11:1728.* doi: 10.3389/fpsyg.2020.01728. Erratum in: *Front Psychol. 2021 Sep 02;12:752308.* PMID: 32903621; PMCID: PMC7438726.

2 Mudrik L, Arie IG, Amir Y, Shir Y, Hieronymi P, Maoz U, O'Connor T, Schurger A, Vargas M, Vierkant T, Sinnott-Armstrong W, Roskies A. Free will without consciousness? *Trends Cogn Sci. 2022 Jul;26(7):555-566.* doi: 10.1016/j.tics.2022.03.005. Epub 2022 Apr 12. PMID: 35428589.

Stress Patterns

When you experience a stressful situation, you may think: *Why is this happening to me?* or, *I do not want this anymore!* or, *Here we go again.* Most of our negative reactions and behaviors are repetitive and they become more and more entrenched over time. They are called stress patterns and they have a major impact on how we react in any situation. To clarify, we are talking about your reaction to situations and people and how you behave in response to them. Other people have stress patterns too. Perhaps another person is triggering you by behaving in a negative way. You may feel that your negative reaction is justified and that they made you angry or upset. However, your reaction is an inside job and it is mostly an automatic reaction based on your own past experiences. Therefore, you and the other person are both reacting based on your own stress patterns. Not a successful way to solve whatever is going on between you, because a part of each of you becomes a little child again, feeling the powerlessness, anger or sadness that went with the earliest experience of this stress reaction. This is called regression and it happens automatically (and most of the time unnoticed) when you are triggered. At that moment, you think and may even behave like that little child with the wisdom you had at that age.[3] Sometimes you may be conscious of the fact that your thoughts, behavior, or voice are somewhat childlike. It goes without saying that it is less than ideal to handle a situation in your adult life like a 5-year-old or 14-year-old would.

Let us take a closer look at how stress patterns arise and how they work. Our perceptions of the world are based on all of our past experiences. Our minds tend to categorize our experiences into groups and then use these to create generalizations or conclusions about ourselves and the world, which become stronger over time. As we experience more situations that confirm these conclusions, we become convinced that these conclusions are always true. They become our truths. These truths influence every choice and observation we make. Whether you call them judgments, generalizations, interpretations, conclusions, decisions, beliefs or truths, they are all examples of how you interpret the world around you. We call them: 'The writings on the walls of our minds.' It is your worldview, but not the reality. A worldview is formed in two

---

3 Lokko HN, Stern TA. Regression: Diagnosis, Evaluation, and Management. *Prim Care Companion CNS Disord.* 2015 May 14;17(3):10.4088/PCC.14f01761. doi: 10.4088/PCC.14f01761. PMID: 26644947; PMCID: PMC4578899.

steps: first, by specific experiences in your life and, second, by the conclusions you draw about yourself and the world based on these specific experiences.

As discussed in Chapter 2, the metaphor of the Table Top with the Table Legs is useful to help you identify which problem you want to address (the conclusion on the Table Top) and which specific events led to this conclusion and made it true (the Table Legs). Now, we want to expand this metaphor further in the next section so that you can get an even deeper understanding of what you need to work on.

The Anatomy of Emotional Problems

As illustrated in Figure 6, the Table Top conclusion, "I am not good enough," is created and supported by numerous specific events (Table Legs), and there are also two smaller tables on top of it, reflecting the concept that emotional problems are layered in time and build upon one another. The example is simple and incomplete, since you may have collected dozens or even hundreds of smaller tables throughout your life that are connected to the big table underneath (this conclusion is your negative core belief, which we will explain below). If you do not resolve the big Table Top, smaller tables will continue to pile up throughout your life.

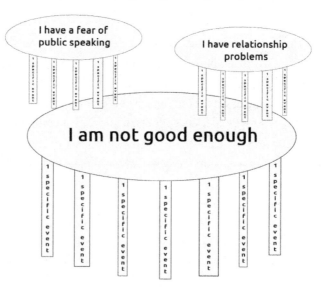

Figure 6. Metaphor of Table Top with Table Legs – Expanded

The big table or issue at the bottom is the result of all the emotional experiences accumulated during the first 6 to 7 years of your life. We explain below how your emotional development is impacted by what happens to you, from the time you were conceived up to the time your brain is fully developed, around the age of 23-24. These years are foundational in the development of various important stress patterns. But, obviously, this development does not stop at age 23-24 but continues for the rest of your life.

Conception to 2 Years: Research has shown that your interaction with the outside world begins approximately three weeks after conception. Until the age of two, a child cannot distinguish between themselves and their environment – they are one with it. During this period, the right hemisphere of the brain is dominant, because the left hemisphere develops at a slower rate. As we have already explained, for the right brain, everything is always happening now and you are connected to everything and everyone. As a fetus, baby and then toddler, you are small, powerless and dependent upon others for your survival. You are not yet able to fully understand what is happening. Things may seem to happen suddenly, which may startle or frighten you, so relatively small events can, therefore, have a big impact. During this whole period, including the time you are in utero, your mother's stress and negative emotions do not go unnoticed; you experience them too. The same applies to the emotions of your father and other people around you. Since you cannot distinguish between yourself and others, you experience their emotions as if they are your own, as if you are the cause of what is happening. If something bad happens, you often conclude it is your fault. This period lays the foundation for our emotional and behavioral responses later in life. Once the child learns to put words around their thoughts and feelings, their implicit conclusion that they are doing something wrong becomes the explicit negative core belief: *I am not good enough.* The vulnerability of babies is also significant because, when they feel they are not okay and that something is wrong with them, that feeling can become a fear of rejection and, therefore, a fear of dying. Because they are so vulnerable at this age, they can die if they are not fed, kept warm and taken care of by others.

From 2 years until 6-7 years: At around the age of 2 years, our left brain comes 'online,' which is noticeable because that is when children usually begin to talk in phrases or sentences. This is almost always the signal for most parents to start 'parenting' in earnest, thinking that, as soon as the child talks, they should be able to listen to reason. This socialization process is necessary, of course, and we are not discussing here what the best parenting approach would be. However, one thing is certain: the way children are parented unfortunately often involves a lot of rejection. Parents tend to focus on what the child does wrong and what they need to change to get approval (love). Also, if parents are not aware of their stress patterns and negative core belief, they may blame the child for their emotions and reactions, telling them it is their fault, they should change their behavior for the parent to feel good again. In this way, the child may literally hear from their parent that they are responsible for what has happened. This is how negative beliefs take root. With each rejection, the child concludes: *If I did not do it right, then they must think I am not good enough.* This soon turns into the general conclusion: *I am not good enough,* or a variation such as, *I do not belong, I should not be here, I do not matter, I am worthless, I am not heard or seen.* We call this the negative core belief. Every child develops a negative conclusion about themselves. This negative core belief is one of the major negative stress patterns that continues to play an important role throughout your life.

In addition to experiencing the rejection of others, we often reject ourselves even more. This is due to the fact that the rejection by others (especially by our parents on whom we depend for food and shelter and love) is so threatening and causes so much stress that we (subconsciously) reject ourselves rather than experience the feared rejection by our parents, and later in life, by others. The logic behind this has to do with the notion that if our behavior is the cause of our parents' behavior, then there is nothing wrong with them, and they can still be the loving, caring parent we need, if only we change our behavior. The latter is in our control, so we just need to do a better job of being a good kid that deserves their approval (love).

Children are in a trance-like state until the age of 6-7 when the brain reaches 90% of its adult size. Until they reach this age, self-awareness develops slowly and magical thinking is characteristic. In this stage, reasoning is still primitive and children ask many questions to understand why things are the way they are. Magical thinking causes them to make all kinds of con-nections between themselves and events in their environment (causal re-lationships) that are in fact not true. For example, many young children of divorced parents truly believe that if they had been more obedient, if they had cleaned up their room and fought less with their siblings, their parents would not have fought, and they would still be together. In other words, they conclude the divorce is their fault. Emotional experiences during this period serve to cement the negative core belief into place. Every rejection, disapproval and criticism result in the activation and reaffirmation of the negative core belief.

From 6-7 years to 23-24 years: Your emotional development does not stop at the age of 6-7. In fact, it never stops. However, by the time you reach the age of 23-24, your brain will be fully developed. The period from 6-7 years to 23-24 years has a huge impact on the development of our self-image and worldview, but the impact is slightly different compared to the period up to 6-7 years. Any negative life experiences during this later period continue to cement the negative core belief into place and reaffirm earlier conclusions about not being good enough: *See, I am not good enough; I knew it, I am worthless; See, I do not belong; I knew it, others are more important.* Beyond that, *I'm not smart enough, I'm not strong enough, I'm not lovable enough, I'm not capable enough, I'm not beautiful enough ....* This voice in your head will become louder and louder. This is your inner critic (your ego[1]) telling you what everything means, like a voice-over to the movie of your life. Everybody suffers from this internal chatter, although some suffer more than others.

A Closer Look at Your Negative Core Belief (NCB)

By now, you may have identified your own negative core belief (NCB). Everyone has one NCB, the negative conclusion about yourself that feels

---

1 The word ego originates from the translation of Freud's work. He uses the German 'das Ich' (the I) and for this term the Latin word 'ego' (I) was chosen by the translator. So, interestingly, the word ego does not appear in any of Freud's texts. He describes das Ich (ego) as the conscious, decision-making part of your mind that you regard as 'I', as when you say: I like my sister or I want to change my hair color or I want to learn EFT. That is your I, your ego. We use the term ego in the same way in this book.

true and is reflected in your self-talk when you feel criticized or rejected. Sometimes other conclusions may also seem to apply, but there is only one true NCB. Your NCB is a feeling described in words, for example, *I am worthless*. In a situation where somebody tells you that you are not good enough to do the job and it should go to a colleague instead, you may conclude: *I am not good enough*. But if you identify with how you feel, you may notice that this remark about not being good enough actually makes you feel worthless, in which case, *I am worthless* is your NCB, which you have had since early childhood, rather than *I am not good enough*. It sometimes takes a little time to figure out exactly what your NCB is. It is important to find the correct wording when identifying your NCB so that you can discover what really resonates with you. To do this, it can be helpful to pay attention to your self-talk when you feel judged, criticized, rejected, unsafe or misunderstood. What do you say to yourself, in your mind?

Your parents and other authorities in your life (such as your grandparents, siblings, teachers, sports coaches, etc.) have a significant influence on the formation of your NCB, as already explained above. If you were often told as a child that you were not good enough, that you were a disappointment or a loser, that your needs were not important or that you did not count, then it is not surprising that you took on those statements as part of your belief system. Again, as explained above, we tend to make generalizations, and therefore the sum total of all these negative statements culminates in one negative core belief that you hold about yourself. At a young age, you were not yet aware that these people were acting out their stress patterns based on their own negative experiences and beliefs, and that the way they treated you had little, if anything, to do with you.

Sometimes the criticism may not have been so overt, but rather subtle, with little negative remarks that consistently undermined your self-confidence and sense of self-worth. Non-verbal behavior also has a major impact. You may feel utterly rejected without a word being said. Perhaps your parents, or other important people in your life, simply gave you a look, or avoided eye contact, or ignored you or just laughed at you.

Or perhaps your parents simply did not have much time for you. For instance, one or both parents may be absent or only focused on their career or their own needs, or parents may be fighting constantly and therefore be unable or unwilling to take up their parental role. In such cases, there may be no ill intent toward their child. They are simply not able to be truly present, loving and nurturing as they have not yet dealt with their own issues. In most cases, parents and other authority figures did not intend to undermine you or make you feel insecure or unlovable. They simply did not realize the impact of their words and behavior. In some cases, however, parents may actually be aware of that impact. Bullying behavior is not only experienced at school, at the hands of other students, but can occur in many situations, including within the family at home, in the workplace and in other relationships.

The Writing on Our Walls

Your negative core belief is a major source of stress, but you have also collected many other negative, limiting beliefs during your life. All experiences are learning moments and the earlier the experiences, the more impact they have. All behavior is learned behavior. You learn from your upbringing and those around you which behavior results in approval (and makes you feel loved) and which behavior meets with disapproval and love being withdrawn (making you feel rejected and alone). All these conclusions become what we call *the writing on our walls*[2] that we continue to consult (mostly subconsciously) for the rest of our lives. This is the same as the aforementioned subconscious database in your long-term memory. We subconsciously live by these negative, limiting beliefs that are, in turn, the basis of our stress.

All of the above is equally applicable to positive emotions. From positive experiences, you draw positive conclusions and they help to develop a positive self-image and worldview. The positive life experiences cement your positive beliefs in place. However, the impact of negative beliefs and behaviors is usually much stronger and more in the foreground and typically results in chronic stress.

---

2 This expression comes from 'The writing is on the wall,' which is a translation of 'mene mene tekel upharsin,' a wordplay in Aramaic written on a palace wall by a disembodied hand as part of a story called Belshazzar's Feast (Daniel 5:5-31). In this context it means very apparent signs that something bad will happen in the future. With EFT we use it in a broader sense, namely all your negative beliefs.

The good news about all these negative limiting beliefs is that not any of them are true and none of them is your fault. You simply came to the wrong conclusions because of what happened in your environment, in combination with your tendency to blame yourself for what is happening to you. You had no idea that you were mistaken and that all these conclusions, which felt very true and still feel true today at a subconscious level, are simply false. Fortunately, this is where EFT can really help. You can use EFT to weaken your negative core belief and dissolve other negative, limiting beliefs so that they no longer feel true and thus no longer have a negative impact on your life. In fact, we know no better approach than EFT to let go of these beliefs and heal the mind.

Every situation properly perceived, becomes an opportunity to heal.

A *Course In Miracles*, Foundation For Inner Peace. Combined Volume, Third Edition, 1975

From Mental Problems to Physical Issues and Back Again

If you have come this far in the book, you are no doubt familiar with our claim that chronic stress is responsible for both mental and physical problems and that the underlying root cause of such stress is specific negative emotional events from our past. Therefore, no matter what your problem is, you need to address those specific events.

For psychological problems, you need to identify the specific events in which you learned to react in this particular way and that led you to believe the conclusions you have reached.

For physical issues, you need to identify the underlying specific events that caused chronic stress that eventually manifested as a physical symptom or illness. The physical symptoms are pointers to these specific events. For simple symptoms, like headaches and stomachaches, the connection may be quite obvious. Most people understand that if they are worried about something and feeling overwhelmed, then they may end up with a headache. Similarly, if a child is feeling anxious or nervous about going to school, parents may not be surprised if they complain of a stomachache. It takes more effort and detective work to identify the emotional connections for more complex physical problems, and it will certainly take more practice. It can also be challenging to fully accept that it is mind over matter in many cases. This is generally not a view most of us learned in school, and it is typically not supported by mainstream medicine. It is not easy to master the mind, but it is a vital part of all spiritual teachings.

Medical professionals and researchers attempt to resolve physical issues by looking for the genetic cause, an imbalance in hormones and other substances, or the one pathogen they think is the culprit. They then attempt to solve each problem using pharmacological or surgical remedies. However, this approach of finding a different solution for each and every problem is focused entirely on the symptoms, rather than on the underlying root cause.

Fortunately, Western medicine has started to pay more attention to the effects of stress in recent years, as reflected in many modern treatment protocols. However, while doctors may encourage their patients to take action to manage their stress, they continue to treat any bodily symptoms in the same way as they have always done, with medication or surgery or some other medical treatment. For more than 20 years, scientific publications have shown that there is a connection between negative early childhood experiences (which involve stressful situations and intense negative emotions) and a wide range of medical problems that develop later in life, from chronic diseases to cancer.[1] And yet, medical science still fails to acknowledge that chronic stress is a major contributing cause of disease. In our view, stress is the root cause of disease, not just a contributing factor. We have held this view since the inception of EFT, and our experience has shown that we are on the right track, as we have been obtaining results that medical professionals cannot fathom and often dismiss as "impossible."[2]

---

1 Felitti VJ, Anda RF, Nordenberg D, Williamson DF, Spitz AM, Edwards V, Koss MP, Marks J.S. (1998). *Relationship of Childhood Abuse and Household Dysfunction to Many of the Leading Causes of Death in Adults.* The Adverse Childhood Experiences (ACE) Study. *AJPM. Volume 14, ISSUE 4, P245-258, 1998.* DOI:https://doi.org/10.1016/S0749-3797(98)00017-8.

2 See emofree.com for examples of 'impossible' healings: https://www.emofree.com/answers/read-this-first.html.

Further Exploring the Root Cause of Physical Symptoms

Not all medical professionals are satisfied with treating only the symptoms of disease without addressing the cause. One doctor who did look further into the underlying root causes of diseases was Ryke Geerd Hamer, a German doctor of internal medicine.

In the 1980s, Hamer discovered the connection between emotionally shocking events and certain reactions of the body. Hamer's research showed that what conventional medicine regards as diseases are, in reality, the body's logical natural reaction. Hamer coined the term *meaningful biological special programs* for these reactions. If you look closely at what happens in the body when you experience certain emotionally shocking events and try to understand the biological meaning of your body's reaction, you will soon realize that this bodily reaction, such as the altered function of an organ or the growth or loss of tissue in the body, is designed to help you survive the problem or situation. When the problem is resolved, the body returns to its normal function. These reactions are part of the solution, but conventional medicine identifies these symptoms as a disease (and thus the problem).[3] Hamer conducted extensive research on his patients (including CT scans, blood work and a detailed examination of their personal emotional experiences) and concluded that there is a logical relationship between how a shocking event is experienced (the emotional interpretation) and the reaction in the body. He summarized this relationship in what he called the Five Biological Laws of Nature.

Given that bodily functions are controlled by the brain, Hamer analyzed the brain scans of thousands of patients diagnosed with all sorts of conditions and diseases – cancer, skin conditions, diabetes, heart problems, muscle issues and so on. He found that the brain scans of patients with the same disease showed the same changes in a very specific part of the brain that controlled the affected organ. Hamer also considered the patients' personal histories and found, without exception, that they had experienced a very specific type of emotional shock prior to the onset of the disease, such as the loss of a loved one, the loss of a job and so on. He found that the psy-

---

3 *The Psychic Roots of Disease*. Eybl, B., Thirty-Three & 1 Publishing; ISBN-13: 9781948909-00-6.

che (where the shock is experienced), the brain (which registers the shock in a particular area) and the organ (controlled by the affected area of the brain) are a biological unit and that they always work in synchronicity. The type of emotional shock and how it is subjectively perceived determines which organ is affected. Once the shock is experienced, a pre-programmed process of either cell growth, cell loss, or a change in function of the organ will begin, in order to facilitate a resolution of the problem.

We are not going to reproduce all of Hamer's insights here, but rather we will focus on the part of his discoveries that provides a practical and useful tool to identify the underlying emotional events that are the root causes of symptoms and diseases. This enables you to use EFT much more effectively, as you can zero in on the specific events that are the underlying cause of your symptoms.

Below is a brief explanation that you can use to identify the emotional root causes of your physical problems. In Part 2 of this book, we will explain Hamer's insights in more detail. Hamer's theory (that stress is a contributor to physical illnesses) is only partially recognized by conventional medicine, but we have taken the same view for years, and his findings fit surprisingly well with our approach in EFT. In short, it comes down to the fact that many symptoms, which we have been taught to regard as disease symptoms, are actually healing symptoms. They are part of a special program the body goes through to return to normal function after resolving a stressful experience.

When trying to identify which stressful specific events to resolve with EFT, it is helpful to remember that many of your symptoms arise in the phase after the stress has passed, which is called the healing phase. Fever, headaches, migraines, fatigue, inflammation and various pains all occur during the healing phase. For instance, you usually experience a migraine attack on weekends or at the beginning of your vacation, when you are off and start to relax because the trigger is not active anymore and the healing can begin. The key is to identify the specific events that have caused emotional stress and that occurred prior to the onset of the symptoms, and then resolve the emotional stress with EFT so that the body can heal and return to a healthy balance.

Hamer's Graph of the Autonomic Nervous System

To understand what is happening in the body, we need to look at the autonomic nervous system. Hamer's graph, shown below, illustrates the normal reactions of the body's autonomic nervous system. It shows how the sympathetic stress reaction and the parasympathetic relaxation response work together, and what happens in your body if and when you resolve an emotional conflict. The graph is divided into four sections, namely the normal day-night rhythm, the conflict-active phase (following an emotional shock), the healing phase (following resolution of the problem) and then the return to the normal day-night rhythm.

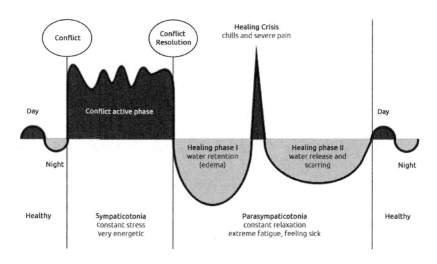

Figure 7. The Hamer graph with the sympathetic response (dark) and the parasympathetic response (gray).[4]

Normal Day-Night Rhythm – Healthy Balance

The first section of the graph, starting from the left, shows the normal day-night rhythm, with the normal amount of stress during the day (represented by a dark semicircle above the line) and the normal relaxation response at night (the gray semicircle below the line). During normal day-to-day activities, our nervous system is in balance. During the day, you have slightly

---

4 *The Psychic Roots of Disease*. Eybl, B., Thirty-Three & 1 Publishing; ISBN-13: 9781948909-00-6.

more sympathetic activity because you are active, physically and/or mentally. Your sympathetic stress response is slightly activated during your daytime activities with small peaks when action is needed. This is useful and necessary to respond properly, for example, when you stand up, catch yourself after almost tripping, maneuver through traffic, catch something, play sports, etc. During the night, you have slightly more parasympathetic activity as you recover from the daytime stress while resting and sleeping. This is the normal, balanced rhythm.

Conflict-Active Phase

When a significant stress trigger or conflict occurs, the sympathetic stress response is automatically turned on and we move into stress mode. Hamer calls this the conflict-active phase. This is shown in the second section of the graph as the larger dark area above the line. The conflict-active phase continues until the conflict is resolved. During the conflict-active phase, we usually experience very few symptoms that we would consider 'disease' symptoms. It may last for only a few seconds, but it may also last for weeks, months, years or even decades. You may feel stressed and tense, but you are generally energetic and capable of getting a lot done during this time. You may also experience compulsive thinking about the problem, high blood pressure, poor sleep, cold hands and feet, little or no appetite, and dry mouth and eyes. Certain conditions also indicate that you are in the conflict-active phase, such as diabetes mellitus, hyperthyroidism (increased thyroid function) and osteoporosis.

Healing or Repair Phase

When the conflict is resolved, the stress reaction subsides, and the healing or repair phase begins. The healing or repair phase consists of three parts:

1. Part 1 of the healing phase (the first grey trough below the line);
2. The healing crisis (the dark peak above the line);
3. Part 2 of the healing phase (the second gray trough below the line).

During Parts 1 and 2 of the healing phase, the parasympathetic response is activated. Parasympathetic activity is much more pronounced than the normal parasympathetic activity you experience at night when you are healthy and balanced. You usually experience fatigue, need more sleep, and you may have headaches. During Part 1, you also retain water, which may result in puffy eyes when you awaken in the morning and swollen hands and feet. You may even gain weight. Swelling may also cause pain in the part of the body that is involved. Therefore, all symptoms of inflammation, fever and pain signify that you are in Part 1 of the healing phase. This includes all flu symptoms, colds, inflammations of skin, joints, or organs, as well as any skin rash.

In the healing crisis, the sympathetic nervous system turns back on, as shown by the dark peak above the line. Its intensity and duration generally depend on the intensity and duration of the conflict-active phase, and it can last from 3 seconds to 3 days. For minor conflicts, the healing crisis may be minimal, and you may simply feel tired and have a headache or you may not even have any noticeable symptoms. However, if the conflict is significant and has been ongoing for some time, the symptoms are usually noticeable and may be severe. You may get a high fever and experience an attack of some sort (such as an asthma attack, migraine, gout or gallstones) or the peak of a flu, infection or skin rash. Sometimes it is so severe it needs medical attention. Part 2 of the healing phase is characterized by increased urination, as the water retained during Part 1 of the healing phase is excreted (although this is not always noticeable). Symptoms rapidly improve and the body returns to its normal function.

How to Use the Graph in Figure 7

You will notice that many symptoms, which Western medicine considers to be a problem, are actually part of the healing phase, such as fever, headaches, painful swelling, and inflammation. It is in the healing phase that 'diseases' are detected, diagnosed and treated. In reality, they are healing symptoms. The conflict-active phase is usually characterized by relatively few symptoms, other than the symptoms you experience when you feel stressed. You can continue in a highly stressed-out state for quite some time, even years. Eventually, you may collapse (often when you go on vacation or retire or when a stressful period has come to an end) and suddenly you may experience all kinds of symptoms. The fact that you experience such symptoms signifies that either the conflict was resolved, or you managed to find a way to cope with it, and thus you moved into the healing phase. To your surprise, you then become sick even though the situation or problem has been resolved.

It is important to remember that these symptoms are part of the healing phase and that your body needs to go through this to return to its normal function. The key is to decrease your stress levels and stay healthy and in balance so that you can avoid severe healing symptoms. You can do this by using EFT to resolve your most important stress patterns on a daily basis, so that your overall stress levels are significantly lower. By doing so, the conflict-active phase will not be as intense or as long, which means that the healing phase will not be as dramatic and the healing crisis will not be as severe. We cannot avoid conflicts in life, but we can choose to focus on resolving them as soon as possible so that we will experience fewer and milder symptoms.

If you think that you may have symptoms that belong to the healing phase, then we strongly recommend that you take the time to identify what specific situation caused you to feel stressed and then use EFT to resolve it. In the action plan below, we will explain the types of conflicts that may be at play and their relationship to physical symptoms and illness. We also want to point out that the graph in Figure 7 is simplistic, as it suggests that you only experience one type of conflict at any given time. However, life is complex, and you are often experiencing several different conflicts or stressful situations at any given time. With respect to one conflict, your symptoms may indicate that you are in the conflict-active phase (for example, very dry eyes), but you may also be experiencing symptoms that are characteristic of the healing phase (such as a sore throat, cold sores or fever blisters). As noted above, Hamer discovered that the type of emotional shock, and how it is subjectively perceived, will determine which organ is affected and what symptoms are experienced. Thus, you may experience a sore throat after resolving a conflict related to not wanting to swallow something, either physically (such as a food item you dislike) or metaphorically (such as harsh words, an unfair accusation, or an insult). You may get fever blisters on your mouth after resolving a conflict related to not wanting or daring to say something, wishing you had not said something, or wanting or not wanting to have contact with the lips (such as wanting to kiss or not wanting to be kissed) or it could be related to eating.

There is one more thing we need to explain about the healing phase. If the symptoms in the healing phase give rise to strong negative emotions, you may get stuck in this phase and the body will not return to its normal function. This is called hanging healing. When this happens, you also need to focus on working on the emotions that the symptoms themselves are giving you.

Below is a brief summary of the examples given in the texts above of symptoms that are experienced in the conflict-active phase, as opposed to all the other symptoms we discussed here that are experienced in the healing phase:

- **Diabetes:** On an emotional level, there may be constant (often subconscious) (i) strong resistance to something or someone, where you feel attacked and want to defend yourself or fight (whether or not you succeed) combined with a sense of powerlessness, or (ii) feelings of fear and disgust towards something or someone.
- **Hyperthyroidism** (increased thyroid function): You may experience yourself as being too slow (to get something that you want or to get away from something that you do not want) and you may be (unknowingly) pushing yourself too much. The same emotional causes are at play with lowered thyroid function (hypothyroidism), where part of you wants to slow you down because you are subconsciously pushing yourself too much.
- **Dry eyes:** You may experience dry eyes when you feel like you cannot see something that you want to see, or when you are seeing things that you consider to be unpleasant, literally or figuratively.

- **Osteoporosis:** This is caused by a generalized self-esteem conflict that involves feeling discarded and/or inferior (which is why it is often experienced by women as they age, particularly in Western cultures where they are usually not valued as much as in the East).

Hamer's research covers many "healing symptoms" that are characterized as diseases by conventional medicine. We will be explaining a large number of these in more detail in Part 2 of the book, with many practical examples and a detailed index, so that you can use this book as a reference to identify the emotional causes of many symptoms you may be experiencing. It takes time to get accustomed to looking for the emotional cause of symptoms in this way, but we are confident that you will find it worth your while.

Resolution of Conflicts with EFT

The healing phase will only begin once the conflict has been resolved, or at least resolved to a sufficient degree to enable the healing phase to start. When identifying the emotional cause, it is important to consider the stress triggers and when they are at play. For example, consider a child who is very quiet, fearful and withdrawn at school, but very talkative, happy and outgoing at home. This shows that the child may be experiencing a conflict at school, which is resolved at home or is not playing a role, and it becomes active again when the child is at school. You can resolve a conflict in a practical way, by deciding to do something to resolve the stress or get yourself out of the stressful situation. Let us look at two examples to clarify this.

Suppose you do not like your job and feel stressed at work. You then decide to enroll in a course that will eventually enable you to quit this job. Your conflict may be resolved the moment you make the decision to enroll, causing you to enter the healing phase. What symptoms will you experience then? That will depend on how you subjectively experience your work stress. If you feel that you are not good enough and undervalued, then you may experience back or neck pain (or a hernia) or muscle pains (such as a flare-up of your fibromyalgia). Symptoms like these are linked to self-esteem conflicts. If you feel completely stuck (trapped) in your job, you may experience restless legs. This symptom is related to feeling-stuck conflicts, which Hamer calls motor conflicts. However, it is also possible that you may simply experience a little fatigue and need more sleep, and this phase may pass almost unnoticed.

Another example might be that someone is not respecting your boundaries during a conversation, interrupting you constantly and not listening to you. If you then express that you want to have your say, you may cough briefly, which would be an indication of a small healing crisis of a shock-fright or speechlessness conflict. You may also cough if you simply decide to say something, as this would also resolve this conflict. The way you subjectively experience each situation determines what type of physical symptoms you may experience. You may, therefore, enter the conflict-active phase several times a day and then do something fairly quickly that will bring you out of it. So, the healing crisis need not be pronounced and often goes unnoticed.

As mentioned above, it is important to understand that you may be going through several conflicts at the same time, which means that several programs are turned on at the same time. Some of those programs might be in the conflict-active phase and others might be in the healing phase. An interesting example where this shows up in the same type of symptoms is psoriasis (scaly skin). Two separation conflicts overlap each other on the same area of the skin, one is in the healing phase (the red skin) and the other is in the conflict-active phase (the scaling part). You might move to another city, lose contact with someone you want to be close to, and at the same time resolve having contact with somebody you do not want to see. Most of the time, however, the various conflicts are different types of conflict and show up in different skin types or organs, as we have seen in the examples above.

If you use EFT to address and resolve a particular problem, then you will enter the healing phase for that conflict and thus you may experience some physical effects. These are usually mild and may include headache and fatigue. The mild or more noticeable healing symptoms you may experience after using EFT are not side effects as such. Rather, they are a completely natural reaction that occurs with all forms of conflict resolution, or – in other words – releasing and resolving stress. You may use EFT immediately to address these physical symptoms until the reaction subsides. The reaction may also be more pronounced, such as a common cold, an asthma attack, an infection or back pain. Again, these are normal physical reactions that are part of the healing phase, so they are actually a good sign that you have resolved the conflict and started the healing phase. To reassure you, again, EFT does not lead to any severe physical reactions. Severe physical reactions occur when you have experienced a lot of stress over a long period of time, which suddenly and dramatically reaches a crisis point because of big changes in your circumstances and/or major, important decisions in your life with far-reaching consequences. With EFT, you are simply processing and releasing negative emotions from past events, one by one, which is a much more gradual process.

Now that you have foundational knowledge, it is time to look at how you can address your problems with EFT.

6 | EFT ACTION PLAN

Every illness is a confession by the body.

Oscar Vladislas de Lubicz Milosz, French-Lithuanian poet, playwright, 1877 – 1939

Introduction

We intend to teach you how to use the basic protocols of EFT to address your problems and any symptoms you may be experiencing. We will provide you with an approach that goes far beyond symptom relief and, when applied properly, you will start to experience real results. Again, we urge you not to start working on your big traumas by yourself. The rule of thumb is that if it does not feel good or safe to close your eyes and really relive the memory as though it is happening right now, then *do not do it*. (We recommend contacting a well-trained EFT professional in the case of major trauma.) Starting with daily stresses and small negatively charged memories will produce huge benefits and results. Once you feel confident about completely neutralizing smaller issues, you may take on slightly larger ones.

However, since our memory works associatively, you may still be reminded of a major trauma even though you are working on only a minor issue. Therefore, we will begin by explaining how to deal with that potential scenario.

Oops – Not This One: Safely Parking the Problem

If you start reliving a moment and then realize that it feels too intense, then stop reliving and thinking about it (how to do this is explained below). Continue to use EFT and simply try to lower your reaction. Recalling a memory that you do not want to relive can happen in many ways, not only when you are using EFT. A memory may come up unexpectedly when watching TV, during a conversation, when reading or when you are simply going about your day. In other words, many situations can trigger you into associating with a memory. When this happens while you are doing EFT, then you know that the intense memory must be somehow related to the issue that you are working on, which can be a helpful realization. If you cannot or do not want to continue with this specific memory, you need to safely 'park' this specific event until you are ready to deal with it or you have engaged a well-trained EFT professional to help you. There are two steps involved in safely parking the problem

1. Take yourself out of the association and address the emotional charge with EFT. To dissociate from the memory, open your eyes and remind yourself that you are no longer in that moment from the past, but that you are here now, in the present moment, and you are safe. Then, continue to use EFT to address any emotional charge that has come up. If you are using Optimal EFT, then instead of closing your eyes (which may lead you to reconnect with the memory), you may find it helpful to look down at a focus point with a soft gaze. Continue using EFT until you feel calm. With Gold Standard EFT, keep tapping with your eyes open.

2. Park the specific event. This can be done using the 'Black Box Technique.' The process is slightly different, depending on whether you are using Optimal EFT or Gold Standard EFT. In both cases, you use your imagination to visualize a sturdy container, such as a safe, a metal box or a shipping container, in which the memory will be stored and put away until you are ready to deal with it. Imagine putting the entire memory and everything related to it inside the container, then visualize it moving away from you until you no longer feel anything. For instance, you may visualize a ship lowering the container into the middle of the ocean somewhere, or a rocket taking the container to the moon, or perhaps the memory is put in a safe and stored in a basement at a distant location. If needed, add to this visualization the notion that the location is unknown to you. Just use your imagination, anything that comes up is fine.

- With Optimal EFT, you may visualize the container being filled with the problem by your subconscious. Then you ask The Unseen Therapist to help you to move the container away from you or simply take it from you and store it safely until you are ready to deal with it.

- With Gold Standard EFT, you again visualize the container being filled with the problem by your subconscious. Then imagine this container going to a far-away unknown location. As you do this, gently do rounds of tapping, without using any Setup phrase. Alternatively, you may tap on one point until you have finished the visualization and the problem is safely stored.

The Black Box technique is also useful when you are working on an issue with EFT but you are running out of time, so you need to park it and continue working on it at a later time. You may choose to keep the visualization more simple than you would for a traumatic memory. The goal is to simply distance yourself from the issue at hand.

The EFT Action Plan Explained

There are four main parts to our EFT action plan:

1. **WMOMD:** the worst moment of my day

2. **Symptom-Focused EFT:** working at the symptom level

3. **Big Cleanup:** clean up as many old memories as possible

4. **Detective Work:** uncovering the origins of stress patterns

Let us now look at each part of the EFT action plan in detail.

1. The WMOMD (Worst Moment of My Day)

Learn to use EFT for the worst moment of your day. By this, we do not literally mean that you choose only one moment or that it needs to be really bad. Perhaps there are several moments. Every day, we experience situations that are not traumatic in themselves, but that evoke negative reactions, nevertheless. Do not limit your selection to situations with a high emotional charge, but also include situations where the charge is low, perhaps only a 4 or 5. For example, someone makes a hurtful remark or gets angry with you, an email or text message frightens or angers you, you feel shocked by violence on TV or about information on social media, somebody interrupts you rudely, something happens in traffic, and so on.

There are three good reasons for this type of daily EFT work:

First: As far as we are concerned, EFT should be used as often as possible to neutralize any stress, very similar to how you would use your toothbrush: if you have a bad taste in your mouth, then you brush your teeth to freshen your breath. If you have a negative emotion, then you apply EFT to become emotionally free again.

Second: Our reactions today are the result of a life-long buildup of stress patterns. Therefore, your daily stress moments are an excellent starting point to identify all the stress patterns that bother you in your present life and that need attention. Most of us are quite unaware of how big a role our negative core beliefs and other important stress patterns play.

Third: Chronic issues are daily problems or frequently recurring ones. If you are suffering from one or more chronic issues, then one or more underlying stress patterns are being triggered on a daily or recurrent basis, otherwise, you simply would not have a chronic issue. Evidently, negative experiences from early childhood play a foundational role in chronic issues. But a stress pattern is not only triggered by very early memories; other specific experiences later in life play an important role too, because they add to and maintain this stress pattern.

By now, you should be familiar with the correct application of EFT: relive the specific moment in an associated way to fully activate the stress reaction and then use one of the Official EFT protocols to bring all nega-tive emotions (and bodily sensations) to zero. Do not forget to test the zero: there should be no charge left, and every moment of the event needs to be neutral. The more often you work on your WMOMD, the greater the effect.

You will discover that there are patterns in the situations and the people that bother you. Many of these situations have to do with your negative core belief: *I am not good enough, I should not be here, I am worthless, I do not matter, I am not heard or seen,...* Do not ignore these moments think-ing they are irrelevant, simply because the intensity of your reaction stays well under 5. Our emotions help us to identify what action is required, but they do not always scream for attention. Remember also that if our nega-tive reactions are the result of our stress patterns, it is quite possible that we are not reacting to the situation at hand, but instead, we are battling with our past experiences. Needless to say, that battle will not produce the most appropriate behavior that serves us and the people around us. Only a peaceful and loving state of mind and looking at the world with forgiving eyes will improve our life and the world at large. Who can claim they are in this peaceful state all day, every day? The challenge is to work towards this goal, one WMOMD at a time.

Our experience of any emotion, be it positive or negative, is in itself very brief. Our first primary reaction of fear, anger or sadness lasts only a few seconds at most. After that, we perpetuate the emotional feeling, because our thoughts turn it into a narrative. It becomes a story that we keep telling ourselves. With EFT, you remove the emotional charge from the event, which will give you the peace of mind to determine what needs to be done in the circumstances. It is utterly impossible to make a sound de-cision when you are still completely caught up in your emotional reaction because this unavoidably brings you into a state of regression, with the accompanying childlike behavior. Daily work on your WMOMD will en-able you to become calmer, more peaceful and less easily triggered. This approach is important for everyone, but if you suffer from chronic issues, whether psychological or physical, the WMOMD is an essential part of an effective approach. Do not save EFT for big, stressful events only. Train yourself to do it every day!

Instructions for EFT on the WMOMD

Identify an unpleasant moment during your day, then decide whether you want to work on it immediately or later. Always relive the moment, even if it just happened, to fully activate the stress response. Then immediately apply EFT to the negative emotions and/or physical reactions. How long should you work on any given moment? That depends on several things: how much time you have, how motivated and energetic you feel and how long it usually takes for you to bring the intensity of a negative memory down to zero. When you are starting out, it is best to practice EFT for 15 to 30 minutes at most. If you have not finished within 30 minutes, then, safely park the issue for next time (as explained on page 96). It is much more effective to keep working on one specific moment until it is completely resolved, as opposed to partially resolving several different specific events. Avoid jumping from one issue to another without first resolving the issue at hand, by bringing it down to a tested zero. We recommend that you keep track of what you are working on, so you may wish to make notes if necessary.

The WMOMD score is < 5: If the initial intensity of the emotional charge of your worst moment is 5 or less, then use EFT to bring the emotional charge down and continue to test until all your reactions are zero.

The WMOMD score is > 5: If the initial intensity of the emotional charge of your worst moment is above 5, use one of the EFT protocols to reduce the emotional charge until the intensity of all negative emotions is less than 5, but not yet zero. Then, we recommend that you use one or both of the following approaches to help you identify the stress pattern that is at play and its origin.

1. Use your negative core belief to identify a related past event: With your eyes closed, stay associated in the WMOMD and allow yourself to really feel your emotions. Then, consider whether your negative core belief is playing a role in this moment. Notice your self-talk. Are you thinking: *I am not good enough, I do not belong, I should not even be here,...?* If so, ask your subconscious (or The Unseen Therapist) if there is a situation from the first 6-7 years of your life in which you felt the same way. Focus on how you feel, rather than getting caught up in your thoughts and stories about your childhood. It is important to note that the situation in which you felt the same way may be completely different, with different people and surroundings. The key is how you feel, not the details of the event. Relax and simply allow any memory to come up, without too much effort. The earlier the memory, the better, but sometimes you may recall events that occurred later in life. That is fine too.

If your negative core belief does not seem to play a role, another important negative conclusion that is somehow related may be involved. For example, *I am all alone, I will never succeed, I am a bad parent, What I feel does not matter, I cannot do this,*... Follow the same approach outlined above. These other negative conclusions may also stem from the first 6-7 years, but sometimes they develop later in life.

2. Identifying a related past event without using your negative core belief: Close your eyes and associate as best as you can in the WMOMD. Then ask yourself, *When have I felt this way before in my life?* Again, remember that the situation in which you felt the same way may be completely different, with different people and surroundings. The key is how you feel, not the details of the event. Pay attention to the first thing that comes to mind. It may be a recent memory, or it may be a memory from the distant past. Do not analyze it, just allow it to surface in your mind.

At first, you may not be able to identify any earlier memories. That is not a problem. You will be able to do so more easily as you continue to practice EFT. If not, we recommend that you seek the assistance of an EFT professional. If nothing comes up, then continue to use EFT to resolve all negative emotions of the WMOMD that you were working on, and then try this procedure on another WMOMD at a later time.

If you have identified a specific event from the past to work on, use one of the EFT protocols to resolve both the past event and the current WMOMD. The order is not important. You can finish the WMOMD you started with, but if the earlier memory has a lot of emotional charge, you may choose to resolve that one first. Make sure you completely neutralize all the emotions from the original WMOMD and the other specific event(s) with one of the

Official EFT protocols and work to a tested zero on all aspects. If more than one earlier memory comes up, choose one to work on – ideally the most intense one (unless you feel that it would be too overwhelming to work on by yourself). It is not necessary to identify past events in this way with every WMOMD, but we recommend doing so as often as possible, whenever you have time. This is one of the most effective ways of resolving the stress patterns that are affecting you on a daily basis, as you are working on both current and past events.

Note: You may notice that previous situations spontaneously surface, without a conscious intention on your part. This is normal and it has to do with the associative way your mind works. It happens both during normal daily activities (when something triggers a memory) as well as during EFT. Make a note of any events that come up and make time to resolve them with EFT. If the surfacing memories are intrusive, park them safely as described on page 96. If this happens while you are doing EFT, tap using Gold Standard EFT or ask The Unseen Therapist to help you focus on one specific moment at a time, because that is the only way to completely resolve an issue.

2. Symptom-Focused EFT

Although the only way to really resolve an issue is to work on specific events, sometimes there is such an intense emotional reaction or physical symptom that using EFT directly on the symptom only is justified. You may be dealing with fear, panic, anger, sadness, some kind of pain, heart palpitations or other unpleasant physical sensations. What is characteristic is that you have an intense emotion and/or physical sensation at this moment. You may obtain results with EFT and bring the intensity down or sometimes even get to zero. However, such results may not be permanent as you have not addressed the root cause. Therefore, we encourage you to work on the related specific moment with the WMOMD approach as soon as you can, to not only reduce or resolve the symptom of that moment but also identify the origin of your reaction.

Instructions for Symptom-Focused EFT

When you experience a severe emotional reaction or physical pain, itching or other sensations, use one of the EFT protocols as described below:

- **Optimal EFT:** Close your eyes and bring yourself into a loving state as best you can, then ask The Unseen Therapist to help you to resolve the symptoms that you are experiencing. Trust that The Unseen Therapist will help you. If possible, take the time to assess the intensity of the symptoms, do a round of the Personal Peace Procedure, then assess the intensity again. Continue to repeat this process until the intensity of the symptoms has been reduced to a manageable level. Alternatively, you may choose to do a long round of the Personal Peace Procedure (a longer meditation of 10-15 minutes) until you feel calmer and more peaceful.

- **Gold Standard EFT:** Simply begin tapping on all the points and do several rounds until you feel the reaction has diminished. As soon as you feel sufficiently calm, start doing the whole protocol, which involves assessing the intensity of your reaction, using a Setup phrase, doing the tapping sequence, and testing the intensity. Continue doing the protocol until the intensity of the symptom has been reduced to a manageable level. You may need to keep tapping for 15 to 20 minutes, or longer.

Working on the symptoms will not resolve the underlying cause and it may take some time, so do your best to be patient and do not give up! If you start to feel frustrated, impatient, or irritable, then work on those emotions. The effects of EFT may continue even after you have finished doing it, so you may notice hours later that the symptoms have decreased even further or disappeared completely.

You may only bring the intensity down by 1 or 2 points. Aim for reducing it to zero, but accept that this may only happen occasionally. Simply try to reduce your symptoms so that you are calm enough to proceed to work on the underlying cause with EFT. Even the slightest improvement in your symptoms shows that EFT is working, which can help to develop your trust in the process. When you are focusing on resolving intense physical symptoms, it may be helpful to focus on the emotions underlying those symptoms, such as anger or fear, rather than focusing on the physical sensation itself. It may be that nothing seems to change at first, but after a while, you may notice the symptoms have decreased or even disappeared.

Chasing the Pain: EFT can be used to relieve emotional issues by resolving related physical symptoms. As we use EFT to reduce or eliminate one painful or uncomfortable sensation in one area of the body, others show up to be resolved, so we 'chase the pain' around the body. Thus, focusing on resolving physical symptoms in this way is called Chasing the Pain. Emotions are expressed as physical symptoms, with each physical symptom representing an aspect of the underlying emotional issue. As we bring relief to each physical symptom, we simultaneously bring relief to an underlying emotional aspect. As we resolve one aspect, another one may arise.

This process is especially useful for people who may not be in touch with their emotions and simply feel pain or sensations in the body instead. It is also helpful for those who are really anxious or too overwhelmed by any mention of the underlying emotional issue, as they can focus on the physical symptoms and thus avoid intense emotional distress. There is no need to mention the underlying emotional issue until the testing at the end.

The first step is to identify the bodily sensation, describe the exact location and assess the intensity. Be as specific as possible. Notice how it feels, whether any pain is dull or sharp, throbbing or pressing, light or heavy. Take note of how large the affected area is, whether it is the size of a marble, a ping pong ball or a basketball. Consider whether it has any color or specific texture. Then use one of the EFT protocols to resolve it. After each round of EFT, notice whether there is any change in the intensity or nature of the sensation or in its location. You may notice with some frequency that the physical symptom has changed location and/or nature. This is a positive sign, and it shows that EFT is working. For example, a headache may change as follows: *throbbing pain at the back right side of my head as big as a tennis ball at an 8* may become *a pressing feeling in the middle of my head as big as a ping pong ball at a 6.*

From Symptom-Focused EFT to looking for the cause: Once you reduce the intensity of your symptoms and feel sufficiently calm, it is useful to dig a little deeper and identify what triggered your symptoms. Consider what was happening before the onset of the symptoms. Did you see or hear or read something that might have upset you? Or were you thinking about something? If you manage to identify and neutralize the related specific event, then you have taken another huge step in resolving the underlying stress pattern.

3. Big Cleanup

The Big Cleanup involves making a list of all the specific events from your past that have a negative emotional charge and then using EFT to address them, one by one. This procedure was first developed by Gary Craig for EFT professionals, who are encouraged to use it to clear their own issues before they start working with clients. However, this method is a valuable tool that can be used by anyone.

Note

In the early days of EFT, the term Personal Peace Procedure was used to describe the process of making a list of negatively charged events from the past, which you then work on with EFT, and many people still use the term in this way. However, when Optimal EFT was introduced, Gary Craig started using the term Personal Peace Procedure to describe each round of Optimal EFT meditation with The Unseen Therapist. To avoid any misunderstandings, we have chosen to give the process of making a list of past specific events a new name, the Big Cleanup.

When applied properly, the Big Cleanup approach can play a central role in your overall well-being and wellness. It involves writing a list of all the negative emotional events (small and large) in your life. It is important to write down everything that comes to mind. The influence from your past experiences may be completely subconscious. Therefore these events may not be in your awareness in your daily life, so include everything that you recall was emotionally charged when it happened, even though you may not feel anything now when you think about it. Then, use EFT to completely neutralize each and every memory, thereby resolving any effect (including any subconscious influence) the events may still have on your present life. If you do this thoroughly and consistently, chances are that you will successfully address the root causes of most (if not all) of your emotional and physical problems. In Part 2, you will see that we regularly recommend the Big Cleanup as a final sweep, to address any residual emotionally charged events.

Instructions for the Big Cleanup

1. Current symptoms inventory: Make a list of all the emotional, mental and physical issues that you experience on a regular basis. Describe each issue and assess its intensity (between 0 and 10) as precisely as possible. For example, panic attacks, 2-3 per week with intensity 8; or headaches, 5 times per month with intensity 7-9. This precision enables you to keep track of any changes. After you have used EFT to work on your Big Cleanup list for 2 to 3 months, describe and assess the intensity of each issue again and compare the two lists. You will be surprised at the dramatic changes you may experience when you do the Big Cleanup and clear out the negative emotions from your subconscious mind!

2. Making the Big Cleanup list: We recommend that you use a notebook or electronic document for your list of events, rather than loose pieces of paper, as it is helpful to keep track of your progress. This will enable you to know which specific events have been neutralized, the intensity of the emotional charge of the remaining specific events, as well as any changes in your physical symptoms. When you make your list, give each specific event a title, being as precise as possible, so that you can immediately step into the situation and relive it. It is best to avoid general titles, such as:

- My dad often belittled me.
- There was always fighting going on at the dinner table.
- I was bullied at school.

Instead, be more specific and use the present tense, such as:

- The moment my dad slaps me on my 8th birthday while everyone is watching.
- The moment my mom gets mad at me when I boldly tell her it is none of her business.
- The moment when [X] pushes me over and I start crying.

It is helpful to include your age or the time/year if you can recall it. Keep the titles brief and succinct. And most importantly, use the present tense for the reasons discussed in Chapter 2:

Age/date/year: the moment when X happens (optional: and I feel Y)

Write down the emotional reaction involved, but only if you know what that is without reliving the event. If not, then just omit it. After all, you can only properly assess whether the memory of an event still has an emotional charge by reliving it in an associated way. You should avoid doing this when making the list, because you may get triggered and need to work on it right away. The goal is to make your Big Cleanup list with as little association as possible. Include everything you know had an emotional charge at the time it happened. Take your time. If you cannot find at least 50-100 specific situations, then you are probably being too selective. Anything you recall being annoying in any way is relevant and worth including on your list. However, if you start feeling overwhelmed, you may also choose to write down only 5 or 10 events and start using EFT to neutralize them. You can then expand on the list at a later date when you feel ready.

You may find it helpful to divide your list into periods of your life, in 5 or 10-year blocks. Or you may have sections for different people, such as a list of events relating to your parents or other key figures in your life. You may want to start with some more recent events first, and gradually add specific events from your younger years. Or you may choose to write down events in no particular order. Feel free to experiment with different approaches and see what works best for you. You do not need to complete the list in one sitting. In fact, it is unlikely that you could do so, as the average person has hundreds of specific events that belong on the list, and more memories will surface once you start resolving the events with EFT. Just keep adding to the list as you go. Start with what you can remember, and you will start recalling other events that you had forgotten along the way. Please take your time and keep in mind that this may be a rather emotional process. If it becomes overwhelming, then just stop. Use EFT to calm yourself down. There is no need to rush or put pressure on yourself.

3. Work through the list and neutralize all events: The Big Cleanup approach will only be effective if you actually do it. Therefore, commit to working on it as your personal project for at least 2 months, and use EFT to neutralize between 1 and 3 specific events each day. Or you may choose to work on it for a few days each week. Whatever the case, decide on the days and exact time of day that you will work on it, making sure that you choose a time when you can work undisturbed for 30 minutes to one hour, and include these in your calendar. Whenever you feel tempted not to do it, remind yourself of the benefits of this clearing work. At the allotted time, help yourself by finding somewhere quiet where you will not be disturbed. Continue applying EFT until each specific event is neutral with no charge. Test this thoroughly. If you cannot get the event to be neutral within the time you have, safely park it and continue working on it at a later time, noting down any aspects that have been resolved and the intensity of any remaining ones. Wait until you can successfully neutralize smaller events with EFT before tackling more intense events. As mentioned, it may be necessary to resolve intense traumatic events with a well-trained EFT professional, rather than by yourself.

Additional Instructions

1. I cannot get it to zero. Sometimes you cannot get the intensity of an event down to zero, even after doing EFT for a long time and quite a few rounds of tapping or meditating (we mean 10 or 20 rounds, not 4 or so).

If that is the case, you can assume that there are previous specific events underneath that are keeping the charge high. Relive the moment of the specific event again, allow yourself to really feel what you are feeling, and ask yourself when you have felt this way before in your life. A memory may surface that is seemingly unrelated, but the first thing that comes to mind is always relevant. If it is not already on your list, add it and work on that one first. Then, return to the specific event that you were not able to neutralize and try again. You may need to do this several times (which means addressing multiple, earlier events before you completely neutralize the later event).

Note: You will recognize the question: *When have I felt this way earlier in my life?* from the instruction for the WMOMD approach. Thus, the starting point (when asking this question) need not be a present-day situation. You can use this question to go back to earlier events from any point in your history. In fact, this way of using how you feel to find earlier memories is a more effective way of finding relevant memories than trying to think about your past and recall such events, since your system is tuned into the feeling. As discussed earlier, quite often, another related memory will surface spontaneously, without you asking yourself this question. That is fine too. If you have time, tackle that one immediately as well. If you do not have time, put it on your list and do it later.

The Big Cleanup and the WMOMD approach complement each other. In the latter, you use a current trigger as a starting point and end up with past events. It is our experience that some events will come up several times. This is usually due to the fact that the event has one or more hidden details or aspects that were not immediately recognized and therefore not yet included in the approach. So, pay close attention when you run into an event that you have already done. Usually you will discover that a different detail is now causing your negative reaction. If you experience exactly the same thing, the event was simply not really neutral yet. It definitely makes sense to tackle it again, and do not get discouraged: persistence wins.

Note: Always finish what you start! Do not jump from one memory to another without neutralizing each one of them.

2. Many similar events. A stress pattern may be composed of many, very similar events. It may therefore seem as if you keep going into the same memory. But you usually switch between different moments of the same type of event, or different aspects in the same moment, without noticing it. If something has happened to you many times, then it is important to deal with a sufficient number of events from this series of similar events. Make sure that each event in itself is as specific as possible. Take being bullied at school as an example. Select some specific moments that represent what happened, for example: you are bullied in class, you are bullied in the hallway near the classroom, you are bullied in the cafeteria, you are bullied in the schoolyard, you are bullied in the parking lot. Choose a representative event for each and stick to that one, do not change it to different scenes. Keep working and testing the exact same scenes until they have been neutralized.

Note: It is not a problem if you do not remember exactly what happened. In that case, make up how it might have happened. This also works because your reconstruction will still somehow be based on your experience of past events. Again, it is important to work with the same made-up moment until it is neutral and then make up a new one if necessary. Experience shows that you need to deal with at least 5 and often as many as 20 specific events of a certain type to get lasting results, so if you have been bullied by two different people, that means 5-20 events with bully A and also 5-20 events with bully B. If you have been bullied for several years, then you may need to do 5-20 events from each year, etc.

The Big Cleanup will bring you a lot of emotional freedom. The challenge is to persevere and follow through. And to get started, of course.

Every day of our lives we are almost on the verge of making those changes that would really make a difference.

Mignon McLaughlin, American author and journalist, 1913 – 1983

4. Detective Work

An important part of EFT involves discovering your stress patterns and then identifying the specific events that contribute to both the emergence of each pattern and its continuation. In other words, you follow the trail of the stress pattern back in time until you arrive at its origin. It is essential to resolve any emotional charge of not only the past specific events where the stress pattern originated but also the relevant specific events later in life up to and including the present. They are all learning moments that contribute to the stress pattern. Hence, you need to address the whole trail of specific events to completely and permanently resolve the whole stress pattern. Once you resolve a sufficient number of specific events, the trail will disintegrate, and the stress pattern disappears because the links between the triggers and the stress response no longer work.

How many specific events should you resolve with EFT? There is no way of estimating this. You simply need to keep working until you notice that your stress pattern has diminished to such an extent that your problem has disappeared. A frequently made mistake is failing to address a sufficient number of specific events.

By way of example, if your problem is feeling insecure, this means you need to work on your negative core belief (NCB). The subconscious belief that *I am not good enough, I do not belong,* or *I am worthless,* ... may cause you to feel stressed, inadequate and/or uncertain in all kinds of situations. To resolve this issue properly, it is not sufficient to only neutralize specific events from your early childhood. You need to work on the entire trail of events, from your early childhood to your school years and throughout your adult life, up to and including the present. You also need to address different types of experiences and different social situations with various people, since your NCB may be triggered differently when you are at home with family, as opposed to when you are in other social situations. Friends may trigger you differently than strangers. It is important to identify enough key moments, and that is what Detective Work is all about. It is about selecting the best specific events to get the best possible lasting results. You could, of course, use the Big Cleanup approach to accomplish the same result because, after all, you are tackling everything and that includes your key moments. However, the Big Cleanup approach usually requires more perseverance and a lot more work than most people are willing or able to do. Detective Work, properly applied, produces results faster.

Instructions for Detective Work

To determine what you are going to work on, you must first identify what the problem is. It may be necessary to break your problem down into parts. For example, if you want to work on weakening your negative core belief that makes you feel insecure, then you need to determine which areas you want to resolve first. Would you like to focus on your insecurity at work and the difficult relationship you have with a colleague or supervisor? Or do you want to prioritize your insecurity in your relationship with your partner, child, mother, or brother?

If you have multiple physical complaints, it is helpful to look at each one individually. Focus primarily on the symptoms, not the illness or diagnosis as a whole. What symptoms do you have, how often do you experience them and what is their intensity? Do not worry if you have multiple problems. Most people have a variety of problems in different areas, some greater, some smaller. Given how much people usually complain about their health, most people will have more than enough physical symptoms to work on with EFT, and by doing so, they can successfully resolve their underlying emotional issues.

Asking the questions

There are a number of key questions that will help you to discover the trail of your NCB. You can use them to identify the specific events so that you know what to work on:

1. How did I learn this feeling / thought / reaction? Who taught me this?
2. When do I experience this problem? What is the clearest, best example of a specific moment when this is happening? When was the first time?

3. When did it start? What stressful issues were at play during that period of my life?

Let us take a closer look at these questions:

1. How did I learn this? Who taught me this?

This question helps you figure out the specific moments in which you learned something and who was involved. Remember that all behavior is learned behavior. If you know who made you feel or think this way, then you can identify the specific moments when it happened. Once you have identified the exact moment, create a precise title for your specific event, as discussed in Chapter 2. Instead of a general title like *My mother was not there for me*, use a specific title like, *The moment when my mom completely ignores me when I say I do not like school and I feel sad*, or, *The moment when I am 5 years old and feel scared because my little brother and I are home alone and we are looking out the window to see if Mom is coming home.*

For example, if you immediately think, *I am worthless,* when someone criticizes you, ask yourself who taught you to think like this in your past. This is an example of your negative core belief (NCB), so in order to identify the foundational early childhood events when the NCB was formed, you need to look at events in the first 7 years of your life. If you think you learned this from your father, then look for the moments when something happened in which he played a role and where you concluded *I am worthless.* For example, *The moment when I discover that dad has thrown my drawing in the trash.* Apply EFT on all the specific events that come up until they become neutral memories.

2. When do I experience this problem? What is the clearest, best example of a specific moment when this is happening? When was the first time?

All these questions should lead you to a specific moment when something happened that is either the starting point of this stress pattern or a good example of a specific moment where this particular stress reaction is again reinforced. The stress reaction may manifest as emotions, feelings, a negative, limiting belief or certain behavior. Use the metaphor of the Table Top and Table Legs to find the specific underlying events. The Table Top is the conclusion that summarizes your problem, such as *I am a bad father, I have a poor relationship with my daughter, I cannot hold down a job* or *My needs do not matter.* The conclusion on the Table Top is almost always a limiting belief. Each Table Leg is one specific event in which you come to this conclusion (often subconsciously) and which, therefore, makes the conclusion seem true. Look for the best examples of situations or moments in which you experience the problem.

If some events took place during a certain period of your life, it can be very effective to identify the first time, if you can. If applicable, also identify the last time it happened. Realizing there is a starting point but also an endpoint to whatever it is can help resolve it more quickly. Your most strongly held beliefs about yourself and the world, including your NCB, come from your younger years. However, significant negative, limiting beliefs may also arise later in life, which will often relate to and build upon earlier ones. Examples include: *I always fall for the wrong men, I will never get rid of this* (a condition), or *I cannot find a good job.* The approach is the same: identify the specific events in which the negative belief comes to mind, ideally starting with your earliest or first memory in which you reached this conclusion, then continuing with other events throughout your life where this same belief played a role. Remember that you do not need to try hard to think of these events, relying only on your conscious mind. Close your eyes, repeat the conclusion as though you really mean it, and then ask your subconscious or The Unseen Therapist to come up with the best example of a specific moment when you learned this. Address all specific events with EFT until they become neutral.

3. When did it start? What stressful issues were at play during that period in my life?

This question helps you to identify which period in your life you should start with. This pertains to emotional problems as well as physical issues. We will focus on physical issues here. Identify when your issue started and what was going on in your life back then. In the case of a disease, this may be earlier than when you received an official diagnosis. It helps to make a timeline from 0 to your age now. Put the ages or times above the line and indicate when each issue started. Put the stressful, negative events from around that time below the line.

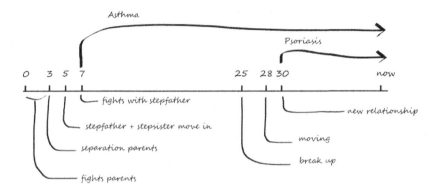

Figure 8: Timeline with symptoms and events

A timeline will give you a better overview of the possible underlying emotional events that may be contributing to your issue. You can certainly apply the Symptom-Focused EFT approach to whatever symptom is bothering you now, but you need to work on the specific events to neutralize the cause and thus resolve the physical issue, permanently if possible.

Additional Instructions for Addressing Physical Problems

In relation to physical problems, we will look at three more issues you can focus on to help you resolve them.

Diagnosis, prognosis and treatment shocks: The key reasons that an illness is intense, takes a long time to heal or becomes chronic is the emotional shock of the diagnosis, the treatment, the consequences and uncertainty about the future, the follow-up visits and any tests you need to undergo. Look for all moments that have a negative emotional charge: receiving the diagnosis and all the other stressful information from doctors and therapists, reactions from the people around you, the stress of hearing about or undergoing treatments and their consequences, hospital visits, waiting for test results, etc. In addition to resolving all of these stressful moments, one of the most important things you need to do is *stay out of fear*. The better you are able to stay out of fear and be at peace with what is happening, the faster the healing process can take its natural course. Letting go of fear enhances the self-healing capacity of your body to the maximum and thus provides you with the greatest chance of full recovery. The only way to let go of fear is to sever the link between any trigger that sets off your fear and the fear reaction itself. So, pay particular attention to and identify all the moments when your fear is activated and keep working on each moment until it is neutral. Do not forget to look for earlier trigger moments if the fear does not subside.

Information stress: It is a widely held misconception that finding information about your particular physical or emotional issue on the Internet is going to help you. On the contrary, it almost always causes more stress! We strongly advise that you do not look for any information about your issues on the Internet. How can general conclusions of what might (or might not!) happen and statistics help you in any way? More often than not, they simply create more fear. It is important to realize that this information is based on the experiences of doctors and patients who believe in illness and in fighting symptoms. That approach will give very different results than what you will get when addressing and resolving the root cause of the symptoms with EFT.

We also highly recommend that you consider not sharing the details of your physical issues and diagnosis with a lot of people. This does not mean, of course, that you should go without support, but choose carefully who you share the information with. When receiving a serious diagnosis, it is understandable that you might want to share it with others. In our experience, however, receiving a pitying look and being treated like a patient have never helped anyone. Nor does it help to hear about what happened to others who struggled with a similar issue. You want to also try to avoid constantly focusing on your symptoms. It can be helpful to make an agreement with those around you to talk about anything except your symptoms. You are not your illness. You have symptoms that have an emotional root cause. You can address these symptoms with EFT. Use EFT to stay out of all stress and anxiety, and let it help you stay out of the patient or victim role. Address everything, including the stress you get from your surroundings and those around you. The calmer you are, the more room there is for your body to heal itself. This is not about denial, but it is definitely a different approach from the norm.

Emotional conflicts leading to physical symptoms: Using Hamer's discoveries, it is possible to determine what type of emotional events you need to look at in order to address your physical problem. In Part 2, we provide clear examples to help you identify the root cause of various illnesses and symptoms. Below is a table that describes various types of negative emotional events (Hamer calls these conflicts) and in what type of tissue or organ the symptoms will show up for each type of conflict.[1] These findings are based on Hamer's research with thousands of patients over many years. We do not expect you to be able to readily identify the conflicts underlying your issues at this stage, but we want to introduce you to these insights here so that you will better understand the emotional root causes that are explained in detail in Part 2.

Hamer identified six main types of conflicts and the type of tissue or organ in which the symptoms of such conflicts will manifest. He classified conflicts based on the way the emotionally distressing event is experienced psychologically and perceived subjectively. For example, a self-esteem conflict involves blaming yourself because you are not good enough and the corresponding tissue that is affected is the musculoskeletal system. So, if you have a problem with your muscles, bones or tendons, then you need to look for specific situations in which you blame yourself for not being good enough. In other words, situations in which your negative core belief plays a role.

If you want to take this detective work a step further, refer to the graph on page 86. Most symptoms that capture our attention occur in the healing phase after the conflict has already been resolved to a significant extent. Therefore, you need to look for what has changed for the better, what situation was stressful but has now passed, and what decision you made that will offer you a way out of a problem. In other words, you need to look

---

1 *The Psychic Roots of Disease.* Eybl, B., Thirty-Three & 1 Publishing; ISBN-13: 9781948909-00-6.

back at the period prior to the onset of the symptoms to find the negative emotional event(s) that is/are the root cause. Resolving a conflict can happen in a few seconds but it can also take hours or days, or even weeks or months. For a minor symptom, like a headache or skin rash, start by looking at events shortly before the onset of symptoms, but, if you cannot find any emotional events, then look further back. For instance, you may have a headache in the evening and realize you had an argument in the morning that was resolved by the afternoon. You may suffer from a skin rash and realize that somebody who had been causing you a lot of stress is no longer in your life now. Or you may have bowel problems after feeling very irritated about a situation that was then resolved. For a more significant problem, like a diagnosis of cancer or heart disease, you may need to look at what was happening a year or more before the diagnosis.

Table 1: Types of Conflicts and Location in the Body[1]

Conflict type	Tissue/organ involved
Chunk Conflict: Not being able to grab or catch something, swallow, digest or eliminate food (the 'chunk'). This conflict may be experienced metaphorically, where you are not able to get what you want or not able to process or let go of what you do not want.	Digestive tract (mouth, esophagus, stomach, intestines), kidney collecting ducts, pulmonary alveoli, endometrium, prostate.
Motor Chunk Conflict: Not being able to move something (the 'chunk'), for example food in the intestines or blood through the bloodvessels.	Smooth muscle tissue.
Attack or Disfigurement Conflict: Being attacked (verbally or physically), being afraid of being attacked from behind, or worrying about being attacked.	Skin (dermis), heart (pericardium), abdominal lining (peritoneum) and lung membrane, nerve sheaths, mammary glands.
Self-Devaluation Conflict: Feeling rejected or not good enough or useless. You blame yourself for not being good enough or having failed (real or perceived). All other Negative Core Beliefs may apply.	Musculoskeletal system (bones, muscles, tendons), lymphatics, ovaries, testes, etc. Symptoms may manifest in the part of the body that you feel has been rejected or is not good enough.
Social Conflict: All conflicts that have to do with the herd / group. This includes Separation conflicts (wanting or not wanting skin contact), Territory conflicts (boundaries not being respected or losing something), Biting conflicts (defending your boundaries, showing someone their place in the pecking order).	The five senses, skin (epidermis), blood vessels, heart, mucous membrane, bronchi and larynx.
Motor Social Conflicts: Being stuck. Not being able to move, not being allowed or daring to move.	The innervation of transverse striated muscles (skeletal muscle and cardiac muscle)

1   *The Psychic Roots of Disease.* Eybl, B., Thirty-Three & 1 Publishing; ISBN-13: 9781948909-00-6.

Summary of Plan of Action

We recommend that you use all of the approaches discussed in this chapter so that you can use EFT more effectively to resolve your issues. See a brief summary below:

- **The WMOMD:** Set aside time every day to resolve your worst moment of the day. Remember that it does not have to be a big, dramatic moment – some days it may be just a very minor irritation. Just pick something that you can identify as triggering an emotion, even if it is short-lived. As often as you can, take time to identify and resolve previous events where you experienced *the same emotional reaction* – this is essential if you are suffering from any chronic symptoms.
- **Symptom-Focused EFT:** Apply one of the EFT protocols immediately until the intensity of the physical or emotional symptom has subsided sufficiently so that you are calm enough to work on the WMOMD or other specific events. If possible, take time to identify what triggered your symptoms, identify the specific moment and resolve it with EFT.
- **Big Cleanup:** If you use EFT to neutralize the emotional charge of all events on your Big Cleanup list, you will resolve the emotional causes of all the issues and problems you are currently experiencing in your daily life. This does require perseverance because this is a very broad approach, and it may take some time before you start experiencing the beneficial effects. But it does not get any more thorough than this, because if you do it right, you will tackle almost everything that has an emotional charge. If you do the work, you will be surprised by the improvements in your emotional, physical and mental well-being. This approach can also be used as a final sweep (after using the other approaches) to dissolve any remaining emotionally charged events.
- **Detective Work:** This involves asking the right questions to help you identify the emotional root cause of your current problem and identifying key events. It is a more focused way of using EFT and usually provides better and faster results.

To find inner peace, you have to finish what you started.

Buddha, Spiritual leader, ca 450 BCE – ca 370 BCE

Additional Techniques and Information

How Long Should I Work, and How Do I Finish an EFT Session?

How long you work on issues with EFT is up to the individual and depends on a number of factors. If you are doing Symptom-Focused EFT, then aim for a zero, but stop after 15-30 minutes. For the WMOMD approach, ideally, you need to be able to work undisturbed for approximately 30-60 minutes. Just like going to the gym, it is better if you use EFT on the WMOMD every day rather than trying to tackle all of the WMOMDs for a whole week in one sitting. For Detective Work and the Big Cleanup approach, you need to create a plan. Do not try to do this work quickly between shopping and cooking dinner. It is better to plan a session of 1 to 1.5 hours once or twice a week, rather than setting an unrealistic goal of two hours every day. The key is to make a plan that works for you and then stick to it.

Using the Black Box Technique: Be prepared to safely park whatever it is you are working on using the Black Box Technique (explained on page 96). Stick to your plan and stop within the allotted time. By now, you should be aware that you will not be able to resolve an issue to zero if it is not specific enough or if other, more foundational events are hidden behind the current issue, or if it is a major event that simply cannot be neutralized within a short time period. That is all fine. Park it safely and continue working on it at a later time. If you are feeling upset that you did not finish neutralizing an event, use one of the EFT protocols until you feel completely calm and at peace with what you have managed to accomplish this time. You can finish it next time and move on. Perseverance pays off.

Working With a Buddy: It can be very supportive to work with a buddy. Not as each other's therapist or coach, but together so that you can be present for each other and motivate one another to stick to your action plan. With Gold Standard EFT Tapping, you can take turns working out loud while the other person taps along for support. In Optimal EFT, it is very helpful to do the Personal Peace Procedure together or even with a small group of 3-4 people. One person can take the lead and follow the protocol out loud. For both forms of Official EFT, the buddy can support the process by working surrogately (which is explained at the end of this chapter).

121

How to Work on Negative, Limiting Beliefs

Even though you may realize by now that EFT is about working on the specific events that underlie a problem, we want to focus once more on addressing a negative, limiting belief, including the negative core belief (NCB). To be effective, you need to understand the difference between Symptom-Focused EFT (working on emotions or physical symptoms) and working specifically (working on the trigger of the emotion). The former may temporarily make you feel better, but only the latter will help you actually solve your problem.

Instead of working on the belief (or thought) itself and the emotions you may have because you are thinking this particular thought, you need to identify the specific moments in which you are triggered into thinking the negative, limiting belief. Using the metaphor of the Table Top and Table Legs again, the Table Top is the conclusion that summarizes your problem, for example, *I am a bad teacher, I will never find a partner,* or *I am not good enough.* Each Table Leg is one specific event in which you come to this conclusion (often subconsciously) and which, therefore, makes the conclusion true for you. If you want to successfully resolve this limiting belief, you need to work on the recent specific moments in which you came to this conclusion, as well as the moments from your early childhood and all the events in between. In other words, you need to work on the whole trail to successfully resolve the pattern. You will notice that, even when you are working on a limiting belief that is not your negative core belief, you will still end up also working on situations where your NCB plays an important role because there is almost always a connection between the limiting beliefs you hold and your NCB. It is very helpful to use the WMOMD approach daily as a starting point and then work your way back to earlier specific moments. See also Section N | Negative Limiting Beliefs.

Note: This instruction also applies to working on undesirable behavior.

Starting in a Dissociated Way: Taking the Edge Off

As mentioned previously, when you start working on events with an intense emotional charge, you may want to start dissociated instead of reliving the specific event in an associated way. We have already advised against working on your major traumas by yourself. However, sometimes you may start to feel an overly intense emotional reaction when you are working on a smaller traumatic memory. Therefore, it can be useful to check whether your emotional reaction may be overly intense before you start. You can check by assessing whether you feel any intensity when you simply imagine that you are going to relive a specific event and then bring this intensity down before you actually start associating with the memory. This is called taking the edge off, which we discussed briefly in Chapter 2. Let us elaborate a little further here:

1. You need to keep your eyes open to avoid association. With Gold Standard EFT Tapping, it is easy to simply keep your eyes open. With Optimal EFT, instead of doing the Personal Peace Procedure with your eyes closed, we recommend that you look down at a focus point with a soft gaze. Then, work on any fear or stress you have when you simply think about reliving the moment. You do not necessarily need to reduce the intensity to zero, but the more you can reduce the emotional charge, the less intense your emotional reaction will be when you relive the event. Aim to lower the emotional charge so that it is between zero and 3.

2. Use reframes if necessary: Useful reframes include:

- I am here now. I somehow got through this, and I can tell the story.
- Nothing can really surprise me. because I know what will happen.
- I do not need this stress reaction anymore, because this is only a memory.
- It is not happening, I am safe now.

These reframes may seem obvious, but only the left hemisphere of your brain knows this is the case because it understands time. The right hemisphere does not know time so as soon as you start to relive the moment and generate images, even before full association, this part may take over, making you feel like you are experiencing it all over again. If necessary, you can first go through the whole event in a dissociated way. Look at the event as if you are looking at a movie and tell yourself, step by step, what has happened, stopping immediately as soon as you feel an emotion. Use EFT until this moment feels calm, at least under 3, but preferably 0. Then, continue with your story. After you have gone through the event step by step in this way, you can then do it again, but now in a fully associated way, by reliving each moment in your story as if it is happening right now. You will find that there is still an emotional charge on the various aspects when you fully associate, although you might have reached a zero when you worked in a dissociated way. This is exactly why we insist on reliving your specific moment in an associated way, once you have taken the edge off so that you do not re-traumatize yourself! Only with full association is the stress reaction completely activated and subsequently completely neutralized, thus severing the link between the trigger and the stress response.

More on Reframes

Reframing is a technique from NLP (Neuro-Linguistic Programming). It can help you to more easily and quickly let go of your negative, limiting beliefs and conclusions that you have drawn during a certain specific event. In short, it helps you to change the meaning you have given to a situation. This happens automatically with EFT because you remove the negative emotional charge from the moment, and this allows you to assess much more calmly what is really going on in the situation you are addressing. But of course, there is no harm in speeding this up. Reframes work most powerfully when they are suggested by someone else and you are a little (but not overly) surprised by them. But there are certain reframes that work really well when you use EFT as a self-help tool.

Let us see how it works. Suppose that as a small child you were severely bullied by your older brother. Possible reframes may include:

- I realize this is his problem, I am just in the way.
- I have carried this long enough and it is time to let it go.

- If I continue to be angry/sad/anxious, I will pay the price (after all, the related stress response happens in my body and wreaks havoc there, not in somebody else's).
- I am not a little kid anymore and I can handle situations like this differently now.
- I can understand now what is going on.
- I did nothing to deserve this.
- It might be time to forgive him, so I can let go and feel peaceful.

With Gold Standard EFT Tapping, you may use reframes in the Setup phrase or during the round of tapping. With Optimal EFT, ask The Unseen Therapist to help you come up with appropriate reframes or use one that appeals to you and ask Her help in allowing it to sink in. In general, reframes work better when quite a bit of intensity has already been resolved. Exceptions include the following reframes, which you can use when the charge is still high and you may want to take the edge off:

- I somehow got through this / I did not die / I am here now, telling the story (for traumatic events).
- I will pay the price if I hold onto this (anger, frustration, resentment...), if the charge does not go down.
- I choose to realize that this event is over, it is history and it will never happen again (for traumatic events and in the case of stuck emotions).

If necessary, you can add words such as *maybe, a little, when I am ready.* This makes the statement less absolute and easier to accept. Use these words while applying EFT until you can fully accept the new insights and let go of any negative, limiting beliefs. EFT aims at neutralizing a negative event completely, step by step so that it no longer affects you. The ultimate goal is complete forgiveness of yourself and the other person. But take your time. EFT is not a disguised form of cognitive (behavioral) therapy, in which you talk yourself into desired behavior or make agreements with yourself about avoiding certain behaviors. For example, if you have been angry with your father for a very long time, it may be completely unrealistic to state that you completely forgive your father, but perhaps considering that you might be able to forgive him someday because you want to put it behind you may be achievable.

Reframe Themes

Undermining the 'true' authority: If someone has been allowed to 'write on our walls' and thus influence our beliefs, we have given them authority to say something about that subject and have come to see that as the truth. You can help yourself realize that that person did not really have the authority to make the statements they made and that you do not need to accept them as the truth. Examples of helpful reframes include:

- If you are upset about something that was said to you as a teenager by a classmate, you may say: *I am a prisoner of the words of a 16-year-old boy.*
- If you have negative beliefs about money that are influenced by what your father told you as a child, even though he was not financially successful himself, you may say: *I am taking financial advice from someone who is/was not good with money.*
- If you feel like you should have handled something better as a young child, you may say: *It would not occur to me now to ask a 3-year-old how to deal with this problem.*
- If you lack self-confidence due to what others have said to you, you may say: *I am accepting judgments and criticism as truth from someone who is far from perfect himself.*

Taking responsibility: It is extremely valuable if you can see that your reaction to a situation involves a choice rather than an unbreakable pattern that is destined to continue with the same burdensome outcome. This insight will empower you so that you no longer feel at the mercy of the situation. Relevant reframes include:

- It is my reaction, and it is an inside job, I am doing it to myself – no one else is doing it.
- It is just my perception/interpretation of the event.
- What the other person says or does is their responsibility, my reaction is my responsibility.
- I will pay the price if I hold onto this (anger, frustration, resentment,....).
- I have carried this (guilt, grievance, sadness,...) long enough.

Connecting to previous memories: Your reaction to the current event is based on memories (specific events) that played a role in creating and maintaining the stress pattern. So, reframes that help you understand that your reaction now is based on previous experiences are helpful. Reframes you could use include:

- I think this reminds me of something in the past.
- This possibly resembles something I experienced in the past.
- This triggers me because I have experienced it before.

If you are already aware of what is underlying your conditioned reaction to a situation, you may find these reframes useful:

- It seems like I am still choosing abandonment. Let me look at how I learned to do this.
- I always choose the wrong type of guy; it is time to work on what causes this.
- My current relationship is not working, just like before. I need to look at the cause.
- Here we go again, I have experienced this before with […]. Let me work on those events too.

Putting the problem in perspective: If the problem seems larger than life, it is useful to realize that your problem may not be that big compared to other problems people have or to remind you that you are not the only one with this problem. Such reframes include:

- We all have our own issues to deal with; no one escapes from challenges in life.
- It was like that before I was born, and it will be like that long after I am gone.
- I am not the only one with this problem, other people have the same problem, and everyone has some kind of problem.
- I do not know anyone who manages to keep everyone happy all the time.
- I wonder if this problem will seem so significant to me in 5 years.

To see the humor in your own beliefs, worldview or memory: Humor generally has a very powerful effect to discharge the intensity of our emotions and reframe our perspective. The conclusions you make as a small child are usually not very logical when you look back on them as an adult. Some of these 'truths' can be quite amusing in retrospect.

- If you developed a distrust of men, you may now challenge your conclusion that *all men are creeps with no exceptions*, and realize that it is quite a silly generalization, as there are in fact exceptions to this rule.
- If you always felt as if you needed your mother's permission, you may say, *Of course, I still have to ask my mom for permission, even though I am 44 years old and realize how absurd that sounds.*
- If you tend to be a people pleaser, you may say, *I still want to be the best boy in the class.*

Unmasking the writing on our walls: Giving yourself the opportunity to examine and acknowledge your beliefs or feelings about yourself and the world may in itself be sufficient to help you let go of those beliefs or feelings. They simply do not serve you anymore or they are no longer relevant. The goal is to expose the writing on our walls – all the 'truths' and beliefs – so that you recognize your own thinking process and have a chance to evaluate it. Usually, you will then see how absurd it was to believe them to be the absolute truth, and if not, you will at least see why your perspective is unhelpful. This process is similar to making people see the humor, but it may not necessarily be humorous. If you are working on a problem and find that you are having trouble letting go of a persistent belief, try using the following phrases:

- Even though I do not feel as bad about what happened, I still have to keep everyone happy.
- Even if I could stop grieving, it is still important for me to feel guilty.
- Even though I can let go of that one incident, I still need my anger, because anger makes me feel (important, powerful, protected, justified...).
- Even though I feel so limited by what my father said, I feel safe in my little prison.

Forgiveness: This powerful reframing tool – and for us the most important tool – will take some work before we can truly forgive. True forgiveness gives you emotional freedom and liberates not only yourself but also others. Many of us have been conditioned to believe that we have to fight to earn a place in this world, that we have to prove that we are good enough and that if the other person gets something and we do not, then we are a loser. If we can realize and accept that these beliefs do not serve us, then this may help us change our perspective. What would the world be like if we no longer thought in terms of *me* versus *you* but in terms of *we*? What if we believed that we are doing well only when everyone else is also doing well? We sincerely hope that EFT will contribute to the expression of more love in the world and less hate, strife, and envy.

We all have stress patterns and those patterns drive our negative behaviors. We are more alike than we are different. The content and details of our lives are different, but our emotional reactions and feelings are recognizable and understandable by everyone. In general, most people are doing the best they can and, even though some behaviors may feel like a personal attack, often they were done with good intentions or the person in question simply was not able to behave any better at that moment (because they were stuck in a conditioned response). The 'bad' behavior may also be due to pure incompetence, powerlessness, or ignorance. The way parents raise us is a good example. Parents quite often give their child love in a way that the child does not want or need at all, yet they usually do so with the best of intentions.

When it comes to situations where someone has used violence against you or displayed other seemingly unforgivable behavior, it may help to see that the person in question was obviously stuck in a pattern or problem of their own that they could not get out of. It may also be helpful to consider that we are never able to really know everything that has happened to other people, and therefore we can never really make an accurate judgment that is fair to everything and everyone, now and in the future. How many times have you been angry at someone or about a situation, only to be able to let go immediately when you better understood what was really going on? True forgiveness is about recognizing that what happened is in the past, it is finished and there is nothing more to it – it is no longer an issue now. Do you want to continue to look back on events with resentment in your heart or are you ready to allow yourself to put it behind you? Let EFT help you take this step. Useful reframes include:

- I realize that he could not have done any better, given his own history, his own traumas and his own worldview.
- She has her own problems that she needs to sort out, and I was just in the way.
- What [the other person] has done says everything about them and nothing about me.
- I understand that he is also only human and therefore does not always make the right choices.

If someone is continually subjected to physical violence or oppression, they need practical help to get out of the situation. Once they have done so, they can use EFT to help them recover and heal. Meanwhile, EFT can still be helpful when one is subjected to ongoing violence – because it can help you release emotions so you can think clearly. This clarity of mind may help you find a way to get out of the situation more quickly – or at least EFT may enable you to suffer less, and get through it with greater peace of mind.

If you are subjected to emotional abuse, then you could use EFT so you can stay centred in peace, despite what others are saying to you, rather than taking things personally. Reframes could include:

- My opinion of me is the only one that matters. No one's opinion of me defines my opinion of myself anymore.
- No one has the power to take away my inner peace, unless I allow them to do so.

In this context, do not forget to forgive yourself. Often, we are much more vicious and hateful toward ourselves than toward those around us. Holding on to guilt and shame does not help you behave better next time – it keeps you stuck and holds you back, helping no one. Using EFT to address your negative core belief is also relevant here, to help you forgive yourself.

We hope that what you have read so far has helped you to see that negative behavior arises from negative experiences that have become stress patterns, and thus the resulting behavior is driven by a subconscious, conditioned response. That does not mean you are not responsible for your behavior. We all need to take responsibility for our behavior. However, it is far better to identify and resolve the emotional root causes of our 'bad' behavior so that we do not repeat it, instead of beating up on ourselves, holding on to our guilt and remaining stuck in our negative patterns. Letting go of our guilt and forgiving ourselves are key.

Useful reframes for self-forgiveness include:

- I forgive myself for making that choice then. At the time, given my age and experience, it was the best that I could do.
- I forgive myself that I could not see it any other way, I was only 3 years old.
- I forgive myself for holding on to this for so long.
- I am only human, and I too make mistakes sometimes.
- I did not judge the situation correctly, and that can happen to anyone.
- I did not know any better.
- I was sincerely trying to be a good (parent, partner, friend,...) but I made a mistake.
- I forgive myself for reacting like a 5-year-old; it is the only way I know.
- I did my best, given my history, my traumas, and my worldview.

> *"When you are sick hasten to forgive your enemies,*
> *for you may get well again."*
>
> Ambrose Bierce, American writer, 1842 − 1914

Another Useful Test: The Validity of Cognition

The Validity of Cognition (VoC) is a term that indicates how true a statement feels to you. You can use this as a test to measure how true your negative core belief or any other significant negative conclusion or limiting belief seems or feels to you. You score the belief using a scale from 0% (which means it does not feel true at all) to 100% (which means it feels completely true). Then, you work on weakening the negative belief with EFT by working on specific events in the usual way. Using the VoC test, you can track your progress by assessing how true the negative belief is and work out whether you have dealt with enough specific events to sufficiently weaken the negative belief until it no longer feels true. Using the metaphor of the Table Top and the Table Legs, you need to completely neutralize enough legs (specific events) to delete the conclusion on the Table Top (your problem, in this case, the negative belief).

How to measure the VoC:

- Close your eyes and say the negative belief or conclusion out loud and mindfully. For example, *I am not good enough*, or *I am a bad father.*
- Feel how true that statement feels right now. We want to see how true it feels emotionally, not rationally or logically. Note down the percentage for later reference.

Then, make a plan to identify specific moments in which this negative belief or conclusion comes to mind, both recent and from the past, and use EFT to neutralize them. Once you have neutralized 5-10 events, repeat this test. You will notice that the percentage will start to steadily decrease, and thus the belief will feel less and less true.

The Generalization Effect

Experience with both Gold Standard EFT and Optimal EFT has shown that if you properly resolve the emotional charge of a series of related specific events, this may have a healing effect on other similar events, even though you have not yet specifically worked on them with EFT.

The generalization effect can be explained by using the metaphor of the Table Top and Table Legs, where the Table Top is the negative limiting belief or main problem (for example, *I have a bad relationship with my sister*, and the Table Legs are the specific events that gave rise to that belief or problem. The details of each specific event may be different, but they share a thread of commonality as they all contribute to the limiting belief or problem. Once you use EFT to resolve a series of related specific events (Legs) that are holding up the Table, this will weaken the remaining Legs (that you have not yet worked on) and destabilize the Table, causing it to collapse and the entire issue to resolve completely. It can help you save time, as you do not need to work on each and every specific event that contributed to a belief or problem. How do you know you are finished? Each specific event that you worked on needs to be neutralized to a tested zero. Then simply test with a VoC (as explained above) as to whether the conclusion on the Table Top is no longer true.

With Gold Standard EFT, the Generalization Effect may occur after resolving between 5 and 20 specific events. However, The Unseen Therapist is much more efficient and after you have enough experience in using Optimal EFT and working with The Unseen Therapist, you may only need to resolve about five specific events to resolve the whole issue.

When EFT Does Not Seem to Be Working

If you are not able to significantly reduce the emotional charge of a specific event, consider whether one of the following applies:

1. Are you properly reliving the specific moment in an associated way? Some common mistakes include: thinking about your problem instead of reliving it, staying dissociated (looking at the situation as if it were a movie), not working with EFT until the intensity of the emotional charge is zero and, finally, not testing properly. The issue does not resolve until you have neutralized enough specific events down to zero, because only then has the link between the trigger and the stress response been severed.

2. Are you being specific enough and working on one event at a time? Or are you thinking of other moments and situations at the same time, thus activating the stress response related to those other moments and events, and therefore making it impossible to neutralize this one. Focus completely on one specific event, working on one specific moment of that event with only one emotional crescendo at a time.

3. Check whether this event is the best one to address your problem. Are there other or earlier situations that have a greater emotional charge? If so, it may be helpful to address the earlier situations first, because they may be distracting you.

4. You may not experience immediate results. Sometimes you simply need to persevere and keep working on it. Give it time.

If you still do not notice any improvement in your issue as a whole, then also consider the following:

5. Are there beliefs at work that are blocking you? You may have certain beliefs about EFT and its application that may be hindering your progress. For example:

- I do not believe I can solve this problem.
- I do not deserve to get rid of this problem.
- This problem is too big for me to overcome.
- It is not safe (or too scary) to get rid of this problem.
- I cannot quite get rid of this problem.
- I cannot get rid of this problem now.
- I do not believe EFT works.
- EFT may work for some people but not for me.
- I have had this problem for so long, there is no way it can be solved so quickly.

If one of these or a similar belief feels true, then, use EFT to release these blocks. First, assess how true the belief feels using the VoC test. Assess how true it feels emotionally, not logically, using a percentage (0% not being true at all, 100% being completely true). If your VoC score is between 0% and 10%, then the blocking effect of the belief is probably negligible, but if the score is above 50%, keep doing EFT until it goes down to 10% or less. When you use EFT to release a blocking belief, make sure that you do not do EFT on the blocking belief itself, but rather use EFT to reduce the emotional or physical reaction that the belief evokes and, more importantly, work on the specific events in which you learned this belief.

6. Is everything on the table? Sometimes, there are hidden aspects. Or you may not yet be ready to really solve a problem. You may even feel unsafe about resolving it, on a subconscious level, because of the consequences. Once the problem is solved, you may have to take action because you no longer have any excuse not to. For example, maybe you

have to go back to work if you no longer have your disabling pain. Your negative core belief may play a role, causing you to feel afraid that you will discover that it really is your fault or that you are a failure (which is not the case, but it may be part of your belief system). This is what your ego likes to do best: try to make situations appear complicated, confusing, and seemingly hopeless, and convince you that because nothing seems to change, it, therefore, never will. If you continue to listen to your ego and remain stuck in your stress patterns, your ego has achieved its goal. Do not let your ego fool you. Persistence pays off. Keep moving forward steadily, even if you are only working with the WMOMD approach. Give yourself breaks too, but do not let that become a habit and lead to you procrastinating. Take your time! You may have been carrying this problem for a long time, but it does not need to be this way. You can overcome it and let it go, once and for all.

7. Do you have realistic expectations? If you have had the same stress patterns for years, there may be thousands of underlying specific events. Addressing 2 or 3 random specific events is unlikely to produce real and lasting results. Fortunately, you do not have to neutralize all of the specific events, due to the Generalization Effect discussed earlier. The key moments will suffice. Identify these using the WMOMD and Detective Work approaches, neutralize them and the Generalization Effect will do the rest.

8. Are you allowing yourself enough time? Have you made it a daily project and really committed to doing it? Are you making room for it? Have you created an action plan that you check every day or every other day? If you are working on a chronic issue, or on something that is bothering you daily, then you will not experience any substantial results if you only do a little bit of EFT sometimes when your emotions are off the chart. For lasting results, you need to work consistently, preferably every single day, on triggers and negatively charged memories from your life. Clear out old baggage and then keep doing maintenance when necessary.

9. Are you paying enough attention to daily triggers? If you have chronic symptoms, then you must be feeling triggered (almost) daily. Otherwise,

the stress pattern would not be continuing. It is not enough to address only early childhood experiences. It is essential to work on the WMOMD on a daily basis and discover the sources of stress in your current life. You also need to use all the other approaches in the action plan – do it all. That takes perseverance and perhaps courage as you start to approach your goals and overcome your problems. Are you ready to look at where you might need to start making different choices once you have fully resolved your problem?

Surrogate EFT

Surrogate EFT is an extraordinary phenomenon. It involves doing EFT on yourself for someone else or another living being, like a pet. This can be done with both forms of Official EFT. As explained in Chapter 3, we are one with everything and everyone around us, even though our sensory experiences usually make us believe that this is not so. We can intuitively sense what is going on and sympathize with another person.

With Surrogate EFT, your intention is key. You are working for the benefit of the other person (or perhaps an animal) – but not with the intention of making them behave in a certain way to satisfy your own needs. This means that if your child or someone else's child is restless and crying, you can use EFT to resolve the restlessness and its cause (whether you know it or not). It does not mean that the crying must stop now because it bothers you, nor does it mean the child has to listen and be more obedient. The same applies to doing Surrogate EFT for adults. You can work surrogately to relieve symptoms in another, symptoms such as: stress, tension, pain. However, this technique should not be used so that the other person does what you want and stops doing what you dislike. This surrogate work is meant to give loving attention to the other person without a vested self-interest. You can do surrogate EFT in two ways:

- **Being the other person.** Imagine that you are the other person and that you are feeling this stress, fear, anger or sadness in this stressful situation. Then apply EFT.

- **Doing it for the other person.** Imagine how it must feel for the other person to have this stress or to be in this situation. In doing so, you keep more distance while you do EFT for the other person.

Actual geographical distance is completely irrelevant. The other person may be in your neighborhood or literally on the other side of the world. Use either protocol to work on reducing stress and creating peace:

- **Optimal EFT:** You can use any metaphor or simply ask The Unseen Therapist to resolve it for the other person. Leave it all to Her and have faith in the process. After all, She oversees everything and knows what is needed. Simply asking The Unseen Therapist to help the other person feel unconditionally loved can be very effective.
- **Gold Standard EFT:** In the Setup phrase, name the problem, using either the I form (if you are imagining being the other person) or the you form (if you are working on EFT for the other person). When tapping, use the words that describe what you are aware is happening, or what you suspect may be going on.

How do you know that you are finished? If the other person is near you, you may observe their behavior and perhaps ask them about the problem that you have worked on surrogately for them. If the other person is not in your vicinity, then continue to work on them with EFT until you feel your attention wane or you get a hunch that you are done. Sometimes, when you empathize with the other person, you can sense the intensity of their problem. If that is the case, continue doing EFT until you feel it has gone down to zero. You may also simply do several rounds of EFT without necessarily feeling anything. Whichever way you do it is fine. It is all about the loving intention.

Do you need permission from the other person to do surrogate EFT? Before answering this question, we ask that you contemplate the following: Think about someone you are angry with or irritated by. Who is that person? What do you think about that person? Close your eyes and take the time to let that person come to mind and feel what negative emotions come up. Stop reading until you have felt this, then continue reading.

Have you visualized this person and how you feel about them? We want you to realize that by doing this, you have thought about a specific person and you have felt negative emotions about them, without hesitation and without asking for their permission. On that basis, why would permission be needed to do surrogate EFT for them that involves giving them loving thoughts and attention? In our opinion, directing loving attention toward another person does not require anyone's permission. However, it is not your place to fix another person or solve their problems. Sometimes, an effect may be noticeable, but the whole issue will certainly not have been addressed or resolved. That should never be the goal.

Consciously giving loving attention to another person can be very supportive. The other person may even experience that support subconsciously. With some regularity, the other person may report that they suddenly thought about you at the time you were doing Surrogate EFT. The intention is to support them, not to solve the problem, so let go of any attachment to a desired outcome. If you are personally involved with the other person and your own emotions are in the way, always do EFT for yourself first. If, for example, you are worried about your child, treat your own worry first with EFT before you do EFT for your child. You can only work surrogately for another when you are in a calm, peaceful state of mind. Do Symptom-Focused EFT to resolve any personal emotions you are experiencing and work on one or more specific events where needed. Try Surrogate EFT. It is a wonderful form of loving-kindness.

Part 2

A disease is never a mere loss or excess. There is always a reaction on the part of the organism or individual to restore, replace or compensate for and to preserve its identity, however strange the means may be.

Oliver Sacks, British neurologist and author, 1933 – 2015

1 | INTRODUCTION

Every truth passes through three stages. First, it is ridiculed.
Second, it is violently opposed. Third, it is accepted as self-evident.

Arthur Schopenhauer, German philosopher, 1788 – 1860

Reading Guide for Part 2

The purpose of Part 2 is to teach you how to apply EFT and inspire you to commit to doing so on a regular basis so that you can effectively resolve your issues.

To this end, we have chosen the following format:

- The sections in Chapter 2 of this Part are arranged alphabetically from A to Z, with each section addressing a certain type of symptom or disease (such as anxiety, digestive issues or sleep disorders), or a certain subject (such as kids or negative limiting beliefs). Since we cannot cover all possible symptoms and diseases, we have selected those which tend to have a major impact, both physically and emotionally. Our selection is also determined by whether the issue can be worked on using EFT as a self-help tool. Appendix 4 contains a list of all symptoms and diseases discussed.
- In each section (A, B, C…) information presented will help you identify the type of emotional conflict that may be underlying the specific type of issue discussed. We use Hamer's discoveries as a guide.

- Each section also contains recommendations for specific ways to apply EFT to resolve those particular issues. Within each approach, we list several different ways to apply EFT. We encourage you to apply EFT in all the ways suggested, in whichever order you wish. Approaching an issue from multiple angles increases your chance of success. It is crucial to carve out time in your schedule to thoroughly address your issues with EFT. If you have had an issue for weeks, months or years, it is not realistic to expect that it will be resolved after doing only a few sessions of EFT. On the other hand, just because you may have had a problem for a long time does not mean that it has to take a long time to resolve it. If you apply EFT as described in this book, we are confident that you will soon see the benefits.

We sincerely hope that you will be inspired to make use of the information provided to tackle your issues!

As you will soon see, the approach to take with EFT is essentially the same, no matter what your issue is. The key difference is the content of your specific events, but the way you address each specific event is the same: you use EFT to neutralize the emotions and feelings until the emotional charge of a specific event is completely gone. By doing so, you sever the link between that previous experience and the stress reaction and thus dissolve the stress pattern so that it no longer affects you in your daily life.

Important reminders before you get started

1. Start with small, manageable problems. We recommend simply applying EFT to the 'worst moment of my day' (WMOMD), as explained in Chapter 6 of Part 1, for a few weeks before you start working on past events. Once you are comfortable resolving daily triggers, use the WMOMD approach in its entirety, which involves not only addressing your WMOMD but also identifying and resolving an earlier memory in which you experienced the same feeling as you did in your WMOMD. You can then move on to the other ways of applying EFT, as recommended in this book.

2. As explained in Chapter 2 of Part 1, use EFT to take the edge off your specific event rather than immediately reliving the specific event in an associated way, if you feel very agitated even thinking about this specific event. While it is necessary to really feel your negative emotions in order to resolve them, it is important to approach issues gradually, so that you are not overwhelmed by your emotions.

3. Commit to using EFT daily, or at least a few days each week, ideally for 30 minutes each time. Put the days and times for doing EFT in your schedule, so that you establish a regular routine. Create a habit of applying EFT consistently to anything that causes you stress.

Emotional Causes According to Hamer

In order to apply EFT effectively, it is important to identify the underlying emotional causes of your physical or mental symptoms. When applying Optimal EFT, you can do a round in which you ask The Unseen Therapist for insights into the cause of your symptoms.

We have also found that Hamer's insights are valuable pointers to the underlying emotional root cause of physical and mental issues. They help to identify the type of emotional conflict involved so that you can zero in on the specific events that are the true cause of your issues and thereby apply EFT even more effectively and efficiently.

Hamer began his research into the connection between emotional distress and physical issues when he was diagnosed with testicular cancer in 1978. Shortly before his diagnosis, he had received the shocking news that his son had been killed. He suspected that his cancer diagnosis was directly related to the emotional distress he suffered over the loss of his son, so he began to investigate the reaction in the body to emotionally shocking events. At the time, Hamer was a doctor of internal medicine in a cancer clinic in Germany. He began interviewing his patients to identify the emotional root cause of various types of cancer and was soon able to confirm that every single one of them had experienced emotionally shocking events prior to their diagnosis. He later extended his research to include other physical problems as well as mental problems. He used CT scans of the brain to study the relationship between the psychologically shocking event and the organs or tissues involved. For more than 30 years, Hamer worked with over 20,000 patients and used their CT scans, blood work, and personal and medical histories to map out the underlying emotional conflicts of almost all diseases known to man.

Hamer's discoveries were received with skepticism by his colleagues in mainstream medicine. There was strong opposition to his finding that addressing the underlying emotional issues would resolve physical and mental issues, as this was contrary to the treatment with medications and surgical interventions recommended by mainstream medicine, which was considered to be superior. Legal action was taken against him, ultimately leading to the revocation of his license to practice medicine and two short terms of imprisonment. Despite this history, there is a rapidly growing interest in his insights and also a rapidly growing body of evidence showing that using these insights to identify the underlying emotional cause and resolving the conflicts involved produces results. We have similar experiences and find Hamer's insights to be very useful when applying EFT, as they help us identify the emotional conflicts underlying physical and emotional issues, which makes it easier to identify the specific events to target with EFT.

Hamer summarized his discoveries regarding the connection between emotional causes and physical effects in his 'Five Biological Laws of Nature.' Below is a brief summary of these laws:

1. Every disease or physical symptom is caused by a biological conflict, namely an unexpected, shocking event that occurs simultaneously in the psyche, the brain and the corresponding organ. While this view is not supported by mainstream medicine, it is generally accepted that stress and unprocessed early childhood traumas play a major role in developing illness (as discussed in Chapter 5 of Part 1).

2. The moment the conflict occurs, the conflict-active phase starts, resulting in stress symptoms. As soon as the conflict is resolved, the healing phase begins (as shown in Figure 7, Chapter 5 of Part 1). Many

of the symptoms experienced during the healing phase (such as fever and inflammation) are regarded as symptoms of 'illness' by mainstream medicine, yet Hamer saw these symptoms as an essential part of the healing process, as they help the body return to its original healthy state. Thus, there is no difference of opinion about the nature of symptoms as such, but rather about the significance and reason for such symptoms.

3. The body's physical reaction to a conflict is determined by the embryological germ layer from which the tissue (affected by a conflict) stems: endoderm, mesoderm or ectoderm. These are the three different embryonic cell layers from which the body develops and they are controlled by different parts of the brain. The tissue in each germ layer always responds the same way to a conflict. During the conflict-active phase, the affected tissue may either proliferate (resulting in a tumor), break down (resulting in an ulcer, holes or tissue shrinkage), decrease in function (for example, diabetes) or increase in function (for example, hyperthyroidism). During the healing phase, the reverse occurs, so that tumors are naturally broken down, holes are refilled by cell growth and function returns to normal. (You do not need to understand this to apply EFT). There is no difference of opinion between mainstream medicine and Hamer regarding the embryonic cell origin of the body's tissues, the nature of symptoms and the way symptoms progress. However, the meaning ascribed to the body's reaction differs completely, as mainstream medicine regards it as a disease process, whereas Hamer sees the process as part of an age-old, meaningful survival program.

4. Bacteria, fungi and viruses (microbes) do not cause diseases; instead, they play a vital role in healing diseases and restoring and returning the body to normal function. For instance, if there is cell growth during the conflict-active phase, microbes serve to break down the tumors during the healing phase. If the emotional conflict is prolonged and intense, there may be a dramatic increase in the number of microbes to help the body heal, which is diagnosed as an 'infection' by mainstream medicine. While mainstream medicine is becoming more aware of the important role microorganisms play in the body (such as the bacteria in our digestive tract), they still distinguish between good and bad

microbes. Yet both species of microbes (good and bad) can be found on your skin and in your gastrointestinal tract, even when you do not have an infection. Hamer does not distinguish between good and bad microbes.

5. Every disease is part of a meaningful biological program created to help the body during periods of unexpected distress. Thus, there is a reason why the body reacts the way it does. The reaction is determined by how you subjectively experience a situation subconsciously, or, in other words, how you perceive it and the meaning you give it, which is why we systematically categorize different kinds of emotional conflicts (listed in Appendix 2) and the relationship between such conflicts and our bodily reactions.

What we call 'diseases' originate in the psyche, so it is the psyche that needs to be healed. We use Hamer's insights in this book not to treat disease, but simply as a guide and tool, to help identify and resolve the potential underlying emotional causes of physical and emotional issues. As previously noted, the information in this book is not intended as a substitute for professional medical advice. The aim is simply to help you release emotions that may be contributing to your issues.

2 | SYMPTOMS FROM A TO Z

Contents

A | ANXIETY

Anxiety is a feeling of unease, such as worry or fear, and it can be mild to severe. While it is normal to experience occasional anxiety, it is not normal to experience frequent, intense, excessive, and persistent worry and fear that interfere with the ability to take part in daily life and that are out of proportion to any actual threat or danger. Examples of anxiety disorders include generalized anxiety disorder, panic attacks, phobias, diagnosis and prognosis anxiety, and fear of failure.

Fear is the most important negative emotion and plays a leading role in all types of anxiety disorders. Anxiety is a reaction to negative, fearful thoughts and negative emotions, rather than a reaction to immediate danger in one's environment (as is fear). Fear often manifests as anger or sadness, so if you take the time to delve into your own or someone else's angry or sad response, you will often discover that there is fear underneath it. Fear is an emotional response to a real or imagined threat. It is a natural and normal response when we feel threatened by people, animals, things, and events in our lives. Fear can protect us from real danger by activating the fight, flight or freeze response (which we explained in detail in Chapter 2 of Part 1).

It is easy to understand how fighting and fleeing help us to survive, but freezing is also a useful survival response. Being paralyzed by fear and unable to do anything can be lifesaving because in some situations, doing nothing is better than fighting back or running away, and it may reduce the likelihood of injury or death. The stress reaction is a survival mechanism, but it does not prevent psychological damage. During the freeze response, you become dissociated from the moment so that you do not consciously experience what is happening. This is designed to protect you from having to fully experience the trauma at a time when you are simply unable to handle it. Later, it may seem as if the event has been forgotten. However, that is not the case. The emotional charge of this event will remain in your subconscious, and the conditioned stress response will continue to affect you. While it is important to apply EFT to release the emotional charge, it is equally important to do so in a way that avoids any risk of re-traumatization.

Accordingly, if you have experienced a traumatic event but you cannot recall the details, you may have dissociated. In that case, we strongly advise that you do not apply EFT to this event by yourself, using only the information in this book. As you work on the event to release the emotional charge, you may start to remember more details about the event. The emotional charge may therefore be more intense than expected, so we recommend that you engage a well-trained EFT professional to assist you.

When you feel anxious, your sympathetic stress response is activated and this usually feels unpleasant. The first step in resolving anxiety is to realize that you are simply experiencing bodily sensations that indicate that the stress response has been activated. You may experience numerous symptoms including rapid breathing, tightness in the chest, dry mouth, heart palpitations, dizziness, nausea, sweating, feeling as if you are suffocating, and so on. These symptoms are not a problem and there is no need to be concerned. Your body experiences these symptoms on a regular basis. For instance, if you have to run to catch a train or flight, you may experience such symptoms without giving them a second thought. In these situations, you know that the symptoms will pass, so you do not worry about them.

However, it can be rather disconcerting if you experience these symptoms in other situations where there is no clear reason for them. You may start to worry about experiencing these symptoms, feeling like you have no control over them, which may result in even more stress. You may also erroneously think that these acute sympathetic symptoms are harmful to your body (which they are not). This may result in fear of the fear. You may even start to worry that you are going crazy or dying when you experience these symptoms. When your stress response is fully activated, you lose the ability to think clearly, so you may start to feel confused, creating even more fear and anxiety, further intensifying the symptoms of the stress response. It is common for people who suffer from anxiety to become anxious about the anxiety. They may be afraid of feeling these unpleasant symptoms again or they may be afraid of the consequences of feeling bad, namely that they may faint, that others will see them lose control, or that they will make a fool of themselves.

All forms of anxiety and fear, regardless of the severity, have a cause: it is learned behavior. You have developed the anxiety and fear during the course of your life from your experiences, thereby creating a subconscious reaction pattern. Whether it is panic attacks, anxiety disorders or phobias, it does not matter. They all arise from specific situations in your life. It has nothing to do with heredity or vulnerability per se. It has to do with the moments in your life when you taught yourself (or learned from others) to react in this way. It may be related to the way you were raised and the types of fearful behavior you have witnessed. There is no doubt that we subconsciously copy the behavior of those around us, especially as children.

It can also be learned later in life, but more often than not, the origin, or the core, of your fearful reaction can be found in early childhood experiences. This means that there are specific events that are the underlying cause of the anxiety, and these events can be addressed with EFT. Those of us working with Gold Standard and Optimal EFT are always amazed when clients tell us that they have been advised by mainstream professionals that they 'just have to learn to live with it,' that their anxiety is 'untreatable,' or that the cause is 'unknown.' These kinds of statements in themselves can be enough to maintain the anxiety disorder or panic attacks and, as far as we are concerned, they are definitely not true and certainly not helpful. It is also not helpful to encourage clients to expose themselves to whatever triggers their anxiety and to ignore their feelings and 'soldier on.' We resolutely advise against forcing yourself to overcome anxiety in this way, because every experience is a learning experience. When your anxiety is triggered, you are simply training yourself even more to turn on the conditioned stress response and feel the corresponding fear whenever you are faced with your particular triggers. As a result, the link between the trigger and the stress response becomes stronger rather than weaker.

Resolving your issue by exposing yourself to anxiety triggers only works if you simultaneously work on severing the link between the trigger and the stress response! And this is exactly what we do when we apply EFT, and that is what makes EFT stand out, head and shoulders above other approaches.

Table 2 contains a brief summary of the different types of fear (or anxiety), although it is not necessary to use such labels in order to address anxiety with EFT.

Table 2: Different Types of Fears and Anxiety Issues Explained

Panic attacks involve repeated episodes of sudden feelings of intense fear that something bad might happen, triggering a severe physical reaction in a short period of time. Symptoms may include shortness of breath, heart palpitations, chest pain and fear of death. Experiencing panic attacks may give rise to a pervasive fear of having another panic attack, thus the fear of the fear plays a big role in the continuation of the disorder. This fear may result in avoiding certain situations that may trigger a panic attack, which can lead to the development of a phobia, such as agoraphobia (fear of open, crowded or unfamiliar places) or claustrophobia (fear of confined spaces).

Phobias are characterized by an excessive and irrational fear of a specific object or situation that interferes with your quality of life and/or ability to function. The fear is disproportionate to the actual threat; thus, phobias are never functional. Phobias are usually accompanied by avoidance behavior and may also provoke panic attacks. Control is an essential theme with phobias: the need for control or the fear of losing control.

Generalized Anxiety Disorder involves persistent and excessive anxiety and worry about a wide range of situations and issues. There is a tendency to overthink and constantly try to find solutions to possible worst-case scenarios and to perceive situations as threatening even when they are not. You may worry excessively about your health and personal safety (and that of your loved ones), your children, your performance at work or in other activities, finances, vacations, natural disasters and future events. This constant worry may result in headaches, muscle tension, restlessness, heart palpitations, sleep disorders, and stomach upset. It may also lead to avoidance behavior (which may interfere with your daily life) and a tendency to overindulge in food, alcohol and/or drugs to escape your anxiety.

Fear of Failure relates to fear of failing in a wide range of situations. It is addressed in this section F | Fear of Failure.

Diagnosis and Prognosis Anxiety relates to the emotional shock you may experience when you are diagnosed with a serious illness or receive a bad prognosis. It is natural to be frightened to death if you receive a life-threatening diagnosis, but if you do not process and release this fear, it will remain in your subconscious and contribute to your stress levels, negatively affecting your health. It is important to address not only the first conversation with the doctor when you received the diagnosis, but also the stress and fear you felt during any treatments or checkups, and while waiting for test results. Even if you fully recover, you may still be holding onto unresolved fear and shock, so it is important to take the time to address and release them.

EFT Approach

When dealing with fear and anxiety issues, we recommend that you start with Symptom-Focused EFT and the WMOMD approach, because it is important to work on the anxiety symptoms themselves. It is also helpful to connect the dots using the Detective Work approach.

Below, we provide a detailed explanation of the approach that we recommend you take when dealing with anxiety.

1. **Symptom-Focused EFT:** As soon as you feel anxious, apply EFT to your symptoms, both your feelings of anxiety and any bodily sensations. Try to reduce the anxiety, but keep in mind that often you may not be able to get rid of it completely. After all, you are only working on the symptom, rather than the underlying cause. The more often you notice what you are feeling and how this naturally expresses itself in your body, the more you will start to realize that it is just a feeling and not a cause for concern. Realize that this is learned behavior, and therefore you can unlearn it by addressing the symptoms of your anxiety with EFT. Give yourself time, and let go of any expectation that your anxiety will immediately disappear, once and for all, after you have applied the EFT protocol only a handful of times. Perseverance is key. You need to unlearn this conditioned response by neutralizing the underlying specific events. It is necessary to dissolve the pattern that you have learned and built up over the years and perhaps decades. Trust the process. With each application of the EFT protocol, the pattern will weaken, even though you may not feel or notice it straight away.

2. **The WMOMD:** Identify the specific moment in your day in which you start to feel anxious. What are you doing in that precise moment? Where are you? What are you reading, listening to or looking at? Apply EFT to that specific moment until the intensity is below 5, but not yet 0. Then, while reliving the specific moment again, ask yourself, *When have I felt this way before?* and identify an earlier moment when you felt the same way. Apply EFT to that earlier moment as well. Also, notice what you are thinking in the precise moment when you start to feel anxious. Our thoughts can turn on our anxiety full blast. Take the time to identify

whether your thoughts relate to the moment itself or to something that happened in the past or to something that might happen in the future. Then apply EFT to your thoughts in the following way:

- If the thought is related to the moment itself and you are using EFT Tapping, then include it in your Setup phrase. For example, you may say, *Even though I read this and think this is never going to work out and I feel fear in my chest with an intensity of 8, I still accept myself.* If you are using Optimal EFT, then simply identify the negative thought, emotion and physical sensation and hand them over to The Unseen Therapist, asking for Her help to resolve them.
- If your thought relates to a past event, identify this specific past moment and apply EFT to that moment in the usual way.
- If your thought is about the future, ask yourself how you learned to think this way. Identify specific moments when you recall learning how to think this way, and when, where, and from whom you learned it. Then work on those moments with EFT to resolve the emotional charge.

Note: If several specific events come up, take the first event, the clearest memory or the best example of a moment when these thoughts played a role.

3. **Detective Work:** Use the following questions to create a list of all specific events that could potentially underlie this problem:

- How did I learn this feeling / thought / reaction? From whom did I learn this?
- At what point am I currently experiencing this problem? What is the best example of a moment when this happens?
- When did it start? What stressful issues were at play during that period of my life? A timeline can help to provide an overview.

B | BONES, MUSCLES AND TENDONS

Your musculoskeletal system consists of bones, muscles, tendons, liga-ments, joints and connective tissue. They work together to support your body's weight and help you move. According to Hamer, the emotional root cause of any issue affecting the musculoskeletal system is a Self-Devalua-tion Conflict. In addition, weakness or paralysis of the muscles involves another type of conflict, namely a Motor Conflict, in which the innerva-tion of the skeletal muscles is affected, not the muscle tissue itself. In our experience, understanding the type of emotional conflict involved helps you to identify the relevant specific events underlying your problem more quickly, so you can then resolve them more efficiently with EFT.

In this chapter, we will explain Hamer's findings as to what happens in the body when the musculoskeletal system is affected by a Self-Devaluation Conflict or a Motor Conflict, as well as the types of symptoms and prob-lems that may arise. We then explain the approach to take with EFT when dealing with such problems.

Meaning of Symptoms: Conflict Active or Healing Phase?

As explained in Chapter 5 of Part 1, Hamer's graph of the autonomic ner-vous system shows what happens in your body when you are dealing with an emotional conflict (you are in the conflict-active phase and the sympa-thetic stress reaction is activated) and what happens when the conflict is resolved (you are in the healing phase and the parasympathetic relaxation response prevails).

We will now explain what happens in the body when a Self-Devaluation Conflict arises which affects the musculoskeletal system. During the con-flict-active phase, there is tissue loss or degradation (resulting in, for ex-ample, less cartilage and/or brittle bones). Once the conflict is resolved, the healing phase begins, in which tissues rebuild and grow. The healing phase may be accompanied by pain and inflammation. Hamer found that the biological purpose of this program is in the healing phase: when you resolve a Self-Devaluation Conflict, which affects your musculoskeletal system, and complete the healing phase, more tissue has been built up and this will make you stronger physically (and often psychologically). This is because more tissue is built up during the healing phase than was broken down during the conflict-active phase, which means you are physically stronger after the healing phase than you were before the conflict or injury occurred. This explains why a fractured bone is stronger after it has healed than it was before the injury. Thus, if you encounter a similar conflict in the future, you will be stronger and better able to deal with it.

You will only notice physical symptoms if the conflict continues for a long time or recurs frequently. The healing phase may take days or up to 6 weeks, but full recovery may take up to three to eight months. If your symptoms last longer than eight months, the conflict may be ongoing (so that you go into the healing phase, get triggered and then go back into the conflict-active phase and continue to go back and forth), or you may be stuck in the healing phase (which remains incomplete because the conflict has not been completely resolved). The latter often happens with serious diagnoses and prognoses as well as painful conditions (where the pain is a trigger in itself) and when your beliefs about the symptoms operate as a trigger.

Of course, not all problems with the musculoskeletal system are due to emotional conflicts. Injuries may occur, including bone fractures or torn ligaments or tendons. However, the fracture or tear often occurs in a weak part of the body where a loss of tissue during the conflict-active phase has made that particular part vulnerable to injury. This may be due to an active Self-Devaluation Conflict.

Why Work on Conflicts When the Symptoms Indicate That You Are in a Healing Phase?

The simple answer is that you want to avoid the repetition of going through a conflict-active phase and the subsequent healing phase, with all their associated symptoms. You may have resolved a current conflict for now, but if a similar situation arises in the future, you may react again in the same stressful way, because the link between your triggers and your stress response has not yet been severed and this is still a stress pattern. This can only be accomplished if you identify the root cause of your stress reactions and have neutralized enough specific events to disable the whole conditioned stress pattern. Please see Chapters 2 and 5 of Part 1 for a detailed explanation.

Right or Left?

It is important to ascertain your biological handedness (whether you are naturally right or left-handed) because this determines whether the emotional conflict manifests on the right or the left side of the body. The clap test can be used to determine whether you are biologically right or left-handed. Many left-handed people were taught or forced to write with their right hand in early childhood, so the hand you write with may not necessarily be your dominant hand. When you clap, the hand that leads is the dominant hand. If this is inconclusive, check which hand you use to open a bottle with a screw cap.

If you are right-handed, the left side of your body is called the 'mother or child' side and the right side of your body is called the 'partner' side, which includes anyone other than mother or child. In left-handed people, your left side is your 'partner' side and your right side is your 'mother or child' side. If you want to work out what conflict may be involved, you need to look at the following:

- If symptoms manifest on the mother or child side, then the underlying conflict is a conflict with or about your mother, you in a mother role, your child, or about you as a child.
- If symptoms manifest on the partner side, then the underlying conflict is a conflict with or about your partner, father, siblings, relatives, friends, co-workers, classmates, teammates, and others, or you in that role.

Symptoms in Bones, Cartilage, Tendons, Ligaments or Muscles Caused by Self-Devaluation Conflicts

Self-Esteem and Your Negative Core Belief

Self-esteem is about how you value and perceive yourself. It is based on your thoughts, feelings, beliefs and opinions about yourself. If it is positive, then you like and value yourself as a person, and you feel that you are worthy, regardless of what others think about you. If it is negative, you may feel dissatisfied with yourself and that you are not good enough. Self-esteem may relate to different aspects of yourself, such as physical self-esteem, intellectual self-esteem, social self-esteem, and self-confidence.

Everyone has one predominant negative core belief, which is our main stress pattern. It is a judgment you have about yourself that is negative and starts with *I am....* It describes how you feel about yourself when you are criticized or judged, by others or by your inner critic. If your negative core belief is active and strong, your self-esteem will be low. Interestingly, our inner critic is often even harsher and more judgmental of us than the people around us and this judgment culminates in what we call the negative core belief. This kind of self-blame leads to a loss of self-worth, and this type of conflict is called a Self-Devaluation Conflict.

Your negative core belief developed as a result of specific events, in which your sense of self was attacked in some way. It may give rise to thoughts such as: *I am not good enough, I do not belong, I should not be here, I have no right to exist, I am unwanted, I do not matter.* Your negative core belief runs like a thread throughout your life, affecting how you perceive situations you encounter, especially those that affect your self-worth. More often than not, it is your most significant stress pattern, and it requires a truly transformational process to weaken it so that it no longer plays a substantial role.

The severity of the conflict determines which part of the musculoskeletal system is affected by a Self-Devaluation Conflict. Severe Self-Devaluation Conflicts manifest in the bones. Lighter forms of Self-Devaluation Conflicts are manifested in the softer structures, such as cartilage and ligaments. When muscles and tendons are involved, the Self-Devaluation Conflicts may be related to movement, literally or figuratively.

The location of your symptoms (where they manifest in your body) helps you determine what kind of Self-Devaluation Conflict is underneath them. Look at the function of the particular body parts, as this may indicate what action, or lack of action, is causing the negative feelings about yourself. Metaphors and expressions are sometimes also good indicators. They are often surprisingly accurate. Here are some examples:

- Problem in the knee: To 'bend the knee' means to submit to the authority of another, with its origins lying in the tendency to kneel or bow to show respect. If you have a knee problem, it may be due to a Self-Devaluation Conflict involving unfulfilled ambition, in the sense that you feel like you are not good enough and have to listen to others or let them handle things you would be capable of handling on your own. Or the Self Devaluation Conflict may relate to feeling frustrated because you are not mobile or athletic enough.
- Pain symptoms in the hands: If you blame yourself for not 'handling a situation' well enough, this may result in all kinds of symptoms affecting your hands. To 'get out of hand' means that you do not have control over something. Or you may 'have your hands full,' indicating that you are completely busy or occupied with something.
- Neck pain: To 'keep your head down' may mean to avoid being seen or noticed or to avoid becoming involved in something. If this is motivated by feelings that you are stupid or unintelligent, it may show up as neck pain.
- Pain in your elbows: The function of the elbow is to enable you to either embrace or hold something or someone or to push away and fend off something or someone. If you are not good enough at either one and blame yourself, this may show up as pain or other symptoms in the elbow.
- Pain in the thoracic spine: If you cannot 'stand up straight,' you may have a Self Devaluation Conflict which results in feeling defeated or humiliated, or you may feel that 'this is more than I can bear.'
- Pain symptoms in feet or ankles: If you 'cannot put your foot down' or 'stand your ground' or 'take a firm stand,' you may experience pain in

the feet or ankles. Also, you use your foot to kick something out of the way, so if you are not able to do that (literally or figuratively), it may also show up as symptoms in the feet or ankles.

Not all expressions are relevant or apply in every situation, of course, but play around with them and see if they resonate. The best time to do so is while you are reliving a specific moment. Then ask yourself which metaphor might be applicable and consider the function of the afflicted body part. This may provide more information about how you are experiencing the situation, which will help determine what to look for. Table 3 describes the meaning of the location of symptoms, according to Hamer.

Table 3: Location and Content of Self-Devaluation Conflicts[1]

Skull, neck, cervical spine	Moral-Intellectual Self-Devaluation Conflict, triggered by not being able to perform an intellectual task, making a mistake, or condescending remarks from others that make you feel slow or stupid (often experienced by overachievers who set the bar high or whose self-worth is based on their intellect). Perceived injustices (This is not fair), dissatisfaction, lack of freedom, disloyalty, dishonesty, ingratitude, and indecency.
Shoulders	'Mother or child' side: Believing that you are not a good enough mother or child, often associated with feeling guilty (left shoulder for those who are right-handed, right shoulder for those who are left-handed). 'Partner' side: Believing you are not a good enough partner, employee, friend, brother or sister, or feeling guilty about that (right shoulder for those who are right-handed, left shoulder for those who are left-handed). Feeling you have performed poorly in sports that depend on shoulder action.
Elbows	Unable to embrace or hold a person or pet or unable to fend off, push away. Feeling like you have performed poorly in work, a sport, or a hobby where the elbow plays a role, for example, unable to hit a ball, throw, shoot, punch or repel.
Hands, fingers, wrists	Believing you have treated someone badly or mishandled a matter. Feeling like you have failed at a task involving your hands (often suffered by perfectionists or people who rely heavily on their hands, for example, surgeons, jewelers, musicians). Feeling awkward or inflexible.
Thoracic spine	Feeling weighed down by life. Feeling discouraged or inferior, humiliated or small.
Lumbar spine	Central Self-Devaluation Conflict that shatters the core of one's self. Feeling unsupported (not backed up) by family, friends, colleagues, or one's employer. Not being able to handle the pressure anymore.

---

1 *The Psychic Roots of Disease.* Eybl, B., Thirty-Three and 1 Publishing; ISBN-13:9781948909-00-6.

Pelvic bone, pubic bone	Local Self-Devaluation Conflicts in this area often relate to sexuality, pregnancy, not performing as expected or feeling devalued below the waist. Also, a local Self-Devaluation Conflict due to a colorectal cancer diagnosis or hemorrhoids.
Hips, femoral neck	Not being able to endure a situation or not being able to persevere or feelings of failure. Feeling like It is too much to bear, This is too much to carry, I cannot handle this, I cannot get through this. Note: Often the person is silently going through this and not asking for help because they feel they should be able to do it all by themselves.
Knees	Unfulfilled ambition or recognition in work, sports, hobbies. Having to submit ('bend the knee') to the authority of another. Not being flexible or being too flexible.
Feet, ankles, toes	Not being able to stand someone or a situation, not being able to kick them away with your foot or crush them with your heel or stand your ground. Not being able to follow your own path. Not being able to walk, run, jump, dance or balance.

Common Symptoms and the Phase in which Symptoms Manifest

For all of the symptoms and conditions listed below, it is essential to identify the underlying Self Devaluation Conflict, which will depend on the location of the symptoms. Please use Table 3 above to help you identify the conflict at play.

Arthrosis occurs during the conflict-active phase; therefore, you need to resolve current stressful situations.

Bone decalcification (osteoporosis) arises in the conflict-active phase. This is more or less a generalized Self-Devaluation Conflict and is often related to situations where you feel old or discarded. Note: In Asia, where elders are valued and held in high esteem, osteoporosis is virtually non-existent.

Arthritis, bursitis, bone marrow inflammation (osteomyelitis) are all signs that you are in the healing phase. Note: Multiple myeloma, bone tumors and cartilage tumors also occur in the healing phase.

Ankylosing spondylitis (calcification of the spine) arises when healing is hanging, which means the Self-Devaluation Conflicts keep repeating as follows: The stress response is activated, the conflict is resolved and the body goes into healing. Then, more triggers arise which again activate the stress response, causing you to go through the conflict-active phase and healing phase over and over again. Calcification occurs in the healing phase and causes stiffening of the spine. Once calcification occurs, it is generally permanent, so it is crucial to address the underlying emotional causes as soon as possible to stop the cycle.

Rheumatism is generally defined to include osteoarthritis, arthritis and ankylosing spondylitis, as well as fibromyalgia and gout, but we will limit our discussion here to chronic polyarthritis or rheumatoid arthritis (chronic problems in multiple joints). According to mainstream medicine, this is an autoimmune disease, in which the body's cells supposedly attack its tissues for no known reason. Even though laboratory tests detect antibodies and an increased blood sedimentation rate, such findings fail to explain the underlying cause. When there is active stress, you are in the conflict-active phase of a Self-Devaluation Conflict, during which you experience little or no symptoms. Acute rheumatism occurs in the healing phase with inflammation and extra bone and connective tissue production, causing increasing thickening and deformation of the affected joint. The increase in tissue is permanent, so it is essential to address the underlying emotional causes to stop this process.

Gout occurs when you have two types of conflicts simultaneously, according to Hamer. There is a Self-Devaluation Conflict that has been resolved enough for you to enter the healing phase, and at the same time, another conflict is active, namely an Existential Conflict. An Existential Conflict arises when you do not feel at home, when you are driven away from your home (like a refugee), or when you are uncertain about your survival. You may feel like a fish out of water, not belonging and out of your element. To resolve gout, you need to resolve this ongoing Existential Conflict and also address the Self-Devaluation Conflict to make sure that it has been resolved completely, to prevent a recurrence.

Neck pain/cervicobrachial syndrome/sleeping hands arise during the healing phase of a moral-intellectual Self-Devaluation Conflict. If blood pathways and nerves of the arms are temporarily compressed, it may cause a numb or tingling feeling in the hands during inactivity. This is because fluid is retained in the first part of the healing phase. It is important to resolve the underlying conflicts to prevent a recurrence.

Carpal tunnel syndrome indicates the persistent healing phase of a Self-Devaluation Conflict due to handling a situation or person wrongly or the inability to hold on to something. The symptoms may be similar to the previous symptoms. You need to resolve all underlying conflicts to heal it permanently.

Sciatica (radiating pain), lumbago (low back pain) occur in the healing phase of a central Self-Devaluation Conflict. You may feel like you have been shaken to the core, in a way that affects your self-worth in a social role such as a mother, a student, a partner or an employee. You may also feel like you are under too much strain or not able to keep up under pressure. Resolving the underlying conflicts is essential to prevent recurrence and permanent damage.

Crooked big toe (hallux valgus) is due to recurrent Self-Devaluation Conflicts where you feel unable to kick something or someone away. It may also relate to the function of the foot, such as not being able to walk, dance, jump, or balance. As the conflict recurs and is healed, a layer of bone is added during each healing phase, causing the toe to become crooked. Resolving the Self-Devaluation Conflicts prevents the toe from becoming more and more crooked. The additional bone tissue is generally permanent.

Fibromyalgia is caused by recurrent Self-Devaluation Conflicts. The acute attack of pain occurs in the healing phase, and the symptom-free intervals indicate that you are in the conflict-active phase. In the symptom-free period, there is a Self-Devaluation Conflict and as soon as you resolve it, you enter the healing phase with accompanying pain symptoms. Breaking this vicious cycle begins with recognizing and resolving the Self-Devaluation Conflicts and paying close attention to anything that activates your negative core belief and then applying EFT to those specific moments.

Muscle Symptoms Caused by Motor Conflicts

Feeling Stuck and Unable to Get Out of a Situation

Conflicts related to the movement of the muscles are called Motor Conflicts, which arise when you are not able to move or feel stuck in a situation. Motor Conflicts affect the transverse muscles of the musculoskeletal system or the skeletal muscles, which you use to move. A Motor Conflict means that you feel stuck or have a fear of being trapped, of being handcuffed, of not being able to escape or of not being able to get away. It can also be about not daring, not being able, not being allowed or not wanting to move. It also includes situations in which you are paralyzed with fear.

In the conflict-active phase, fewer nerve impulses are transmitted to the muscles, causing a loss of muscle function. Depending on the intensity of the conflict, muscle weakness or even total paralysis of the muscles may result. The biological purpose of the paralysis originates in the freeze response (which you see when prey animals play dead when chased by a predator). Therefore, not moving can increase your chances of survival.

Note: At the start of the healing phase, the paralysis may briefly become even more severe because of the retention of fluids all over the body. This temporarily enlarges the space between the nerves themselves and between the nerves and muscles, further disrupting nerve signals to the muscles. This is actually a good sign, but it is often misinterpreted as an aggravation of the symptoms. In the healing crisis, uncoordinated muscle spasms may occur, which can often lead to a mistaken diagnosis of epilepsy. These wrong conclusions (and the associated fears that then arise) can create a vicious cycle.

Muscle pain may also occur without underlying emotional events triggering the stress response. Overuse of muscles may lead to pain, stiffness and sometimes even tears. However, a muscle tear is often caused by an underlying active Self-Devaluation Conflict with the accompanying tissue breakdown. Also, various medications may have adverse side effects, causing painful, stiff muscles, muscle spasms or even weakness and paralysis. Thus, you may want to consider the potential side effects of any medications you are taking, (such as blood pressure medication, cholesterol-lowering drugs, and psychopharmaceuticals) when attempting to identify the cause of any muscle pain.

Table 4. Location and Content of Motor Conflicts[1]

Shoulder and back muscles	Not being able to get out of the way or step aside (to avoid someone or something).
Arm and leg flexors	Not being able to hold or embrace someone or something, not being able to draw something or someone to oneself.
Arm and leg extensors	Not being able to push someone or something away, not being able to fight someone off (by punching or kicking), or not being able to defend oneself, for example, being forcefully held down (abuse, injection, a fight).
Legs	Not knowing where to go. Not being able to escape, flee or run away (literally or figuratively, for example, from a workplace or relationship), not being able to follow, not being able to jump aside, not being able to run fast enough and keep up, not being able to climb up (for example, not being promoted), not being able to jump, balance or dance.

---

1 *The Psychic Roots of Disease.* Eybl, B., Thirty-Three and 1 Publishing; ISBN-13:9781948909-00-6.

Common Symptoms and the Phase In Which They Manifest

For all of the symptoms and conditions listed below, it is essential to identify the underlying Motor Conflict, which will depend on the location of the symptoms. Please use Table 4 above to help you identify the conflict at play.

Muscle paralysis can result in a diagnosis of Multiple Sclerosis (MS), infantile paralysis (polio) and amyotrophic lateral sclerosis (ALS) if the Motor Conflicts are not resolved and there is hanging conflict activity. Unfortunately, being diagnosed with one of these diseases produces an additional Motor Conflict, especially if you are told there is no cure, as you may feel trapped in the disease, believing you cannot get out of it, expecting to end up in a wheelchair. It is essential to understand the connection between emotional conflicts and how they can be expressed in the body and to do lots and lots of EFT to resolve all conflicts and stress.

Epilepsy or convulsions occur during the healing crisis of a Motor Conflict. If you experience repeated spontaneous convulsions, with or without loss of consciousness, you may be diagnosed with epilepsy (which is viewed as an illness by mainstream medicine, as opposed to simply a sign that you are healing from an emotional conflict). See also the information given in J |Juvenile Myoclonus Epilepsy.

Diaphragmatic Cramps/Spasms occur during the healing crisis of a Motor Conflict, especially during the healing phase of a conflict where you feel like you are not getting enough air, or like you are not able to breathe, either literally or figuratively (you may be in a situation where you feel oppressed or where you cannot get enough air or room or you feel the need to take a deep breath).

Parkinson's disease with symptoms such as tremors (twitching of muscles), muscle stiffness and the slowing of movement are symptoms of a Motor Conflict in hanging healing. The tremors (which occur in the healing crisis) themselves become a trigger, interrupting the healing and moving you briefly back into the conflict-active phase, and then another healing crisis follows, so the healing phase is never completed. As with MS and ALS, the condition worsens because of the negative prognosis and fear of becoming disabled, which causes more Motor Conflicts. It is essential to resolve all the conflicts (including your fears about the symptoms and prognosis and your beliefs about the illness) so that the healing phase is not interrupted and complete healing can occur.

Restless legs arise from a fear of being stuck in, or not being able to escape from, a place or undesirable situation (for example, literally feeling stuck behind a desk at school or work), or not being able, allowed or daring to move (literally or figuratively). It may occur during the healing crisis of the hanging healing of such a Motor Conflict. Isolated cramp attacks at night are a brief healing crisis of this type of conflict.

EFT Approach

Musculoskeletal symptoms almost always involve Self-Devaluation Conflicts, except for the small group of muscle-related symptoms described above, which are caused by Motor Conflicts. The more you address the Self-Devaluation Conflicts from both the past and the present, the faster you will get results. Therefore, it is necessary to identify and neutralize current triggers in your daily life as well as resolve old negative memories from the past. Since the foundation of your negative core belief (NCB) is established in the first 7 years of your life, it makes sense to focus on this period and start applying EFT to events during this period, in order to weaken its origin. When dealing with a Motor Conflict, it is also particularly useful to address your NCB, because that may play a big role in causing you to conclude that you are stuck in a situation and cannot do anything to get out of it. For the more serious diagnoses, it is also important to neutralize the diagnosis and prognosis shocks and beliefs as well.

1. **Negative core belief:** Identify the exact wording of your NCB (using the guidance at the beginning of Chapter 5 in Part 1). For example, *I am not good enough* or *I am not worth it* or *I do not belong.*

   VoC (Validity of Cognition) of your NCB: Assess how true your NCB feels so you can use it as a benchmark to measure your progress. Repeat your NCB out loud, really focusing your attention on it, then notice how true it feels emotionally, not rationally (where 0% is not true and 100% is completely true). Test the VoC of your NCB with some regularity (every 6–8 weeks) so you can determine if it is becoming less true. Identify current specific events in which you draw this negative conclusion about yourself, and neutralize them with EFT, so that over time, your NCB will feel less and less true and its influence will largely or completely disappear. Aim to bring the VoC down below 10%.

2. **The WMOMD:** Identify at what specific moment your NCB is activated (for Self-Devaluation Conflict symptoms) or you feel stuck (for Motor Conflict symptoms). What are you doing at that moment? Are you reading or hearing or witnessing something? Apply EFT to this specific moment until the intensity of the emotional charge is below 5, but not yet 0. Then while reliving it, ask yourself, *When have I felt this way before?* and identify an earlier moment. Apply EFT to that moment as well. Use this approach every day, beginning with a recent moment as a starting point, which makes it easier to identify key events from the past. This approach helps to both weaken your NCB and address events in which you feel stuck.

3. **Detective Work:** Make a timeline. When did you first experience the symptoms? What stressful events were going on in your life before the onset of the symptoms? What has changed? If the symptoms suggest that you are still in the conflict-active phase, identify what was going on during the onset of the symptoms. What is still going on?

   For Self-Devaluation Conflict issues: Ask yourself the following questions, *How did I learn my NCB?* and *Who taught me this and at what age?* Identify the specific moments in your early childhood in which you learned to draw this negative conclusion about yourself. Look at the roles played by your parents, grandparents and siblings, as well as others like teachers, friends, or sports coaches.

   For Motor Conflict issues: Ask yourself, *What situations made me feel like I was stuck and could not get out?* to find out what specific situations and events are involved in the underlying conflict. Start with early childhood events, but make sure that you also include recent events as well. When you are experiencing a recurrence of symptoms or persistent symptoms (longer than 2-4 weeks), then recent stressful events always play an important role.

4. **Big Cleanup:** You may not need to do any Detective Work if you can immediately make a list of specific events. If so, do that and work on it regularly. The more you resolve the events in which your NCB is activated, the weaker your NCB becomes, and the less impact it has on your life. The same applies to your efforts to resolve any events where you felt stuck, which have resulted in a pattern of feeling stuck. The more EFT you do to neutralize these events, the weaker the stress pattern and the less intense the symptoms will become. If you are anxious about or feel stuck in a diagnosis you received, make sure you neutralize every specific moment that is related to it, including all conversations with doctors and therapists, all examinations, all test results, reactions from the people around you and every moment in which you were frightened by what you read, heard or saw in connection with the diagnosis.

5. **Symptom-Focused EFT:** When needed, use EFT to work directly on your symptoms, either physical (aiming at reducing them) or emotional (aiming at calming yourself down sufficiently so that you can switch to working on specific events).

C | CHRONIC FATIGUE

For our discussion here, we use the term chronic fatigue to also include chronic fatigue syndrome (CFS), myalgic encephalomyelitis (ME), burn-out, surmenage and chronic stress with depressive symptoms. Any of these diagnoses may be given in cases of severe fatigue. Whatever the diagnosis, it is necessary to determine what is causing the fatigue. You may have been in the conflict-active phase for a long time (months or even years) and therefore feel exhausted. Or perhaps you have resolved a significant long-standing conflict and have already moved into the healing phase, and thus you are experiencing the intense fatigue that is characteristic of this phase.

Websites that provide information about the above diagnoses show a striking overlap in symptoms and the explanations given are, as far as we are concerned, disappointing. Apart from pointing out that the symptoms are caused by too much stress, there is no explanation given as to what causes this stress (other than that you are apparently not very good at dealing with stress). And the recommended solutions lie mainly in avoiding everything that can give rise to stress, which involves adjusting your life and applying stress-reducing methods. Even when you do so, you do not solve the cause of the stress. The fact that these kinds of websites then report that recovery is often very slow or only partial seems almost logical since the cause of the problem is not resolved. This will indeed lead to many people claiming that once they experience these kinds of symptoms they never quite get back to their 'old self.' If you do not tackle the cause, we understand that this would be the case. We are not claiming that if you 'just' start working with EFT, all your symptoms will disappear immediately because these types of symptoms did not just appear overnight. There are precise reasons why these symptoms developed, reasons that may have continued for years before the symptoms arose, so it is necessary to take the time to identify and resolve these causes. If you really want to do this, you will probably need to make some radical changes and decisions about the way you live your life. If you choose to see these symptoms as a wake-up call, they may be the catalyst for a true transformation in which many positive changes are possible.

We will now explain how chronic fatigue develops. Normally, we expend energy during the day, which makes us tired, and then at night, we recover and replenish our energy reserves. When we encounter challenging situations, we may call on our reserves and continue to perform at a high stress level 'because we have to.' For example, there may be a serious family circumstance to deal with or extreme work pressure, often in combination with other stressful events. If you are suffering from chronic fatigue, this means that you have been drawing on your reserves for months or years. When your reserves are finally depleted, it can feel like falling into a black hole, with no one to help you. You may feel like you are on your own and that you just cannot handle anything anymore. It is difficult to put things into perspective and you may feel overwhelmed by your negative feelings, spinning around in negative, despondent thoughts, and feeling exhausted.

You can find many lists of symptoms of chronic fatigue on the internet. Some websites list 5 symptoms, others may list 10 or 20, and we even came across a website that listed 73 possible symptoms of chronic fatigue. Below is a list of possible symptoms you may have:

1. Fatigue
2. Memory problems (forgetful, difficulty learning)
3. Difficulty concentrating
4. Difficulty sleeping, insomnia
5. Unrefreshing sleep (tired upon waking)
6. Feeling weak
7. Frequent headaches
8. Dizziness
9. Frequent sore throat
10. Palpitations
11. Stress, tension
12. Feeling anxious, nervous, panicked
13. High blood pressure
14. Strong sense of restlessness
15. Brain fog
16. Difficulty thinking and making decisions
17. Enlarged lymph nodes in neck and armpits
18. Unexplained muscle or joint pain
19. Nerve pains
20. Fainting, feeling light-headed
21. Intestinal discomfort, IBS
22. Poor fitness
23. Chills and night sweats
24. Vision issues: blurred vision, seeing spots
25. Allergies and sensitivities
26. Frequent urination
27. Shortness of breath
28. Extreme exhaustion after physical or mental work
29. Skin reactions (eczema or acne)
30. Hormonal imbalance
31. Trembling
32. Suicidal thoughts
33. Overly critical, complaining a lot
34. Feeling insecure, worrying a lot
35. Guilt and shame
36. Heavy pressing feeling in chest
37. Social isolation
38. Fear of failure
39. Unable to let go of control
40. Migraine attacks

In short, you may be faced with a long list of possible symptoms but given very little direction as to how to overcome them. Even if you have not been diagnosed with chronic fatigue, you may recognize that you have experienced some of these symptoms. Whatever the case, the starting point is to figure out why you have these symptoms, so you can resolve them with EFT.

Which Factors Are Involved?

The first step is to observe how you experience stressful situations and notice the meaning you give such situations because that will help you determine which stress pattern is activated. Certain personal characteristics contribute to the risk of chronic fatigue. These include a strong sense of responsibility, perfectionism, a high degree of empathy, high standards, and a tendency to be overinvolved, too caring or conflict-avoiding (for example, people in social professions who give too much but feel unappreciated). Personal circumstances may also be relevant. For instance, feeling unsupported (either at home or work), losing a loved one, stressful or dysfunctional relationships, serious illnesses and other drastic events. It may be helpful to consider your life from a more spiritual perspective to help determine the underlying conflict. For instance, perhaps you are not following your inner calling, or you feel that you have taken the wrong path, and thus your life has become increasingly meaningless. If you are on the wrong path, cut off from your purpose and sense of fulfillment, you may run out of steam and burn out.

Which Emotional Conflicts?

If chronic fatigue has been going on for years, the underlying emotional conflict is almost always related to 'having taken the wrong path,' hence the name Wrong Path Conflict. It may involve your personal circumstances as well as your work. Quite often, there are multiple issues at play in both areas. If this is the case, you are in the conflict-active phase. If you are honest with yourself, you know that drastic changes are needed to get out of this conflict. Of course, this in itself may cause a lot of stress.

If you have developed fatigue or burnout after a short period of chronic stress (which lasted weeks or months, but no more than a year), then the underlying emotional conflict usually relates to Territorial Conflicts or Attack or Disfigurement Conflicts. If this is the case, your symptoms arise during the healing phase. However, it is likely that several conflicts are involved, so you may be in the conflict-active phase with respect to ongoing problems and in the healing phase with respect to other conflicts you have already resolved (and thus experience fatigue). Finally, generalized Self-Devaluation Conflicts are another group of conflicts to look at, since they almost always contribute to the conflicts listed in this paragraph.

Below is an explanation of the potential underlying conflicts involved:

Wrong Path Conflict: Feeling like you are on the wrong track, that you have made the wrong decision, that you have gone 'off course' or that you are on a slippery slope. Feeling like you or something has fallen into the wrong hands. In other words, you have chosen the wrong partner, the wrong job, the wrong house or place to live.

Territorial Conflict: Territory includes your home, workplace, school, playground, community centers and the village, city and country where you live. It includes 'pack' members in the territory, namely your parents, spouse or partner, child, relatives, friends, colleagues, clients, neighbors and pets, as well as assets in your territory, for example, car, jewelry, money, stocks, investments, a license, an immigration status or a club membership. Territory can also be your body or your time. There are several types of Territorial Conflicts: Territorial Anger, Territorial Fear, Territorial Loss, or Territorial Marking. See Appendix 2 for the definitions of these types of conflicts.

Attack or Disfigurement Conflict: Feeling attacked, disfigured, tarnished or you feel violated (literally or figuratively) or dirty in some way. It may be a physical or verbal attack, such as being slapped in the face or sworn at. A surgery or a biopsy may be subconsciously perceived as an attack on, or disfigurement of. the body, and even a medical diagnosis or announcement that you need an operation can trigger such a conflict. You may feel soiled or dirty if you come into contact with something you perceive as disgusting (such as vomit, urine, blood or feces) or if you are touched or embraced by someone who you perceive as repulsive or who you believe has an infectious disease.

Self-Devaluation Conflict: Self-devaluation or loss of self-worth. Feeling rejected, not good enough, useless or a failure. This type of conflict involves self-blames. It arises when you judge yourself as not being good enough in some way. Thus, the way we perceive ourselves and our self-talk can create a Self-Devaluation Conflict. Examples of generalized Self-Devaluation Conflicts: feeling humiliated (by accusations, scoldings, derogatory remarks), being abused (physically, sexually or verbally), failure (at work, at school, in sports, in a relationship, as a parent or partner), a poor performance, feelings of shame and guilt, loss of a status or a workplace, illness or injuries (causing one to feel 'less than'), and aging (*I am not as good as I used to be, I am old and useless*).

EFT Approach

Concerning your symptoms, it is important to identify when the symptoms started and what stressful things are or have been going on in your life. Take your time and go easy. If you have realized that you are in the healing phase, then it is important to take care of yourself during this period and take time to rest. If you have more energy, then make time to dig deeper and address events that occurred prior to the onset of your symptoms. If you are still in the conflict-active phase, it is imperative to resolve your ongoing conflicts as soon as possible. You need to do so in two ways: by applying EFT and also by taking concrete actions and making decisions. Keep in mind that you will then enter the healing phase, which will give rise to even more fatigue. It is important to be aware of this so that you do not become stressed (again) by wrongly assuming your condition is getting worse. Fatigue is a natural part of the healing phase, and it is designed to enable (or force) you to rest so that you can recover properly. All you need to do is listen to your body and follow its cues.

1. **Determining whether you are in the conflict-active or healing phase:** You may still be in the conflict-active phase if you experience the following: feeling rushed and restless but tired, unable to sleep well at night, teeth grinding, waking up early and feeling like you have a lot on your plate and need to keep all the balls in the air. Indications that you are in the healing phase include intense fatigue, feeling heavy and languid, a great need for sleep, unable to get out of bed, feeling weak and/or suffering from all sorts of physical problems and pain. If you have made radical (and often difficult) changes and had assumed that you were finally out of the woods but you are now experiencing pain and fatigue, this suggests that you have resolved a major conflict and entered the healing phase. See also the explanation of the healing phase in Chapter 5 of Part 1 and section H | Healing Symptoms.

2. **Detective Work:** Use the following questions to create as complete an overview as possible of the specific stressful events which may be underlying your symptoms and mark them on a timeline:

   - When did the fatigue begin? If you know that you are still in the conflict-active phase, identify what stressful things have been going on since you began experiencing fatigue. If you know you are in the healing phase, identify what stressful issues were involved prior to the onset of the fatigue and what changes have occurred in your life. If it is still unclear, make a note of everything that was going on in your life a year or two before the fatigue started, as well as everything that is going on now, which could be a source of your stress. Use the description of the conflicts above to help you identify what may be relevant.
   - At what times do I experience stress? For everything on your timeline, identify the clearest examples of the moments when this stress is activated. Then start making a list of specific events. Use the phrase: *The moment when X happens and I feel Y.*

3. **The WMOMD:** Identify the specific times during the day when you feel stressed. What are you doing at that moment? Are you triggered by something you are reading or hearing or witnessing? Add that moment to your list of events and then apply EFT until the intensity

of the emotional charge is below 5, but not yet 0. Then, while reliving it, ask yourself, *When have I felt this way before?* and identify an earlier moment. Apply EFT to that moment as well. Initially, limit yourself to more recent moments, as the aim is to address your current stress triggers.

4. **Big Cleanup:** Make a list of any negative stressful situations you have experienced, from birth until now, that you have not yet identified with the Detective Work approach. Make time to apply EFT to these events on a regular basis. The more diligently you apply EFT in this way, the less influence your past will have over your life now. However, if you are still in the healing phase and experiencing a lot of pain and fatigue, then it is best to focus on the WMOMD approach and Symptom-Focused EFT. Once you have recovered and have enough energy, start applying the Big Cleanup Approach as well.

If you have received a diagnosis, in relation to your fatigue symptoms that you are anxious or worried about, make sure you neutralize every specific moment related to the diagnosis, including all conversations with your doctor or therapist, stressful moments when you underwent procedures or examinations or when you were awaiting or receiving test results, and any moment when you felt startled by what you read, heard, or saw in relation to the diagnosis.

5. **Symptom-Focused EFT:** This involves applying EFT directly to your symptoms.

Additional Tips

1. **Distinguishing between effects, thoughts, and causes**

Effects: Chronic fatigue often results in feeling tired and miserable. You may be experiencing all kinds of emotions about what is not working in your life anymore, which may seem to have come to a screeching halt. You may feel despondent like everything is hopeless. Perhaps you do not see the light at the end of the tunnel. In that case, apply Symptom-Focused EFT to everything you feel.

Thoughts: Sometimes it is your thoughts that are causing your stress as opposed to the effects of chronic fatigue. Identify the moments when you have thoughts that cause you stress, for example, *This will never work out, I messed up, I will never get another chance like that, I am on my own, No one understands me, I will never get over this.* First of all, apply EFT to the emotions that arise when you think these thoughts, rather than applying EFT to the thoughts themselves. For example, if you feel despondent and anxious when you think I am alone, then apply EFT to those emotions. Second, address each stressful thought by identifying how or from whom you learned to have that particular thought. Ask yourself, when in my life have I had the thought *I am alone* or *No one understands me.* Then apply EFT to all the details and emotions of those specific moments. By doing this, you will identify and resolve specific events that are contributing to your problems, as they are playing a role in the background, activating your stress.

Causes: Once you have successfully applied EFT to your emotions, feelings and thoughts related to your problem (in this case, chronic fatigue), it is easier to look for the real causes of your problem. You may feel calmer so there is more room to step back and look at what stressful life circumstances have been involved. We recommend that you wait until after the healing phase when you have the energy to deal with things again before you start addressing these major causes. It is important to address these underlying causes to prevent a recurrence, but there is no rush, so wait until you feel better.

2. Do not be too quick to assume that nothing can be done about it

Here, we are referring to the life circumstances that are causing you stress, as opposed to your symptoms. A serious illness, a broken relationship, a burned-down house, a bankrupt business or an unexpected dismissal can cause a lot of stress and when facing such major life challenges, it is difficult to stay optimistic about the future. However, if you take the time to apply EFT to bring down your stress reactions, you will be able to think more clearly and make better decisions, increasing your chances of a positive outcome. When you are in fear and feel extremely stressed, there is a tendency to go into regression, which results in you feeling and reacting like a small child rather than an adult, and thus it is no wonder that you feel there is no way out.

3. Take your time

A situation that started years ago and is still ongoing does not go away in a few days or even a few weeks, but that does not mean that it will take years to resolve. Try to be realistic when setting your expectations and just take the time to apply EFT in the ways we recommend. Even though your issue may not resolve completely in a short period, you will start to see improvements, which will give you the confidence and motivation to continue. Make sure to take inventory of all your symptoms (physical and psychological) before you start and assess their intensity as precisely as possible. Rather than checking every week, we recommend that you reassess the intensity of your symptoms every 4-6 weeks and make a note of any improvements.

D | DIGESTIVE TRACT ISSUES

In this chapter, we will discuss the following digestive tract issues:

- Stomach issues including gastritis (stomach inflammation), heartburn (gastric acid), peptic ulcers (gastric ulcer), stomach polyps and stomach cancer, and
- Intestinal problems including celiac disease (gluten allergy), inflammatory bowel disease (IBD) which includes both Crohn's disease and ulcerative colitis, colon cancer, irritable bowel syndrome (IBS), colon polyps and intestinal obstruction (ileus).

Like all physical issues, symptoms that manifest in the stomach or intestines are triggered by underlying emotional causes. Mainstream medicine looks for the cause in the organ or tissue itself, which yields few explanations because cause and effect are again reversed. Let us look with different eyes at what may be going on.

The stomach is on the left side of the upper abdomen, below the diaphragm. When empty, it has a volume of about 1.5-2.5 oz (45-75 ml), but it can expand to about 34 oz. (1 L). It receives food from the esophagus and releases it to the duodenum, the first part of the small intestine, which is 8-11 inches long (20-30 cm). The small intestine is about 20 feet long (6 meters) and has a surface area of 1700 - 2700 square feet (150-200 square meters). This is where the absorption of food takes place. After the small intestine, the food moves into the large intestine, which is 3-5 feet long (100-150 cm). The large intestine absorbs water, converting food waste from liquid into stool. When the stool enters the rectum (the last part of the large intestine), it triggers the urge to defecate.

The main function of the stomach and intestines is to digest food, and the main emotional conflicts that occur in this area are related to this function, literally, but more important, figuratively. These conflicts are called Chunk Conflicts and they relate to the inability to swallow, digest, grab or eliminate a 'chunk,' which may literally be food or could be something that needs to be digested or processed emotionally. While animals usually experience Chunk Conflicts in the literal sense, humans most often experience these conflicts as 'indigestible annoyances' regarding people or situations. Metaphors may assist in identifying the conflict, such as *I cannot stomach it, I do not have the stomach for it, This turns my stomach, This is gut-wrenching.*

Sometimes, we may not even be aware that we are annoyed. We are usually aware of annoyances that manifest in the stomach area, but annoyances that manifest further down the digestive tract into the intestines tend to be more subconscious. The deeper down the annoyance manifests, the more subconscious it is. We often find that when we start working with EFT on the emotional causes of intestinal symptoms (like lower abdominal pains), people are surprised to discover how often and how much they are annoyed.

Stomach Problems

In addition to Chunk Conflicts, Territorial Anger Conflicts and Identity Conflicts may also manifest in the stomach.

Chunk Conflicts involve not being able to digest a chunk (food or something else) that feels heavy in the stomach. This is quite often experienced figuratively (for example, a family dispute over an inheritance) and it may relate to any area of one's life, including work, education and relationships.

Territorial Anger Conflicts manifesting in the stomach often involve aggression, either one's own anger or another person's anger. Such conflicts may arise in situations involving boundary disputes with neighbors, in-laws or co-workers. You may also feel forced to submit or comply or you may feel belittled.

Identity Conflicts may arise if you do not know where you belong or what decision to make, for example, not knowing which partner to choose.

Chunk Conflicts induce cell growth in the digestive tract during the conflict-active phase, usually with few or no symptoms, although you may experience nausea. Upon examination, this may lead to a diagnosis of a 'benign' polyp or 'malignant' stomach cancer (adenocarcinoma). In the healing phase, cellular degradation takes place, as the additional cells are broken down by fungi and bacteria. During this phase, you may experience severe fatigue, night sweats, mild bleeding and pain, and possibly black stools due to gastric bleeding.

Territorial Anger Conflicts and Identity Conflicts may result in heartburn (if the esophagus is involved) or an ulcer during the conflict-active phase, and there may also be pain in the stomach area. In the healing phase, there may be blood loss due to bleeding from the ulcer (which may pass unnoticed). If there is a severe healing crisis, there may be gastric colic, gastric bleeding with black stools, chills, cold sweats and possibly absence seizures.

Intestinal Issues

Problems in your intestines are caused by Chunk Conflicts (situations you find hard to process or digest), which usually trigger an intense feeling of annoyance. You may be annoyed with people, animals or situations, or by comments (accusations, criticism, insults) or other information. In the small intestine, the Chunk Conflict may relate to a loss of some sort, fear of poverty or unmet needs, or fear about income, benefits or bonuses. If the conflict manifests in the large intestine, the conflict is experienced as ugly, mean or despicable. Annoyances about deceptions and scams also often show up in the colon.

To better understand the types of symptoms experienced, it is helpful to examine what happens in the conflict-active phase and the healing phase. In the conflict-active phase, cell proliferation of the intestinal mucosa occurs, which may result in tumors forming, which are then broken down in the healing phase. The tumors may grow either on a flat plane (absorptive type) or take a cauliflower-shaped form (secretory type). Depending on the size of these tumors and the rate at which they grow, they may be diagnosed as colon polyps ('benign') or colon cancer ('malignant'). Tumors that stay flat often go undetected. In this phase, there are usually no symptoms unless a cauliflower-like tumor is obstructing the bowel. In the healing phase, the tumors are broken down by fungi or mycobacteria. In this phase, you may experience fever, night sweats, bleeding and diarrhea. If the healing crisis is severe, there may be more bleeding. If the muscles of the intestines are also involved, you may also have intestinal cramps and colic.

Celiac disease (gluten intolerance): This indicates that you are stuck in the healing phase. With long periods of conflict and a lot of repetition of conflicts, too many villi (which form the lining of the intestine) are broken down and nutrient absorption is hindered, which can lead to malnutrition.

Crohn's disease or ulcerative colitis: There is no real distinction between these two conditions. The former can occur anywhere in the intestines; the latter is thought to occur only in the colon. It is a chronic recurrent process where you alternate between being in the conflict-active phase and the healing phase of a conflict. Tumors grow in the conflict-active phase, mainly flat-growing (resorption cells) and sometimes polyps (absorption cells). In the healing phase, the tumors are broken down, so you may have blood and mucus in the stool, diarrhea, constipation and night sweats.

Irritable bowel syndrome (IBS): This affects the smooth muscles of the intestines. These muscles propel food chunks through the intestines so that they can eventually be expelled once all the nutrients are absorbed. When you experience an indigestible annoyance, there is a 'motor failure,' resulting in a vicious cycle of conflict-active phase and healing phase. In the conflict-active phase, you may experience a bowel blockage because there are enhanced muscle contractions at the location of the blockage, holding the food chunk in place. There may also be tumor growth (especially polyps). In the rest of the intestines, there is little, if any, muscle movement. This immobilization of the intestines is the most noticeable symptom. On examination, this may be diagnosed as paralyzed bowels or intestinal obstruction (ileus). In the healing phase, there is increased muscle activity and intestinal colic (a cramp-like pain) in the area of the intestines that was immobile. Thus, you may alternate between having constipation (in the conflict-active phase) and diarrhea (in the healing phase). You may also have a bloated abdomen or flatulence during the healing phase.

In mainstream medicine, IBS has long been seen as a psychological disorder because a physical cause has not been found. This is, of course, correct, but not in the way this argument is used. Unfortunately, the modern understanding now is that there is no psychological cause, but that it is simply a disorder in the function of the gastrointestinal tract with an unknown cause. This is a step in the wrong direction. Moreover, people with such symptoms are given little direction as to how to resolve them. To confuse matters further, it is generally accepted in the mainstream that stress and anxiety can trigger these types of symptoms, but that such symptoms can be experienced by people with IBS as well as by people without IBS. This seems contradictory, given that IBS is diagnosed as a disorder. In our view, this is not surprising, given that the symptoms are not a disorder as such, but are in fact caused by emotionally stressful events. If you look for the underlying emotional causes of your symptoms and resolve them with EFT, you may find that your symptoms improve and may even disappear because you are finally addressing the root cause.

EFT Approach

1. **The WMOMD:** Start by taking note of what times of day you get annoyed and neutralize any specific moments with EFT. If you experience symptoms like heartburn or ulcers, look for Territorial Anger Conflicts and Identity Conflicts. As often as possible when reliving the WMOMD, take time to identify earlier moments when you felt the same way. It is essential to apply the WMOMD approach every day, especially if you have chronic symptoms. The more moments you address each day, the more you will resolve and the more insight you will gain into your patterns.

    Note: If you do not immediately recognize that you are annoyed or angry, simply start by applying EFT to all negative moments, whenever you feel angry, sad or anxious. Also, pay attention to being annoyed about feeling annoyed! The fact that you are beginning to realize that this annoyance is the cause of your symptoms is a valuable insight, but it will not resolve the pattern. It is essential to neutralize all the specific situations in which you feel triggered by this annoyance, so you can steadily reduce this pattern, and eventually resolve it so you are no longer annoyed.

2. **Detective Work:** Make a timeline and look for a connection between the emotional causes and the symptoms you are experiencing. More often than not, if you are experiencing symptoms, you are in the healing phase, which means the conflict has been resolved. So, start looking for what you were angry or annoyed about immediately before you started experiencing symptoms. You will find your most important stress moments in the preceding, symptom-free period. However, certain symptoms, like heartburn and peptic ulceration, occur during the conflict-active phase, so you need to identify what was going on at the time you experienced those symptoms. With IBS, you experience constipation in the conflict-active phase. Cramps and diarrhea are more common in the healing phase. Make lists of the specific events that cause you to feel annoyed. Use appropriate wording to make it really specific: *The moment when X happens and I feel Y.*

   Ascertain the origin of your problem by asking yourself the following questions:

   - How did I learn to feel annoyed? Who did I learn this from?

   - At what point do I experience this problem? What is the clearest, best example of a specific moment in which this is happening?

   - When did it start? What stressful issues were at play during that period of my life?

3. **Big Cleanup:** Make lists of all the events related to your symptoms that have caused you stress, including any moments relating to your diagnosis, tests, information provided, reactions from those around you and anything you have read on the internet or elsewhere. This approach is designed as a final sweep to identify any events that have not yet come up after using the Detective Work approach.

4. **Symptom-Focused EFT:** Apply EFT to your physical and emotional symptoms, especially to any feelings of anxiety, impatience, anger and annoyance. It may take time to resolve any tendencies to feel anxious, impatient and annoyed, so be patient and do your best to keep working on your issues.

E | EATING DISORDERS

In this chapter, we discuss the two most common eating disorders, anorexia nervosa (anorexia) and bulimia nervosa (bulimia).

Anorexia Nervosa

Anorexia is an eating disorder that is characterized by extreme food restriction, abnormally low body weight, intense fear of gaining weight and a distorted body image. The fear of gaining weight is the main trigger and being thin is equated with self-worth.

In the case of anorexia, two underlying emotional conflicts are active simultaneously. You have an Identity Conflict (not fitting in) or a Territorial Anger Conflict and, at the same time, you also have a Shock-Fright Conflict, a Sexual Conflict, a second Identity Conflict or a Territorial Marking Conflict. So there are two active conflicts, one of which is related to 'mother or child' and the other is related to 'partner.' See Appendix 3 for an explanation of the 'mother or child' side versus 'partner' side.

As soon as both conflicts are active, it will become evident in your mood, which may be either (slightly) manic or (slightly) depressed. The first conflict (the Identity Conflict or Territorial Anger Conflict) almost always arises from the emotional impact of specific events in which derogatory comments were made about your weight, you were bullied or teased about your body shape, or you felt inadequate compared to others who you perceived as slimmer and thus more attractive (such as a friend, sister, classmate, model or celebrity).

Anorexia can affect anyone but it is more common among young girls and adolescents, who are especially sensitive to comments concerning their appearance and weight. However, increasing numbers of children and older adults of both sexes are being diagnosed with anorexia.

Bulimia Nervosa

Bulimia manifests as compulsive binge eating followed by compulsive purging in which you try to get rid of the excess calories consumed by vomiting, excessive use of laxatives or diuretics, fasting or compulsive exercising. Bulimia can affect anyone, but it is more common in girls and women and typically develops during adolescence or early adulthood. Unlike those with anorexia, people with bulimia are usually at a normal, healthy weight (or are even overweight), but like those with anorexia, they usually have a negative perception of their weight and/or body shape.

The emotional conflicts underlying bulimia involve one or more of the following: Fear-Disgust Conflict, Territorial Anger Conflict, Resistance Conflict or Identity Conflict. As with anorexia, two underlying emotional conflicts are active simultaneously. One conflict relates to 'mother or child' and the other conflict relates to a 'partner.' See Appendix 3 for an explanation of the 'mother or child' side versus 'partner' side.

Note: Mainstream medicine distinguishes between bulimia and binge eating disorder, where there is no compulsive purging. For our purposes, the distinction is not important, as the underlying emotional conflicts are essentially the same, although when there is compulsive purging, the Fear-Disgust Conflicts or Resistance Conflicts tend to be stronger and have more emotional charge than any Territorial Anger Conflicts or Identity Conflicts.

The following types of conflicts may cause bulimia:

- **Fear-Disgust Conflict:** In this context, the conflict usually arises from a distressing sexual encounter, such as sexual abuse or molestation, forced oral sex, exposure to pornography, disgusting first-time sex or dirty sex.
- **Territorial Anger Conflict:** Due to annoyances in the parental home (fighting parents, fights with a family member) or arguments at school (bullying, being treated badly by a teacher).

- **Resistance Conflict:** Where you want to reject or oppose or fight against somebody or something; being forced to do something against your will, not being able to decide what you want or do not want (a child being forced to wear clothes they do not like, having sex against your will).
- **Identity Conflict:** Feeling like you do not fit in, possibly caused by the loss of a parent (emotional neglect, divorce, death) or the loss of a close friend or your first love.

EFT Approach

Eating disorders are more common than you may think and they often go unnoticed. They may be partial, meaning the behavior is followed on certain days and under certain circumstances but not daily. Also, they are often 'self-limiting,' especially in teenagers, and tend to be more chronic at older ages. Anorexia lasts around 2-3 years, whereas bulimia lasts 5-8 years on average. The reason for this is that the condition stops when one of the two conflicts stops being active. However, this means that the condition may return when the conflict is active again. While conventional treatments may help to relieve the symptoms for a short period, any success is usually short-lived as the underlying emotional conflicts are not addressed. Thus, we highly recommend that you use EFT to resolve the underlying causes to shorten the duration and prevent a recurrence.

1. **Detective Work:** Start by asking yourself when it started and what stressful things were going on during that period of your life. It is important to identify the type of conflicts involved (using the guidance above) and the specific events underlying each conflict. Be aware that (i) both conflicts are active, so you need to identify the current daily triggers, and (ii) one conflict is related to 'mother or child' and the other relates to 'partner.' Make a note of every specific event and then take the time to neutralize each event with EFT.

2. **The WMOMD:** Several of your WMOMD are likely connected to the underlying conflicts you have identified. In particular, pay attention to everything that happens around eating or not eating, including your feelings and the reactions and comments of those around you. Pay attention to any negative emotional situation regarding your body and how you look. Also, take the time to work on your negative core belief (NCB) and address any situation where your NCB is activated. As often as possible, take the time to identify specific events in your past in which you felt the same way, by asking yourself while reliving your WMOMD *When did I feel like this before?*

3. **Big Cleanup:** Make a list of all other events you have not yet identified using the Detective Work or WMOMD approach and pay particular attention to events from the first 7 years of your life when you formed your NCB.

   If you have fears or worries about your condition, neutralize every specific moment in which you felt such fear or worry, including during conversations with your doctors and therapists, when undergoing medical examinations and awaiting or receiving test results, and when dealing with reactions from people in your life. Include every moment in which you recall feeling startled or scared by what you read, heard or saw in relation to your diagnosis.

4. **Symptom-Focused EFT:** Apply EFT immediately to your symptoms (for example, feelings of fear, disgust, sadness) whenever you experience such intense emotions. If at all possible, make that moment a specific event and address it using the WMOMD approach.

F | FEAR OF FAILURE

Most of us have experienced fear of failure at some point or another. We may have experienced exam anxiety, fear of public speaking, anxiety before a job interview or even stage fright. Who does not know someone who experienced fear of failure before their driving test? Your negative core belief (NCB) is your most important stress pattern and it plays a major role in any fear of failure. A certain amount of performance anxiety is normal and may even be helpful, as it may motivate you to take positive steps to ensure that you do not fail. For instance, a student may study hard before an exam to ensure they do well. Typically, with normal performance anxiety, any nervousness you feel should go away once you start the exam, interview or other activity.

However, when the fear of failure is extreme, it may give rise to uncomfortable physical sensations (such as tightness in the chest, heart palpitations, sweaty hands or a dry mouth and sometimes even a black-out) which do not go away once you start performing the activity and which are not in proportion to what is happening. This fear of failure may result in an actor on stage forgetting their lines or a baseball player striking out. Intense fear of failure may cause you to put off or avoid any activity in which you see a potential for failure, and that might negatively impact your ability to function in daily life and reach your full potential.

Fear of failure may be generalized in the sense that you have low self-esteem and you think you will fail at everything, so you do not dare to try new things or take any risks. This is related to a very strong NCB and a build-up of negative experiences, usually starting early in life. A fear of failure may also arise later in life, related to a sporting achievement or some other performance or social situation. You always need to adopt a two-pronged approach to successfully work on weakening your NCB. You need to neutralize all the specific events in which you learned the fear of failure in relation to the particular activity and you also need to go back to your early childhood experiences (paying particular attention to the first 6-7 years) to identify the origin of your NCB and neutralize those specific events with EFT.

EFT Approach

The first step is to identify exactly what your fear of failure is about. Identify the specific situation in which you experience the fear of failure. Frequently, you will feel fear and anxiety coming on before you are required to perform, such as prior to an exam, interview, presentation or performance. If you think about your performance in the days or weeks leading up to it and feel anxiety or tension, you can immediately work on those symptoms by applying Symptom-Focused EFT. However, while that may alleviate the symptoms temporarily, it does not solve the problem! The only way to effectively resolve any fear of failure is to address both your feelings of fear and anxiety (with Symptom-Focused EFT) as well as the underlying cause, namely the specific events that caused your fear of failure. It is therefore essential for you to look back and identify the specific moments in your past when you previously experienced this fear of failure. After all, most behavior is learned behavior. Therefore, the question *How did I learn this fear of failure?* is the most important question you must ask yourself in order to discover the cause of your fear of failure. Once you have neutralized enough of the past events in which you learned the fear of failure, you can check whether you have neutralized enough events by looking ahead to the future performance and assessing whether your level of anxiety or fear has gone.

Below is the step-by-step approach that we recommend you take:

1. **Identify your Negative Core Belief (NCB):** First, determine what your NCB is (if you do not yet know it). You can do this by choosing a moment when you felt rejected, criticized, or verbally attacked. Relive the moment in an associated way and listen to your inner critic. Is it saying: *I am not good enough, I do not belong, I should not be here,* or something else? Once you have identified your NCB, assess its strength using the Validity of Cognition (VoC) test below.

VoC test: Close your eyes and say your NCB mindfully out loud. Then assess how true this statement feels to you emotionally, not logically. Score the belief using a scale from 0% (does not feel true at all) to 100% (feels completely true). Write down this number and retest the VoC regularly. The VoC test is a useful way of tracking your progress, enabling you to assess whether your NCB is weakening. As you address more specific events, your NCB will weaken until it no longer feels true. As it weakens, you will likely notice your fear of failure diminishing too. Aim to work the VoC down to lower than 10%. If you require a more detailed explanation of the NCB and VoC test, see Chapter 5 of Part 1.

2. **Detective Work:** At what times do you experience this fear of failure? What are the clearest or best examples of times when this fear is activated? When was the first time? Make a list of all these events using the phrase *The moment when X happens and I feel Y.* Be sure to make the events brief (10-20 seconds each), so that there is only one emotional peak. For example, if your fear relates to giving a presentation, you may identify several moments, such as the moment you hear your name signifying it is your turn, the moment you stand up, the moment you walk toward the stage and the moment you stand on the stage and look out at the audience. Each of these moments is a specific event. Neutralize every event on your list with EFT. Your list should contain at least 10-20 specific events. Work on an event until the intensity drops below 5 but is not yet 0, and then ask yourself if your NCB is playing a role and notice how you feel while you are reliving the moment. Then ask yourself when you have felt this way before, earlier in life (the earlier, the better). If possible, try to identify events during the first 6-7 years of your life. Neutralize every specific event you find. The more often you can apply EFT in this way, identifying not only present events but also those in the past when you have felt the same way, the faster you will see results.

3. **The WMOMD + Symptom-Focused EFT:** Apply EFT as soon as you start to feel anxious in the period (hours, days or weeks) leading up to your performance. Work until the intensity has subsided, aiming for a 0 (which will usually be temporary). The more often you do this, the

more often you turn off your stress response – that in itself has a positive effect.

However, it is much more effective to work on the underlying cause of the fear, namely the specific events which gave rise to the fear of failure. In order to identify those events, notice whenever you feel the fear coming up then ask yourself what aspect or detail is causing you the most anxiety right now. For example, when giving a presentation, you may feel anxious when you see all the eyes of the audience looking at you. If that is the case, identify the best example of a previous event in which you experienced this. Then apply EFT until you completely neutralize this specific event – not just the aspect of 'all eyes looking at me' but all the aspects of the entire event. It is never just one detail that is responsible for your fear, there are usually many aspects involved, including your thoughts about not being good enough (your NCB). When you are working on this event, apply EFT until the intensity of the fear is below 5, but not yet 0. Relive the event and check to see if your NCB is playing a role. If so, ask yourself when you have felt this way earlier in life. The first memory that comes up is relevant. Neutralize this event completely as well and test properly to make sure everything is 0. In this way, you are very effectively addressing multiple moments of this stress pattern. This is the fastest route to get results.

4. **Big Cleanup:** As a final sweep, we recommend that you make a list of any emotionally charged events from your past that you have not yet addressed, especially those related to your NCB, and take the time to neutralize them with EFT.

G | GESTATION (PREGNANCY)

EFT is an effective method of dealing with any trauma regarding pregnancy, such as infertility, abortion, miscarriages, and traumatic births. In this chapter, we focus on the emotional causes that can be addressed with EFT.

The main emotional cause of infertility is chronic stress in both women and men. Your chronic stress may be caused by a variety of issues, which may or may not be related to your desire to have children. Thus, all types of emotional conflicts may be at play here. In addition, when you are trying to get pregnant and it does not happen straight away, you often start to feel stressed. It is necessary to apply EFT to all the moments in which you experience stress associated with trying to get pregnant, as well as any associated relationship problems. This may include moments in which you see other people with a baby or child, when you receive a birth announcement from friends or when other people talk about having children. Mainstream medicine only starts to address possible causes of infertility after a couple has been trying to conceive for at least a year. However, you do not need to wait that long. As soon as you realize the problem could be emotional, take the time to deal with it immediately with EFT. If you have not yet become pregnant, it may be helpful to look specifically for past events related to the following experiences: sexual abuse, rape, circumcision, loss (or fear of loss) of a loved one, partner or pet. For women specifically, it may be helpful to address any conflict around being female such as feeling disrespected, dishonored, insulted or slandered, usually by a man (often one's partner). Also, a Territorial Loss Conflict of a sexual nature may play a role. For men specifically, any Territorial Conflict or Self-Devaluation Conflict may be a cause.

You may also encounter stress around an unwanted pregnancy or abortion. If you have an unwanted pregnancy, use EFT to address every related detail, including the moment you discovered the pregnancy, other people's reactions and any relationship issues, as well as any relevant previous experiences that may trigger the stress response. Regarding an abortion, while it may bring a sense of relief for people who do not want to have a child, it can also cause trauma, guilt, shame and other forms of stress. The medical procedure itself is often quite traumatic. Again, it is necessary to address every moment that triggers the stress reaction, including the attitudes or reactions of your partner, family, friends and others, as well as any previous experiences.

Finally, miscarriages and traumatic births can also create a lot of stress. Again, it is necessary to identify specific moments in which the stress reaction was triggered, including the moment you realized there was a problem, other people's reactions and any relevant previous experiences.

EFT Approach

If you experience any physical problems, they may point to specific emotional conflicts. In these cases, you can refer to other sections of this chapter for guidance. For example, if you suffer from a skin rash, this suggests there is a Separation Conflict. If you experience musculoskeletal problems, it would be worthwhile addressing any Self-Devaluation Conflicts. If you experience muscle weakness or paralysis or have epileptic seizures, there may be Motor Conflicts that need to be resolved.

However, you may not experience any physical symptoms, only psychological stress symptoms. In that case, you can address such issues as follows:

1. **The WMOMD:** Identify what is causing you stress as well as the specific moments in which you feel stressed, and then resolve those moments with EFT. Once you have reduced the intensity of a moment to below 5 but not yet 0, look for another event in the past in which you felt the same way and apply EFT to that moment. Use this approach to resolve not only general stress but also stress that is specifically related to pregnancy or childbirth, such as stress related to your efforts to get pregnant, other people's reactions to your inability to get pregnant or your decision to have an abortion.

2. **Focusing on the traumas:** Make a list of any traumatic events related to pregnancy or childbirth. You may wish to consult section P | Post-Traumatic Stress Disorder for more detailed instructions on addressing trauma. Address each specific traumatic event you are able to work on by yourself, one at a time, with EFT. If you have any major traumas, we recommend that you work with a well-trained EFT professional.

3. **Negative Core Belief (NCB):** If something in your life is not working out as you would like or you feel that you are failing in some way, your NCB is no doubt playing a major role in the amount of stress you are experiencing. Work on any moment related to your NCB, including those that may be unrelated to pregnancy or childbirth. Make a list of the moments when you feel like you are not good enough (or not worthy, or that you do not belong and so on) and neutralize them with EFT. Also, identify specific moments from your past (ideally in the first 6-7 years of your life) in which you learned your NCB and resolve those moments with EFT.

4. **Big Cleanup:** As a final sweep, we recommend that you make a list of as many stressful negative experiences from your life as possible. Make time to resolve these events, at least a few times a week, working on one or two moments each time.

Tip: Are you pregnant and want to address your stress with EFT, but you are afraid the baby in your womb may suffer from the stress reactions you evoke when you relive a stressful moment from the past? If so, we recommend applying EFT in the following way:

- **Gold Standard EFT:** Include wording in the Setup phrase that makes it clear to your unborn child that what he or she is feeling has nothing to do with him or her. This only has to do with their mother who still has something to resolve. For example, *Even though you may feel my tension or emotions, this has nothing to do with you and you do not need to deal with this at all. I am resolving this myself. I love you and I fully accept myself.*
- **Optimal EFT:** Do a meditation with The Unseen Therapist, in which you ask Her to explain to your unborn child that what he or she is feeling has nothing to do with him or her, but with the fact that their mother is resolving something.

H | HEALING SYMPTOMS

We decided to dedicate a chapter to healing symptoms because so many of the symptoms people experience during the healing phase are often diagnosed as disease symptoms by mainstream medicine. When you receive a diagnosis, it often gives rise to fear and worry that can interfere with healing (often to a significant degree). We, therefore, want to give you a more detailed explanation of the healing phase and an indication of the symptoms you may experience so that you will hopefully worry less about these symptoms and let go of any fears.

What is healing? It is defined in various dictionaries and online sites as 'making healthy,' 'recovery from an illness,' 'the process of becoming healthy again,' 'getting well,' and 'restoration.' In Chapter 5 of Part 1, we introduced you to Hamer's discoveries and the way he explains what happens during the healing phase after a conflict is resolved. If you look at what is happening in the body from Hamer's perspective, you see an entirely different picture, as the symptoms that arise during the healing phase are interpreted in a completely different way. Instead of viewing such symptoms as a problem, you begin to understand that they are simply a sign that your body is healing. Understanding more about the healing phase will not only help you identify the underlying emotional causes more easily, but it can help you to relax and let go of your fears that your body is somehow failing you because now you understand that your body is doing the exact opposite: you are healing. Even though you do not need to do anything in particular during the healing phase, since the body is going through the appropriate program by itself, it can be very helpful to do EFT. Our main concern is fear and pain, which can both impede our ability to get through this recovery period with all its symptoms, which can be severe and frightening. Aim to let go of any fear with EFT first and then focus on dealing with any pain with EFT. It is also very important to realize that while you may have sufficiently resolved a conflict to enter the healing phase, this does not mean that the underlying stress pattern has been resolved. To avoid

203

being triggered again by a similar conflict in the future (which will involve a repetition of both the conflict-active phase and healing phase, with all of the associated symptoms), you need to identify the specific events that maintain this stress pattern and neutralize them with EFT, so that you can resolve the stress pattern once and for all.

If you look up the definition of 'disease', you will no doubt find many more definitions than for 'healing'. You may find a variation of the following: 'abnormality', 'disturbance of health', 'physical disorder', 'defect', 'malfunction of the body and/or mind, often caused by germs', 'a health problem', or you may find a long explanation like the following: 'any process in the body that has a harmful effect on the functioning of tissues in the body, which disturbs the functional balance of body and mind and results in a reaction of restoring this balance.'

In short, it is generally believed that an illness occurs because something goes wrong in the body. But is that really the case? If you look at Hamer's Five Biological Laws of Nature, Hamer discovered that the organs and tissues of your body function normally when nothing is wrong, but they adopt a special function or program to help you through a shocking emotional conflict. Thus, the body functions differently when you encounter a problematic situation, but that does not mean that something is going wrong in your body. Rather, it is evidence that everything is going according to plan. When the emotional conflict has been resolved, the body enters the healing phase with the accompanying symptoms to return the body to balance and its normal function. Unfortunately, in mainstream medicine, symptoms in the healing phase are usually labeled as a disease, causing a lot of unnecessary stress, especially when it is a serious diagnosis. If you are anxious about a diagnosis or prognosis or any proposed treatment, it is necessary to address this anxiety with EFT. Everything around your illness can be perceived as threatening, which creates more conflicts that may give rise to more reactions in the body.

If you are going through the healing phase of a major conflict and then receive a serious diagnosis that shocks you, the healing phase can be so intense that your chances of survival may be reduced even further. However, if you look at your symptoms from a completely different perspective, with an understanding that they are simply part of the body's survival program, then you will realize that there is no need to fear these symptoms, as they are actually increasing your chance of survival. When you encounter an emotionally shocking event, your body first switches to a special function or program to cope with the shocking event (during the conflict-active phase), and once the conflict has been resolved, it switches to the recovery function. The associated reactions in the body are thus part of the solution, not the problem.

Below, we describe the characteristics of the conflict-active phase and the healing phase (see also Figure 7 in Chapter 5 of Part 1):

Conflict-active phase: Psychological symptoms include feeling stressed and tense, compulsive thinking about the problem and poor sleep. You may have high blood pressure, increased heart rate, cold hands and feet, little or no appetite, trouble sleeping, weight loss and increased levels of stress hormones, such as adrenaline and cortisol. At the organ or tissue level, there may be cell growth or cell loss, resulting in an increased or decreased function of the affected organ or tissue, depending on the type of emotional shock and the tissues involved. This chnge makes sense when you look at the biological reason for the program. For example, in the case of a Separation Conflict, the sensitivity of the skin diminishes in the conflict-active phase, helping you to forget the missing or unwanted skin contact.

Healing phase: You usually experience a sense of relief that the conflict is over. You may feel at peace with whatever happened and even feel that you can forgive and forget. Physically, you may feel tired, need more sleep and have headaches. During the first part of the healing phase, you retain water as healing always occurs in a fluid environment, so there may be edema (swelling) in the organs or tissue affected by the conflict (including in the part of the brain that controls that organ or tissue) and inflammation, which may cause pain. You may also notice your eyes are puffy when you wake up in the morning, and your hands and feet may be swollen. Water retention may show up as temporary weight gain. You may also experience a fever or infection (as microbes may multiply to assist with the healing). Thus, all cold and flu symptoms and any inflammation of the organs, joints or skin (such as a skin rash) are signs that you are in the healing phase.

Your appetite usually returns, your hands and feet become warm again, and your blood pressure and heart rate go back to normal. There will either be cell loss or cell growth (the opposite of what happened in the conflict-active phase) in the affected organs or tissues, and function will be restored to the affected organs or tissues.

Healing crisis: Psychologically, you may experience a brief flare-up of the emotions experienced during the conflict-active phase, which may manifest as an attack of fear or anger, nightmares or sleepwalking. At the organ level, there may be a brief attack of symptoms that may be clearly noticeable, such as an asthma attack, a migraine, vomiting, dizziness, cramps, and sometimes even an epileptic seizure or convulsions. You may experience chills and night sweats. There may be a discharge of blood (to eliminate the by-products of the healing process), either when you cough or in your stool or urine, or you may get a nosebleed. However, most of the time, the symptoms are mild, such as a slight headache, hiccups, twitching eyelids, sneezing, coughing, fatigue and sleeping longer than usual or this moment may go entirely unnoticed.

After the healing crisis, symptoms improve as the body returns to its normal function. This latter part of the healing phase is characterized by increased urination, as the water retained during the first part of the healing phase is excreted, although this may not be noticeable. All in all, the healing phase of some conflicts can take 3 to 6 months or sometimes longer, but usually, the intensity of the symptoms decreases rapidly. If symptoms remain severe for a longer period, this may indicate that fear and / or the severity of the healing crisis symptoms are a trigger that keeps you stuck in the healing phase, in other words the healing phase is 'hanging' and it will not come to an end. However, the whole process from the initial trigger to the resolution can also be very short and be completed in only a few minutes.

Examples of healing symptoms

Below are some examples of the types of symptoms you may experience during the healing phase:

General symptoms

- **Dizziness:** Short-term dizziness is a common sign of a healing crisis. If it is accompanied by a tendency to fall, the direction in which you fall is relevant and may help you identify whether the conflict is related to 'mother or child' or 'partner.' First, you need to determine whether you are left or right-handed. See Appendix 3 for an explanation of biological handedness and the 'mother or child' versus 'partner' side. For those who are right-handed, a tendency to fall to the left suggests there may be a conflict related to 'mother or child' and a tendency to fall to the right signifies a conflict related to 'partner.' For those who are left-handed, it is the opposite, so falling to the left indicates a conflict related to 'partner' and falling to the right signifies a conflict related to 'mother or child.' Falling forward or backward does not point to such relationships.

- **Fever:** All fevers occur during the healing phase. It is a general symptom, in the sense that it does not point to a specific cause or emotional conflict. You may get a fever whenever there is any inflammation or infection, and that is a natural part of the healing phase. In the healing crisis, you may experience the peak of a fever, which may include shivering and night sweats.

- **Headache:** If a headache is mild to moderate, it is a sign that the body is in the healing phase, whereas a severe headache or migraine is part of the healing crisis. A headache does not point to a specific emotional underlying cause but is simply a sign that a conflict has been resolved and you are healing. For migraines, see below.

- **Inflammation:** Inflammation is a common healing symptom. An inflammatory response can be intense, causing anxiety, and it can also be very painful. In particular, fear and pain can be triggers in and of themselves, keeping you in stress and preventing you from getting through the healing phase. This is the reason why you should always resolve your fears and pains with EFT as best you can and take any other measures to reduce them. If you are anxious about something, prioritize resolving your anxiety over everything else. We cannot discuss all forms of inflammation, but if it involves the skin, see section Z | Zits and Other Skin Problems.

Specific symptoms that point to particular conflicts:

- **Bronchitis:** This may occur during the healing phase of a Territorial Fear Conflict or a Shock-Fright Conflict, which affects the mucous membrane of the bronchi. For instance, you may be afraid of losing your territory (such as your job or partner) or your position in the territory.

- **Coughing:** You may cough during the healing crisis of a conflict that affects the throat, larynx or bronchi. It may be a tickly, itchy cough or you may cough up mucus. The underlying emotional cause may be either a Territorial Fear Conflict, a Shock-Fright Conflict or a Speechlessness Conflict. The specific events giving rise to the conflict may involve fear regarding a job, business, money, your home or partner or fear that something terrible might happen, such as being scared that you will receive bad news or being afraid to speak up or not being able or willing to speak up.

- **Hay fever:** Allergies are always based on recurring triggers, such as pollen, dust mite droppings, and the like. An allergy is not an immune response randomly targeting a foreign substance, but rather a reaction to a trigger, which is an aspect of a severe emotional situation from your past. The 'allergic' reaction is a manifestation of the stress reaction, which is triggered by the substance, as it reminds you of the upsetting event. The types of underlying conflicts that cause hay fever are the same as those that give rise to nasal congestion, rhinitis and sinusitis (see below).

- **Hemorrhoids:** Superficial hemorrhoids (which are the most common) are the healing phase of an Identity Conflict (not knowing where you belong, which decision to make or which partner to choose). Less often, they arise during the healing phase of a Territorial Anger Conflict. In the healing crisis, there may be bleeding, possibly chills. If the voluntary anus muscle is also affected, sphincter spasms (tenesmus) may occur. In rare cases, the hemorrhoids are internal, which points to the healing phase of a Chunk Conflict: indigestible anger, not being able to get rid of something unpleasant ('crap').

- **Laryngitis:** Laryngitis may occur during the healing phase of a Territorial Fear Conflict, a Shock-Fear Conflict or a Speechlessness Conflict, which causes inflammation of the larynx, resulting in a hoarse voice, coughing, fever and/or pain. It could also be a Speechlessness Conflict where you do not dare or are not able to express yourself, and you may feel *I was struck dumb* or *The words stuck in my throat.*

- **Loss of smell:** If you have rhinitis, you may also experience a loss of smell. If you do not have rhinitis, a loss of smell may signify that you are in the conflict-active phase of a Stink Smell Conflict, which means you may be stressed about something that smells or because you cannot pick up the scent (to identify if there is danger and/or where the danger is coming from).

- **Loss of taste:** If you have rhinitis, you may also experience a loss of taste. If you do not have rhinitis, a loss of taste may signify that you are facing a conflict related to your sense of taste. It may arise if you tasted something very unpleasant, but often it is experienced figuratively, for example, when something happens that leaves you with a bitter or sour taste in your mouth.

- **Migraine:** A migraine may be experienced during the healing phase of several short, intense conflicts and is most intense during the healing crisis. The underlying conflicts are usually a combination of a Stink-Smell Conflict and a Powerlessness Conflict: a situation where you feel a sense of injustice that you are powerless to defend against: *This is not right (it stinks), but I cannot do anything about it.* Other conflicts that may play a role include a Shock Fright Conflict, a Territorial Fear Conflict, a Frontal-Fear Conflict, a Resistance Conflict or a Biting Conflict.

Note: With migraines, you may sometimes experience pain in the conflict-active phase, especially behind the eyes, prior to the onset of the migraine during the healing crisis. It is also possible that you do not have any pain in the conflict-active phase but a lot of pain in the first part of the healing phase, then only a little or no pain in the healing crisis, followed by reduced pain during the second part of the healing phase.

- **Muscle pain:** Pain in the muscles is a symptom of the healing phase of a Self-Devaluation Conflict. See section B | Bones, Muscles and Tendons.

- **Musculoskeletal symptoms:** These symptoms are explained in section B | Bones, Muscles and Tendons.

- **Nasal congestion, rhinitis, sinusitis:** You may experience a stuffy nose, runny nose, itchy watery eyes, sneezing, or swelling of the sinuses during the healing phase of a Stink-Smell Conflict. A Stink-Smell Conflict involves not wanting to smell something and is often used in a metaphorical sense, such as *This situation stinks, Something smells funny here,* or *This does not smell right.* A Stink-Smell Conflict may also arise if you cannot pick up the scent, for example, you are not able to smell (or know) what or when something is going to happen or coming toward you (a danger). It is similar to the way a dog sticks its nose in the air to detect a scent. If there are persistent or recurring symptoms (due to a pending conflict that has not healed), you may be diagnosed with allergic rhinitis or hay fever by mainstream medicine.

- **Pharyngitis (sore throat):** This may occur during the healing crisis of a Separation Conflict, which affects the throat mucosa. The conflict may involve not wanting to swallow something, or wanting to spit something out again, literally or figuratively. For instance, you may say, *I am fed up* or *This is hard to swallow.*

- **Pneumonia:** This may occur in the healing phase of a Fear of Death Conflict and affects the alveoli (tiny air sacs in the lungs). It is often due to a diagnosis or prognosis shock. See section L | Lung Diseases for further information.

- **Skin symptoms:** These symptoms are explained in section Z | Zits and Other Skin Problems.

- **Sneeze:** A sneeze is a short healing crisis of a Stink-Smell Conflict.

EFT Approach

It is crucial to ensure that you do not get stuck in the healing phase but rather that you complete the healing phase and let your body return to a healthy balance. If you experience healing symptoms, that is a sign that you have resolved the conflict sufficiently to enter the healing phase, so you do not have to 'do' anything other than get through the healing phase as best you can.

However, if you notice that you are experiencing these healing symptoms on a regular basis, it suggests that there are repetitive triggers that keep reactivating the stress response, causing you to repeat the cycle (so you get triggered again, return to the conflict-active phase, resolve the conflict, start healing, only to get triggered again). In that case, it is definitely worthwhile to identify and resolve the underlying emotional causes, which means you need to identify and resolve the underlying stress patterns and triggers. And this is exactly what you can do if you properly apply EFT. Also, when you use EFT to address your daily triggers on a regular basis, the negative emotions do not build up, so you will be less likely to have an over-the-top intense emotional reaction and therefore an intense healing phase.

If the healing symptoms are still intense, we recommend that you focus your energy on healing first (using Symptom-Focused EFT whenever helpful), then, once you feel better, you can take the time to address the underlying emotional causes and stress triggers.

Below is the strategy we recommend:

1. **Symptom-Focused EFT:** Use EFT to neutralize any fear you feel about your symptoms and any diagnosis or prognosis you have received. Staying out of fear is the fastest route to recovery. Whether the symptoms are mild or intense, it is essential to remember that they are a natural part of the healing process and that nothing is going wrong in your body. The more you are able to stay out of fear about this, the faster your recovery will be. Of course, this can be challenging because you are not yet used to looking at symptoms of illness in this way.

    It is also important to consider whether you are feeling alone and unsupported, abandoned or not cared for properly or at all, including feeling out of your element or like a fish out of water. You may not consciously be aware that you are feeling this way, so it is important to dig deep and consider whether you are feeling this way subconsciously. These types of feelings can lead to another conflict, namely an Existential Conflict, which may cause further fluid retention and thus more pain. So, if your healing symptoms are severe with intense pain, this almost always indicates that an Existential Conflict is exacerbating the symptoms. You need to address these emotions and feelings and the related specific events in your approach.

    Apply Symptom-Focused EFT to all your physical symptoms. The sooner you notice that your symptoms are decreasing in intensity, the more confidence you will have in your ability to recover. We want to emphasize that Symptom-Focused EFT does not address the underlying emotional causes, only the physical and emotional symptoms you are experiencing in the moment, which is our priority in the healing phase. You can address the underlying emotional causes and past specific events later, once you are feeling better.

    Pain can be a trigger in and of itself, so try to make yourself as comfortable as possible. If at all possible, refrain from using anti-inflammatory medication (such as diclofenac) or painkillers (such as paracetamol and ibuprofen), as they interrupt and thus prolong the healing phase. If the pain is intense or the fever is high, you may be able to naturally stimulate the sympathetic response (the stress phase), in order to dampen the healing symptoms by drinking black tea or coffee (but not too much), by gentle activity indoors or taking a walk outside in cold air, or by drinking herbal tea (peppermint, willow bark, sage, arnica, or thyme). If you have a severe headache, use cold compresses on your head to cool it down, take a walk outside in cold air, and take a little dextrose (sugar) regularly. A good massage is very supportive, especially a foot massage. Finally, do take a painkiller if the pain is too severe and stressful and the other measures do not help.

2. **Detective Work:** As soon as you feel well enough, apply EFT to all the specific moments when you feel stressed or fearful about your diagnosis, prognosis or the proposed treatment. Focus on specific moments, such as when you first received the diagnosis, when the doctor explained the prognosis and proposed treatment, the reactions of your friends, family and others, as well as any moments when you read, heard or saw something about your issue which scared or shocked you. We highly recommend that you do not tell everyone about your diagnosis. Rather, be selective about whom you discuss it with. Other people's fear will not help you, and it may actually make things worse. While it is helpful to feel supported by the people close to you, it is not helpful to constantly talk about your diagnosis and receive compassionate looks and questions like *Are you okay?* as this pushes you into the patient role, which is similar to the victim role. This is not an empowering role and we recommend that you do everything you can to stay out of it.

3. **Big Cleanup:** After you have recovered from the symptoms associated with the healing phase, use the information above to identify any relevant conflicts and related specific events that you need to work on to neutralize any other stress triggers so that you can complete the healing phase and avoid a recurrence of the conflict.

I | INCONTINENCE

Incontinence, urine leakage and bedwetting are almost always due to a Territorial Marking Conflict. Such conditions may in turn result in feeling ashamed, embarrassed or not good enough, leading to Self-Devaluation Conflicts. A Territorial Marking Conflict may arise when you are not able to set your boundaries and 'mark your place.' When animals experience such a conflict, they usually experience it literally and respond by peeing to mark their territory. We, as humans, usually experience Territorial Marking Conflicts in a figurative sense. Perhaps others cross or do not respect your boundaries, either because you have not set boundaries around your territory or you have not set them clearly enough. Or maybe you feel like you cannot or dare not set boundaries, or maybe you do not know where or how to draw the line. Incontinence may also develop if you are under pressure, or you are unsure and easily influenced regarding your own decisions.

If a child (or even a teenager) starts wetting the bed (known as nocturnal enuresis), even though they have already learned to control their bladder, this suggests that they may have experienced a Territorial Marking Conflict, in which their boundaries were significantly overstepped. The involuntary urination takes place during the healing crisis of the Territorial Marking Conflict, which typically occurs at night. The conflict may arise due to a new situation within the family (such as moving, parents separating or having a new partner, boundary fights with siblings, no longer having a room of their own), a situation at school (such as being bullied, a teacher overstepping their boundaries, fights with classmates, a new school), or similar situations in other areas of their life (such as sports or hobbies). It is also relevant to consider how the family responds to the child when they wet the bed, how they inform others of the problem at sleepovers, and so on. These situations can, in and of themselves, be so upsetting for the child that they cause another Territorial Marking Conflict, thus keeping the conflict going, or they may result in a Self-Devaluation Conflict.

Incontinence may also affect seniors who may become incontinent after moving to a nursing home or into a hospital nursing ward. Here, too, boundaries are often crossed, as people can simply walk into their room unannounced, wake them up and wash and dress them, with no respect for their privacy or boundaries. Or they may be required to share a room with others against their will. Incidentally, seniors are sometimes put in a diaper to drain their urine, so they do not need to ask the staff for help to go to the bathroom, which ends up making them incontinent. It goes without saying that this can cause all sorts of other emotional conflicts.

Boundary issues may also play a role if you have an overactive bladder with a constant urge to urinate small amounts. You may not be able to pass urine with sufficient force as your limits are not being respected by others, because you are too weak to enforce them. Frequent urges to pee also occur with cystitis (which is a symptom of the healing phase of a Territory Marking Conflict).

If for any reason you cannot pee, you are not allowed to pee or you dare not pee when you are out of the house (for example, in a public restroom because you find it dirty or you do not want others to hear you pee), then coming home (where you can pee) can be such a relief that you go straight into the healing phase. The bladder muscles may cramp up considerably, making the urge so great that you can barely (or not) make it to the bathroom in time.

There are two more situations in which incontinence may develop, namely stress incontinence, for example, after pregnancy (where small amounts of urine leak out when lifting something, laughing, sneezing or coughing), and incontinence after prostate surgery. In these situations, bladder-related Self-Devaluation Conflicts (due to urine leakage itself) usually play a role. As a result, it is an active conflict that is self-perpetuating, usually with transient symptoms.

Finally, advanced age in and of itself can also be a cause of incontinence, without any underlying emotional conflict. However, it always makes sense to identify and address any possible emotional stress that may also be at play.

EFT Approach

Ask yourself where and when your boundaries are being crossed, and in what area or situation in your life this is happening. It could be situations in your environment (at school, at work or at home). Reflect on the way other people treat you, either verbally or physically, in relation to your body, your home, your thoughts and ideas and also your time.

Here is the approach we recommend you take:

1. **The WMOMD:** Identify the specific moments in which your boundaries are crossed and resolve these moments with EFT. As often as possible, take the time to identify previous events with the same emotional reaction, when you are working on the WMOMD. Bring the intensity of your WMOMD down until it is lower than 5 but not yet 0, then relive the moment again and ask yourself when you felt this way before. Neutralize both the past event and the WMOMD. Also, apply EFT to moments when you experienced the urine leakage itself and the emotions you feel when you relive them and then address any Self-Devaluation Conflicts related to these experiences. For incontinence after pregnancy or prostate surgery, use EFT to resolve both the emotions about the urine leakage itself, as well as on the emotions you have about any belief that you are 'incontinent from now on,' as well as any other Self Devaluation Conflicts.

2. **Big Cleanup:** Make a list of all the specific situations in which your boundaries have been crossed, from the time your symptoms first started. Neutralize each event with EFT. For incontinence after pregnancy or prostate surgery, work on a list of specific events when you experienced urine leakage but also pay attention to the shocks you received when you discovered the problem, anything you were told about the condition by doctors and other people, as well as your reactions when reading information about it (for example, on the internet). Also, neutralize any situations where your self-esteem is affected because of incontinence.

3. **Detective Work:** Using the following questions, identify the specific events that are at the root of this stress pattern. In other words, how did you learn that you cannot or should not set boundaries?

    - How did I learn that it is not OK to set boundaries, or that I am not allowed or cannot set boundaries? From whom?
    - What negative conclusions have I drawn that make me unable, unwilling, or afraid to state my boundaries? Find related specific events.
    - What are the key moments in the first 7 years of my life where this happened?

    For incontinence after pregnancy or prostate surgery, also ask yourself: How did I learn that this condition is not curable, that I should 'learn to live with it,' or that it will worsen over time? Who told me that? At what point? Use EFT to weaken (and eventually eliminate) these negative self-limiting beliefs.

4. **Symptom-Focused EFT:** Apply EFT immediately to any emotions or bodily sensations you experience in the moment you feel urine leaking or fear that urine is about to leak until the intensity of any emotions or sensations has subsided and you feel sufficiently calm. If possible, make that moment a specific event and address it using the WMOMD approach.

J | JUVENILE MYOCLONUS EPILEPSY

Juvenile myoclonus epilepsy (JME), also known as Janz syndrome, is the most common generalized epilepsy syndrome. It usually starts during the teen years and is characterized by the presence of absences, myoclonic seizures and tonic-clonic seizures. Infants and young children can also have epileptic seizures, which are quite often 'benign' convulsions. For instance, febrile seizures may occur when a young child has a fever. Adults may also have epileptic seizures (often during the healing crisis of a Motor Conflict or Separation Conflict).

For the purpose of this discussion, we will not make distinctions based on age. Instead, we will look primarily at the symptoms of the three most common types of seizures. By examining the symptoms (as opposed to the labels or diagnoses given by mainstream medicine), we can use Hamer's insights to uncover the possible emotional root causes that underlie the symptoms.

There are three main types of seizures:

- **Myoclonic seizures:** These involve brief, jerking spasms of a muscle or muscle group, often in the arms and shoulders. This type of seizure may occur during the healing crisis of a Motor Conflict, which may arise if you feel stuck in a situation, unable to get out of something, or unable or unwilling to move.

- **Absence seizures (petit mal seizures):** These are very brief, sudden lapses of consciousness, during which the person stops what they are doing (but does not fall) and stares blankly into space, usually for less than 10 seconds. Other signs include fluttering of eyelids, twitching of the mouth and small hand movements. Then, they quickly return to their normal level of alertness and continue what they were doing, without any memory of the absence. An absence seizure may happen during the healing crisis of a Separation Conflict. The fluttering of the eyelids is the healing crisis of a visual Motor Conflict (in which you cannot or do not dare to open or close your eyes) and the twitching of the mouth is the healing crisis of a Biting Conflict (which may arise when you want to snap at someone but cannot or do not dare to do so).

- **Tonic-clonic seizures (grand mal seizures):** These involve a sudden loss of consciousness, then 15-20 seconds of muscle stiffening followed by violent muscle twitching in the arms and legs for 1 to 2 minutes. Then, the person falls asleep and may be confused for a while afterward. Here, multiple conflicts are involved, all of which are in the healing phase, resulting in several things occurring simultaneously, namely two healing crises of a double-sided Motor Conflict plus the healing crisis of a Separation Conflict. A Motor Conflict occurs when you feel stuck like you cannot, are not allowed to or do not dare to move or leave. A double-sided Motor Conflict means there are two Motor Conflicts, where one Motor Conflict has to do with 'mother or child' and the other conflict has to do with 'partner.' See Appendix 5 for an explanation of the 'mother or child' side versus the 'partner' side.

  At the same time, there is a Separation Conflict in the healing phase, which means you have healed a conflict where you experienced an unwanted separation from something or someone, or you had unwanted contact with something or someone, like an unwanted advance.

  Muscle twitches and muscle spasms have already been addressed in the section B | Bones, Muscles and Tendons.

Even though an epileptic seizure may look very violent, it is rarely acutely dangerous. Mainstream medicine claims that seizures are caused by abnormal electrical activity throughout the brain or some kind of short circuit in the brain. It is also suggested that they may result from damage to the cerebral cortex (the outer part of the brain) due to a brain infection, a severe head injury, cerebral hemorrhage or vascular malformation, a brain tumor, or congenital brain abnormalities. However, in about half the people with epilepsy, mainstream medicine concludes there is no apparent cause.

It is true that the cerebral cortex (the motor cortex of the brain responsible for controlling the muscles) plays a role when seizures occur. Hamer found that when an emotionally shocking experience occurs, which relates to a Motor Conflict, there is always a corresponding reaction in the motor cortex of the brain. He found evidence in CT scans of a cerebral hemorrhage or a brain tumor in the healing phase of such a conflict, consistent with the findings of mainstream medicine. However, while mainstream medicine would diagnose such a finding as a disease symptom that requires treatment, Hamer sees such a tumor as a natural part of the healing phase, like any infection. Thus, the findings are similar but the meaning given to such findings are radically different, representing two completely different views. Mainstream medicine would treat a brain tumor with medication or surgery in which the affected part of the brain is removed, and sometimes in small children, an entire hemisphere of the brain is taken out. While Hamer would not recommend such treatment, it is essential to identify and resolve the underlying conflicts, to avoid a recurrence of these symptoms.

If we look at the underlying emotional causes from Hamer's point of view, we need to identify and resolve all conflicts that involve wanting to move but feeling stuck or not being able or allowed to move, which may have preceded the epileptic healing crisis. When epilepsy is reported in babies and young children, it is necessary to also consider the possibility that they felt stuck in the womb or birth canal, and use EFT to resolve that. In older children and teenagers, the conflict of being stuck may be experienced physically (where they are not allowed to do what they want or go where they want) or metaphorically, if they feel stuck in a difficult or oppressive situation at home or school, perhaps with a parent or teacher who literally does not give them any space and represses them.

EFT Approach

If there are only absence seizures, you need to focus on identifying and resolving Separation Conflicts. If you only have muscle twitching, look for Motor Conflicts. If you have both absence seizures and muscle twitching, you need to identify how both types of conflicts play a role in your life. If your child is experiencing seizures, you could accomplish a lot by yourself, but it may be wise to contact a well-trained EFT professional, especially in situations where you, as the parent, may be part of the conflict. If you know or suspect this may be the case, make sure you also use EFT to address your stress patterns and emotions. It may also be useful to read the next chapter, which is dedicated to using EFT with children.

1. **Detective Work:** Using the information above, identify whether you need to look for a Motor Conflict, a Separation Conflict or both, based on the type of seizure you (or your child) are experiencing. Ask yourself when the epileptic seizures started and look for the situations where you felt stuck and/or where there was a Separation Conflict. When looking for Separation Conflicts, consider whether you have experienced any loss (such as the loss of a pet or loved one), or whether you have felt any irritation about having contact with something, such as squeezing into clothes that are too small or feeling uncomfortably cold. When identifying Motor Conflicts, consider whether you feel stuck in any situation, which could even be feeling stuck in a medical diagnosis or treatment. You may also have been literally stuck, for example, in a car accident. Ask yourself, *At what point do I suffer from this conflict?* and make a list of specific events. Use the wording, *The moment when X happens and I feel Y.* Neutralize all the events you identify with EFT.

2. **The WMOMD:** There may be several moments during the day when you feel stuck, or when you feel like getting out of a situation, but you do not dare to, you are not allowed to or you are simply unable to get out. Also, take note of any moments with people or animals you no longer want to have contact with or when you are doing things you do not want to do. As often as possible, look back at earlier events with the same emotional reaction, and ask yourself, while you relive those events, *When did I feel like this before?* Do this when the emotional intensity of your WMOMD is below 5, but not yet 0. The more often you use the WMOMD approach to identify and resolve both current and past specific events, the faster your stress pattern will be cleared.

3. **Big Cleanup:** Make a list of any emotionally charged events you have not yet identified using the Detective Work approach and the WMOMD approach. Include events that may be relevant to the formation of your NCB during the first 7 years of your life. You will no doubt find events in which you felt not good enough, or not worthy of attention, and in

which you also felt stuck. If you have fears or worries about a diagnosis, neutralize every stressful specific moment that relates to your diagnosis, for example, any examinations or tests, information provided by doctors and therapists, the reactions of those around you, as well as every moment when you felt startled by what you read, heard or saw in relation to your diagnosis.

4. **Symptom-Focused EFT:** Apply EFT immediately when you experience an intense emotion. If possible, make it a specific event and resolve it with the WMOMD approach.

K | KIDS

This chapter is for mothers and fathers, aunts and uncles, grandparents, and anyone else who is responsible for taking care of children. EFT can be done very successfully with children. If they are very young, EFT Tapping is more appropriate. Teenagers can tap but they would also be able to use Optimal EFT since they are old enough to meditate and work with The Unseen Therapist. Ultimately, it depends on the child as to which protocol will be most useful. In addition, it is possible to apply EFT surrogately for children. See Chapter 5 of Part 1 for an explanation of how surrogate EFT works.

EFT is safe and can be used effectively with children of all ages. All of the information in this book applies equally to children and adults since children can experience all the same types of emotional conflicts. As explained in Chapter 5 of Part 1, our negative core belief (NCB) develops during the first 6 to 7 years of our life and usually starts forming while we are still a fetus in utero. It is formed by specific events that negatively affect our self-esteem (Self-Devaluation Conflicts). Every time a child feels rejected, they make a negative conclusion about themselves, such as I am not good enough, I do not belong, or I should not be here. After the age of 7 and before the brain is fully formed at the age of 23-24, any negative life experiences continue to cement the NCB into place and reaffirm earlier conclusions about not being good enough *See, I am not good enough; I knew it, I am worthless; See, others are more important,* and so on. This voice in our head (our inner critic or ego) causes a lot of suffering, although some children suffer more than others.

How amazing would it be if you could prevent early childhood experiences from having such a negative impact and causing numerous problems later in life? Is there such a thing as an ideal childhood with an ideal upbringing and ideal parents? Of course not. Life is like a classroom and involves all sorts of experiences, some we perceive as good, others as bad.

Mistakes are made and people get hurt, but we learn and grow through our experiences. Negative childhood experiences do not only occur in seriously dysfunctional families with major problems and unsafe home environments. A child can also be traumatized by incidents that may not have any effect on us as adults. Arguments between parents and other family members can be immensely stressful for children. School can also be a major source of stress, even if children do not have learning difficulties or issues with bullying, because their NCB can create problems. In addition, children may encounter serious accidents, illnesses or the death of loved ones. Would it not be wonderful if you could help children to process these experiences so they can continue to develop, emotionally unimpeded, into balanced adults?

We recommend that you always work on your own emotions first, before addressing your child's issues. If you are scared, angry, frustrated, full of rage or feel powerless, you cannot be there for your child. No matter how understandable your emotional state may be, your child suffers if you do EFT with them when you are not in a loving state. Therefore, we urge you to be aware of this and make it a priority to do EFT on yourself first, so that you can maintain a state of calm, even when your child is acting out.

We also suggest that you let your child know that you are using EFT yourself to regulate your own emotions, rather than keeping it a secret. Explain to your child that it is natural to have negative emotions, that we all experience them and that it is ok to feel angry or sad or frustrated. Show them that you want to take responsibility for your emotional state by processing and releasing these negative emotions with EFT. Setting a good example is worth its weight in gold.

Often, children experience issues and conflicts involving one or both parents. The child may feel that another sibling is their parent's favorite child, or perhaps they are resistant to doing their chores or homework. If you suspect that you are part of the conflict, it is probably not effective for you to do EFT with your child. You may be able to teach them the basics of EFT and help them resolve smaller issues that do not relate to you, but you may not be the best person to help them address their bigger issues. In that case, it may be necessary to contact a well-trained EFT professional to assist your child.

When your child is dealing with a particular issue, you will often realize (consciously or subconsciously) that they learned this behavior or habit from you. Rather than blaming the child, we need to be honest with ourselves and recognize that we all have stress patterns that we learned from our parents and others around us during childhood. You may see parts of yourself in your child that you do not like. Use EFT to let go of any guilt or judgment of yourself or your child and simply get to work. Follow the strategy below and address your issues and those of your child with EFT, so that you can work towards freeing yourself and your child from these negative patterns.

Finally, while you may believe that EFT is very useful, your child may decide that they do not like it and simply refuse to engage in the process. If that is the case, do not force them. You will not achieve anything if you try to make them do it. Instead, you could do EFT surrogately for your child, in addition to applying EFT to your own issues.

Scoring the Intensity of the Experience

Just like with adults, it is helpful to score the intensity of the emotional response with children so that you can measure whether the charge is down to 0. With school-aged children, it works well to use the score of 0 (nothing) to 10 (a lot). For small children, you can ask them to indicate how bad something feels using the distance between their hands: hands all the way apart indicates a lot and hands together indicates not at all. This works amazingly well. Children are usually able to indicate the intensity very accurately. With babies and toddlers, you can look at what effect EFT has (including using surrogate EFT): does the child become calmer, do they fall asleep, do they start laughing or stop crying and other such feedback?

Gold Standard EFT with Kids

When young children tell you about an upsetting event, they are usually already associated with the event and their feelings, so you do not need to ask them to relive the event in an associated way, as you do with adults. But if they are not connected to their feelings, then just ask them to close their eyes, step into the moment, and pretend it is happening right now.

When creating the Setup phrase, rather than saying *I accept myself*, it is better to emphasize that they are loved. This is one of the most important affirmations children need to feel safe. Teens and adolescents also like to hear this. In fact, who does not? So you may use a variation of the following: *Even though I am really angry and I threw my food on the floor, Mom and Dad still love me.*

You can teach children to tap on the points by themselves while you are repeating the Setup phrase and the reminder phrase, or you can tap on them. Many children like to be tapped on. We frequently hear from parents who do EFT regularly with their children that they ask if they can be tapped on for a while.

Note

Sometimes children do not like being tapped on. You may be tapping too hard without realizing it, so try to tap gently. An alternative is to use the Touch and Breathe technique as follows: without tapping, place your finger on a point and let the child breathe in and out quietly and then move to the next point. Breathe along with your child, so you do not move too fast from one point to the next. With very small children, it is sufficient to simply breathe in and out very gently yourself, as their breathing will usually naturally synchronize with yours.

Optimal EFT with Kids

It has been our experience that the Optimal EFT protocol itself does not need to be modified. However, when explaining what The Unseen Therapist is, keep it simple. If the child has a positive image of God, then you could explain that The Unseen Therapist is like the Holy Spirit or use any other name in your culture or religion. But you could also describe The Unseen Therapist as an angel, an imaginary friend or even a cartoon character, provided that it is perceived as positive and supportive. The loving moment may be something very simple, such as an experience your child enjoyed or a cuddle with their pet or favorite toy.

EFT Approach

The strategy described below assumes that you are working with your child.

1. **The WMOMD:** We recommend that you start by working on a WMOMD, if possible. If something happened at school, apply EFT as soon as they tell you about it, when they get home. Apply the WMOMD approach in the usual way, by first reducing the emotional charge of the WMOMD to below 5 but not yet zero, then asking your child to relive it (by imagining it is happening right now), and finally asking them if they can remember feeling the same way before, in order to identify past events. You will soon find that there will be past events that need attention, especially situations in which their NCB is involved. This is a great way to ensure that their experiences do not further strengthen their NCB. You can also use the VoC test to measure how true their NCB feels and repeat the test from time to time to see how things are going. You can do this by asking them to close their eyes and repeat their NCB and then ask them how true the statement feels (0% means feeling not true at all and 100% means feeling completely true). Of course, do not use percentages if your children are very young. Instead, ask them to show you how true it feels using their hands. The VoC tends to fluctuate a little, so the percentage may be higher during a stressful period, but if you continue to apply EFT, it will decrease again. It is usually not possible to get the NCB down to zero permanently, but you can aim to keep it below 10%.

   EFT is a wonderful addition to the bedtime ritual. You can ask your child to tell you why they cannot sleep, whether they are not looking forward to school tomorrow, whether they are afraid of not passing a test, etc. While they talk, you can gently tap on them. You can also work with The Unseen Therapist and either ask for Her help while you listen to your child, or do a meditation with your child and ask for Her help together.

2. **Detective Work:** Although your child does not yet have a long history of negative past events, it is worthwhile using what you find with the

WMOMD approach to look for deeper causes. Once you have identified a problem, use the following questions to look for the specific events that are at the root of this stress pattern:

- How did my child learn this? From whom?
- What are the best, clearest examples of specific moments when this plays out?

3. **Big Cleanup:** Encourage your child to make a list of any events they find upsetting (or do this together), then help your child to resolve them with EFT, one by one. Take your time. Perhaps you only address one event together each week. Whatever you do, do not force them, otherwise, this may turn them off. Patience is key.

4. **Symptom-Focused EFT:** Apply EFT immediately if your child is experiencing any intense emotions until the intensity of the emotions has subsided sufficiently. EFT works particularly well with children when applied to pain and other physical issues. This could be because they are less influenced by limiting beliefs about pain and illness (and more open to expecting results!). Also, remember you can always do EFT surrogately when working with them directly is not possible.

L | LUNG DISEASES

In this chapter, we will take a closer look at bronchial asthma, bronchitis, and pneumonia. The lungs are housed in the chest cavity and the left lung envelops your heart. Your heart lies almost in the middle of your chest behind your sternum (two-thirds of the heart is to the left of the center and one-third to the right). The left lung has two lobes and the right lung consists of three lobes. The lung lobes contain the bronchi (passageways connecting the windpipe to the lungs) and the alveoli (tiny air sacs). When we breathe, the air moves down the bronchi into the alveoli. The total surface area of the alveoli is 860-1075 square feet (80 -100 square meters), and this is where the uptake of oxygen and the release of carbon dioxide take place.

The following types of emotional conflicts are expressed in the lungs:

- Fear of Death Conflict (this affects the lung alveoli and may result in a diagnosis of pneumonia);
- Territorial Fear Conflict or Shock-Fright or Speechlessness Conflict (this affects the mucous membrane of the bronchial tubes, which may result in a diagnosis of bronchitis or bronchial asthma).

Pneumonia

The main function of the lungs is the process of gas exchange called respiration (or breathing). In respiration, oxygen from incoming air enters the blood, and carbon dioxide, a waste gas from the metabolism, leaves the blood. Hamer describes the same process differently: the function of the lungs is to 'digest' chunks of air. From his research, it became clear that if we encounter a life-threatening situation and suffer a Fear of Death Conflict, the lung alveoli react by making more cells to be able to process more oxygen and improve the function of the lungs. The symptoms you experience during the healing phase of such a conflict are diagnosed by mainstream medicine as pneumonia.

The most common situations that lead to a Fear of Death Conflict are diagnosis shocks, such as a cancer diagnosis that is associated with a death sentence, or prognosis shocks, such as *This tumor is very malignant, you have six months to live, go home and put your affairs in order.* Or it may be a self-diagnosis shock, where you discover a lump or see blood in your stool and associate it with cancer or some other serious disease. You may also suffer from such a conflict if you are literally threatened with death (for instance, if someone comes at you with a knife), or if you encounter a situation you perceive as life-threatening, such as an accident. Even receiving non-medical information that is perceived as threatening can result in a Fear of Death Conflict. Finally, you may fear the death of a loved one and suffer from a Vicarious Conflict.

During the conflict-active phase of a Fear of Death Conflict, the body responds by cell growth of the alveoli, as explained above, to increase lung function so that we are better able to cope. This usually does not involve any symptoms. However, if you undergo a medical examination at the same time (such as a chest X-ray or an MRI), the extra cells produced (tumors) may be diagnosed as lung cancer. According to Hamer's findings, if there is only one lung tumor, this signifies that you are afraid that somebody else will die. If there are many, often small, lung tumors throughout the lungs, this signifies that you fear that you will die.

Once the conflict has been resolved because you are no longer afraid that you or somebody else will die, the body moves into the healing phase and the extra cells are broken down and decomposed by tuberculosis bacteria (mycobacteria) and fungi. It is during the healing phase that you may be diagnosed with pneumonia. During this phase, you may experience a productive cough (to expel the discharge caused by the decomposition of the extra cells), which may include blood. Other symptoms include difficulty breathing, extreme fatigue, night sweats, fever, bad breath and tightness of the chest. During the healing crisis, you may experience a lot of pain, severe shortness of breath and a high fever. After the healing crisis, during the final part of the healing phase, the symptoms diminish, but you may again have a productive cough for a considerable period thereafter. Depending on the intensity and duration of the conflict-active phase, the healing phase may be quite severe, so it is essential to rest and take good care of yourself so that you can heal.

EFT Approach for Pneumonia

If you have pneumonia, then in principle, you have already resolved the underlying Fear of Death Conflict sufficiently to enter the healing phase. However, it is important to ensure that you will not get triggered again and interrupt the healing, which could cause you to get stuck in the healing phase, or cause another conflict and thus another bout of pneumonia. Therefore, it is essential to address the underlying emotional causes with EFT to make sure they are completely resolved. Any situation that involves fear always deserves a lot of attention because fear not only makes symptoms worse but also hinders healing. In addition, you need to address the healing symptoms, which can create even more fear. Finally, if your healing symptoms are very intense, it is unlikely that you will have any energy, so it may be worthwhile to contact someone who can do EFT with you or even work surrogately for you.

1. **Symptom-Focused EFT:** Apply EFT to each symptom. Take your time and be patient as healing needs to take its course, so you may not get immediate results. If you are feeling very fearful and anxious, make it your priority to resolve those emotions. The more you stimulate the relaxation response with either EFT protocol and let go of fear and anxiety, the easier and faster you will get through the healing phase.

2. **Big Cleanup:** Identify all situations that may have triggered the fear of death response. This may include the moment you or a loved one received any serious diagnosis, any fearful stories you heard about others, anything you read or saw, and all other moments in which you were afraid that you or another might die.

Bronchitis

Bronchitis is characterized by inflammation of the bronchial mucosa. Air comes in through the nose or mouth, moves through the trachea (windpipe), and enters the bronchial tubes, which let air in and out of your lungs. The bronchial tubes are lined with a mucous membrane (bronchial mucosa).

The underlying emotional conflict is either a Territorial Fear Conflict or a Shock-Fright or Speechlessness Conflict. A Territorial Fear Conflict involves fear about your territory, such as losing part of your territory or fear concerning members of your territory, including yourself. For example, the loss of a loved one (partner, child, friend, pet), loss of property or losing your job or position. You may not have lost anything yet, but you may deeply fear that you will. Your territory could also include your schedule or time; thus, the conflict may involve someone putting you under pressure or imposing a deadline or telling you how to spend your time.

A Shock-Fright or Speechlessness Conflict occurs in situations where you are startled because of a sudden threat or noise (including somebody suddenly yelling very loudly at you). Or it may be a situation in which you are not able to speak loudly enough or scream, feeling like you have lost your voice or not daring to express yourself. The words may be stuck in your throat or you may feel 'struck dumb.' It is a passive reaction to a threat. A child may suffer a Territorial Fear Conflict or a Shock-Fright Conflict when they are reprimanded, punished, yelled at or screamed at. They may also suffer from such a conflict after watching a scary movie, having a nightmare or due to a fear of sleeping alone.

The Territorial Fear Conflict is an active reaction to a threat to your territory. The Shock-Fright or Speechlessness Conflict is a passive reaction to the same types of situations. Typically, the active reaction involves an attack (wanting to take action against the threat), and the passive reaction involves fright (staying put, not taking action).

The function of the bronchial musculature is to expand and contract to allow breathing. In the conflict-active phase of a Territorial Fear or Shock-Fright or Speechlessness Conflict, there is tissue loss in the bronchial mucosa, but you do not have any symptoms other than feeling stressed.

According to Hamer, the biological purpose of the tissue loss is to widen the bronchial tubes so that more air can be taken in, enabling you to cope better.

Once the conflict is resolved, the ulcerated area will be refilled and replenished with new cells. During the healing phase, there will be swelling, as healing always occurs in a fluid environment, and that may cause breathing difficulties and pain. You may start with a hacking, unproductive cough, that may become productive within a few days (with thick yellow mucus). You may also have a fever, sore throat, headache, fatigue, tightness in the chest, runny or blocked nose and muscle pain. In the healing crisis, you may have coughing attacks or cramps and a very high fever.

During the first part of the healing phase, there is a buildup of tissue, which is a natural part of healing, but if you undergo a medical examination, this may be interpreted differently by mainstream medicine and diagnosed as bronchial cancer. As a result of your symptoms (and any diagnosis received) during the healing phase, you may feel alone, abandoned, displaced (especially if you have to go to the hospital) or feel like you are not being properly cared for, which could give rise to an Existential Conflict. If you experience an Existential Conflict, there will be even more swelling, more tightness in the chest and further inflammation of the bronchi, which may intensify the healing symptoms.

EFT Approach for Bronchitis

Like pneumonia, bronchitis is a symptom of the healing phase, which means that you have already resolved the conflict to a significant degree. However, to avoid a recurrence and getting stuck in the healing phase, you need to address the underlying emotional causes with EFT and also address any fear about the healing symptoms themselves. If you have recurring bronchitis, this could eventually lead to blocked bronchial tubes (due to swelling during healing) that can be serious, so it is essential to identify what is triggering you and resolve those triggers. If there is a lot of fear, this deserves careful attention. Fear aggravates any symptoms and hinders healing. Again, during the most intense part of the healing phase, you may not have any energy at all to do EFT. In that case, consider finding someone who can help you apply EFT effectively or who can even work surrogately for you.

1. **Symptom-Focused EFT:** Work on all physical and emotional symptoms with EFT. Take your time and do not expect immediate results. The more you stimulate the relaxation response with either protocol, the better. If you have a lot of fear or anxiety, work on those emotions immediately. The less fear and anxiety you have, the faster you will get through the healing phase.

2. **Big Cleanup:** Identify any events with Territorial Fear, Shock-Fright or Speechlessness and neutralize them with EFT.

   If the symptoms themselves cause you anxiety, then neutralize every specific moment that makes you feel anxious, including conversations with doctors, medical examinations or tests, reactions from others, and any moment in which you felt frightened by what you read, heard or saw in relation to your diagnosis.

Bronchial Asthma

An asthma attack may occur during a severe healing crisis of either a Territorial Fear Conflict, or a Shock-Fright or Speechlessness Conflict. A second conflict from this group is also at play, as explained below.

Asthma has nothing to do with allergies, strong smells, physical exertion, food, laughter or temperature changes per se. These factors can play a role, but only if they are a stress trigger (which is usually subconscious). The belief or conviction that such factors are the direct cause seems to be proven with every attack because the asthma attack does tend to occur after exposure to such triggers. However, this only occurs because two other things are happening simultaneously, namely the resolution of an underlying emotional conflict while (at the same time) another conflict is still ongoing.

According to our experience with EFT and working on emotional underlying causes, a person can be 'allergic' to anything, not just to a substance they touch or consume. Every detail we perceive with our senses at the time we experience an emotional shock (which activates our sympathetic stress reaction) is stored in our long-term memory for later use and protection in the future. Thus, any such detail can serve as a trigger and give rise to an allergic reaction that, depending on the type of conflict involved, may manifest as an asthma attack, a skin rash or a stuffy nose, etc.

Unless you are aware that there is a missing link, you may simply assume that the body has developed an allergic reaction to something for no apparent reason, so you may never take the time to identify and resolve the root cause of your symptoms.

Let us now look at the underlying emotional causes of an asthma attack, so you can start exploring for yourself what happens when you resolve the emotional causes with EFT. At least two conflicts are at play during an asthma attack. As mentioned above, one of the conflicts is a Territorial Fear Conflict or a Shock-Fright or Speechlessness Conflict, which has been resolved and is in healing crisis. At the same time, another Territorial Fear or Shock-Fright or Speechlessness Conflict is either in the conflict-active phase or in healing crisis. One of these conflicts is related to 'mother or child,' while the other is related to 'partner.' See Appendix 5 for an explanation of the 'mother or child' side versus the 'partner' side.

EFT Approach for Bronchial Asthma

When you are having an asthma attack, focus on applying EFT to the acute symptoms you are experiencing. Once the asthma attack has subsided and you feel better, take the time to identify the underlying emotional issues and start resolving them with EFT. The goal is to clear the stress patterns so that you prevent a recurrence. Again, if you are very fearful, focus on resolving your fears with EFT because fear tends to make the symptoms worse and hinders healing.

1. **Symptom-Focused EFT during an asthma attack:** Apply EFT to any tightness in your throat and your shortness of breath, as well as any feelings of anxiety, fear or panic. The calmer you are, the faster it will pass.

2. **Fear of an attack:** Between asthma attacks, resolve any fear you may feel about having another attack. Identify any specific situations in which you are afraid of having an attack, as well as your actual experiences during a past attack that may have been severe and upsetting. Make a list and neutralize these experiences with EFT.

3. **Detective Work:** Start by asking yourself when the asthma attacks started and identify the specific situations in which you may have experienced a Territorial Fear Conflict or a Shock-Fright or Speechlessness Conflict, shortly before the attack and also during the attack. Start with the last asthma attack you experienced, neutralize that experience with EFT, then continue to work backward in time until you identify the specific situations in which you first started experiencing asthma attacks. They may involve different circumstances and different people. If you were too young, then ask your parents or caregivers to help you identify the situations. Relevant questions to ask include: *In what type of moment did I have an attack? Who was involved?* Make a list of events using the sentence *The moment when X happens and I feel Y.* Then make a plan to neutralize all those events with EFT.

4. **The WMOMD:** Focus on identifying one or two situations each day that relate to the type of emotional conflicts underlying asthma attacks, as noted above. When addressing a current event, dig deeper to find earlier events once you have reduced the intensity of the current event to below 5 but not yet 0. You may find that your negative core belief (NCB) also plays a significant role in the specific moments you identify.

5. **Big Cleanup:** Make a list of any other negatively charged events that you have not yet identified using the approaches above. Use this as a final sweep to find any other events that could be related to your asthma attacks and then neutralize them one by one.

If you feel worried or anxious about the symptoms themselves, identify any specific events related to such worries, such as upsetting conversations with doctors or therapists, any medical examinations or tests and their results, reactions from others, as well as every moment you were shocked by what you read, heard or saw in connection with your diagnosis.

M | MEDICALLY UNEXPLAINED SYMPTOMS

The diagnosis of Medically Unexplained (Physical) Symptoms (MUS or MUPS) is made when you have ongoing physical symptoms, such as headaches, dizziness or pain, which do not match any recognized medical condition. The prevalence of MUS is estimated to be greater than 25%, which means that about 1 in 4 people who consult a doctor have physical symptoms the doctor cannot explain.

If you have read up to this point, you may not be surprised that we take a different view, based on Hamer's discoveries, which is that there are no unexplained symptoms as such, there are only doctors who may not be able to explain the symptoms.

All physical and psychological symptoms have a root cause, which is either an emotionally shocking unexpected event (which causes chronic stress) or external forces that have a direct effect on the body (such as a fall, being hit by an object, etc.).

All the details of every stress-inducing event you have ever experienced are stored in your long-term memory. Anything that reminds you (usually subconsciously) of a stressful situation from the past can therefore trigger your stress response, which becomes a conditioned, automatic response. In this sense, all physical and psychological symptoms are psychosomatic symptoms, although we do not mean this in the way that it is often communicated by doctors. It is not helpful to be told there is nothing wrong with your body and that it is all in your mind. There is clearly something wrong since you are experiencing real physical symptoms, which is why you consulted the doctor in the first place.

Chronic stress can lead to many problems. Stress can cause symptoms that may be experienced as a psychological problem only, but there is usually a physical reaction in the body as well. The fact that mainstream medicine does not identify any specific cause is not proof that there is (or was) no stress reaction. Our minds are extremely powerful and they instruct our bodies how to heal and repair themselves. Many physical reactions to stress are temporary and heal by themselves without us needing to do anything. Of course, there may also be permanent changes in the body that continue to affect us. Either way, it can be upsetting and frustrating to go to a doctor and be told there is nothing wrong.

In this chapter, we will look at several symptoms that are medically unexplained and help you to understand what is happening in your body and why and how you can address your issues with EFT. So, you do not need to give up and think there is nothing you can do about your medically unexplained symptoms. We hope this chapter inspires you to feel empowered and take action!

Predisposition and susceptibility to symptoms?

If you look up what causes medically unexplained symptoms on the Internet, you may read that some people simply have a predisposition and susceptibility to certain symptoms such as abdominal pain, back pain, headaches, fatigue, or itchy skin. We do not agree that some people are randomly predisposed or susceptible to certain symptoms while others are not. Let us look at this concept from a different perspective. These types of symptoms are almost all healing symptoms that you will go through during the healing phase after a stressful event has been resolved. Abdominal pain may occur in both the conflict-active phase and the healing phase. Lower abdominal pain is usually a healing symptom, while upper abdominal pain is usually related to an active conflict, which means that something is causing you stress at the time you experience the pain.

In our view, you may be predisposed to certain conditions but only if you have learned certain stress patterns from your past experiences, which we discussed in Part 1. Similarly, you may be vulnerable or susceptible to certain symptoms but only if you have developed a conditioned stress response, which may then manifest as physical or psychological symptoms. Thus, these symptoms are neither random nor unexplained. There is a reason for them (the underlying emotional conflicts) that can be addressed with EFT.

For example, abdominal pain is often associated with anger and issues that you cannot digest or process (defined as a Chunk Conflict), back pain is often associated with the resolution of a Self-Devaluation Conflict, fatigue is a common and general symptom of healing of all conflicts, and itchy skin is related to the resolution of a Separation Conflict.

The way we develop stress patterns (which are caused by our past experiences and then manifest as symptoms) is the same for everyone and has nothing to do with predisposition or sensitivity.

Your Beliefs Play an Important Role

Your thoughts and beliefs have a major influence on your symptoms. If you are frightened by your symptoms and are convinced that something is seriously wrong, this intensifies the stress response in your body and may lead to you developing negative expectations and beliefs as to the outcome. Experiences and expectations around illnesses clearly play a significant role. If you have had certain symptoms, you may be convinced that you will suffer from them again or fear that they will come back. If a family member suffers from a certain condition, you may fear that you will end up with it too. If you believe that heart disease is hereditary and you are aware that several family members suffered from it, you may conclude that you too will end up with heart issues. In that case, it is not surprising if you feel very stressed if you get minor heart palpitations or slight chest pain.

Many beliefs develop from looking up information about illnesses, diseases and ailments on the Internet. Similarly, negative limiting beliefs are created by the way doctors explain and treat symptoms, since these explanations and treatments are based on the view that symptoms are a sign that something is wrong, as opposed to the view that most symptoms are part of your body's natural healing response.

A well-known phenomenon is the fear of heart disease which, ironically, may arise as a result of medical tests and checkups. Say you are experiencing some symptoms and your family doctor recommends that you get an ECG (electrocardiogram). The results show no problem but you still have symptoms the doctor cannot explain satisfactorily. So, your doctor refers you to a cardiologist. Your doctor may hope this will reassure you, but it usually creates more fear, as you may start to worry there really is something wrong with you. You may think that the doctor must have found something, why else would they refer you? The cardiologist does another ECG but cannot find anything wrong either, so they order more tests. The cardiologist may hope to reassure you by doing an ultrasound of your heart and a stress test on a treadmill or bicycle. Unfortunately, you as the patient (because that is what you have become since consulting the doctor about your symptoms) conclude that there must be something seriously wrong, otherwise, the cardiologist would not run all these extra tests, and your fear escalates. It can be difficult to get out of this negative spiraling thought pattern, which causes more stress and may result in (or intensify any) heart palpitations. This example shows how our beliefs about illness and health develop and how they play a substantial role. They can play a crucial role in determining what symptoms you experience and how long they last.

Pain is also an important factor. Severe or prolonged pain is a trigger in itself, creating an Existential Conflict (as you consciously or unconsciously feel that your life is threatened). It is not uncommon to feel despondent or hopeless in the face of pain. This stress and the associated emotions can lead to the belief that you will never get rid of the pain, especially if you have had the pain for a long time.

Body and Mind (Psyche) Form One Unit

More and more websites with medical information agree that the body and mind form one unit. Holistic approaches and integrative medicine that are completely or in part based on this idea are becoming more widely accepted, although mainstream medicine is a little slower to fully integrate this concept. The fact that the medical field as a whole is expanding its scope is hopeful and a step in the right direction, because it is always mind over matter, not only in our opinion but also based on our practical experience, (except in situations where there is a direct physical impact on the body). What happens in the body always starts in the mind. What happens in the mind may be completely unconscious, so it may seem that you suddenly have a symptom out of nowhere. But any symptom is always preceded by stressful, negative experiences and your subjective interpretation of those experiences (which may be conscious or unconscious).

We will now discuss the most common medically unexplained symptoms and how to best approach them with EFT. As we have emphasized previously, persistence pays off, so do not give up. It may take some time to get used to this new way of looking at your symptoms, and you may be skeptical at first. That is fine. We urge you to persevere anyway and do lots of rounds of EFT, not only on the symptoms (which may produce results but usually only temporarily) but also on the underlying emotional root cause, the specific events.

Commonly Misunderstood Symptoms

Chest tightness / chest pain: You may suffer chest pain or tightness because of emotional conflicts. There are many different reasons why you might have chest pain or tightness. They may originate from symptoms in the esophagus, stomach, heart, lungs, muscles, tendons, or cartilage due to a variety of underlying conflicts. General stress can also cause tightness and discomfort in the chest. The good news is that this symptom is almost always experienced during the healing phase. This means that the conflict has largely been resolved, so you can focus on resting and healing, instead of delving into fearful thoughts. What follows is a summary of the most common underlying causes:

- **Esophageal spasm:** This may occur during the healing crisis of a Chunk Conflict (which involves not being able to get something). It may concern a job, a promotion, a position, a purchase, an inheritance, an apology, or a proposal. It can also be the healing phase of a conflict where you cannot swallow something literally or figuratively because it is too much to handle, such as an insult, an accusation or a diagnosis.
- **Gastric acid and esophageal inflammation:** This occurs during the conflict-active phase of a conflict where you (literally or figuratively)

have swallowed something negative (or revolting) that you cannot spit out, or during the healing phase of a conflict where you were not able to absorb something positive.

- **Heart:** For heart palpitations see below. For pain in the heart area: If you suffer from a literal or figurative attack on your heart, you may experience chest pain once the conflict is resolved. For instance, you may be physically threatened with a knife, or you may get a diagnosis of a heart problem that feels like an attack on your heart, especially if the doctor recommends surgery. There may be pain behind the breastbone early in the healing process. If you experience a Territorial Loss Conflict (loss of job, home, business, etc.) or a Sexual Conflict (sexual abuse, loss of sexual partner, circumcision, rape, etc.), you may have mild chest pain in the conflict-active phase or severe chest pain in the healing crisis. Even mainstream medicine recognizes the broken heart syndrome. It is a condition with symptoms that may feel like a heart attack with chest pain and shortness of breath, but it is caused by going through an emotionally stressful event, not by clogged arteries. It may be triggered by very stressful situations, such as the death of someone you love.

- **Inflamed pleura (pleuritis):** If you experience a situation as an attack on the lungs or chest, you may suffer from pleuritis (inflammation of the serous membranes that surround the lungs) during the healing phase of that conflict, which may involve chest pain or tightness. The attack may be a literal attack. This may involve a punch or fall or you may have a lung tumor that requires surgery. Sometimes a breast amputation is felt like an attack on the chest. It could also be a figurative attack or a threat from within (such as strong pain in the chest cavity).

- **Muscles, tendons or cartilage:** You may experience tightness or pain in the chest during the healing phase of a Self-Devaluation Conflict. You may have experienced muscle pain after strenuous exercise but think that you did not do anything that would explain the pain. If you look closely at what happened, the strenuous exercise may have resolved part of your Self-Devaluation Conflict (perhaps you achieved or finished something and felt good about yourself, etc.). Or there may have been some other Self-Devaluation Conflict (unrelated to the exercise you did) that you resolved just before the pain appeared.

Dizziness and tendency to fall: You may feel dizzy if you have had a fall or feel like you are about to fall. This includes not only a literal fall but also a figurative one, such as losing your position or status or reputation. Consider the expression a fallen woman. Or perhaps you feel disappointed that you could not do something or did not persevere. You may also be afraid that someone else will fall, literally or figuratively. Or you could feel like you have fallen from grace. Use your imagination and broaden your perspective to find the possible underlying causes. If you experience a tendency to fall, the direction in which you fall is relevant. For right-clapping people, a tendency to fall to the left indicates an underlying conflict related to 'mother or child' and a tendency to fall to the right indicates a conflict related to 'partner.' For left clappers, it is the other way around. (See Appendix 3 for an explanation of 'left clappers' and the 'mother or child' side versus the 'partner' side.)

Heart palpitations: This is a completely normal reaction that can occur whenever the stress response is activated. Your heart might feel like it is pounding, fluttering or beating irregularly, often for just a few seconds or minutes. Heart palpitations may also occur in the following situation:

- If you are stressed about your heart or afraid that something is wrong with it (or you are stressed about somebody else's heart), you may experience palpitations during the healing crisis of such a conflict. In our experience, this type of fear is one of the most common causes of palpitations. The idea that something might be wrong with your heart causes a lot of stress. So, it is important to know that these palpitations are healing symptoms so that you can get out of the vicious cycle of being afraid that something is wrong with your heart. Another emotional cause of palpitations is the thought, *my life is not flowing anymore.* You are not following your path or you are losing yourself.

- When you feel overburdened, overloaded, overwhelmed or like you cannot handle a situation mentally, involving other people or animals, you may experience palpitations during the healing crisis. This usually involves a rapid, irregular heartbeat. Often, you may feel like you want to help someone, but you are not able to do so for some reason. It is never just a matter of too much work. Other people have to be involved and the situation must really bother you.

- When there is extreme tension due to too much almost unbearable stress, then you may experience palpitations during the conflict-active phase. Think of situations where you cannot get something or you just cannot let go. Everything feels like it is just too much. It may also involve wanting something or not wanting something anymore, which feels very intense.

Headache: This is a common symptom of the healing phase. We have already discussed it in section H | Healing Symptoms. Note: You may have a headache because you have sufficiently resolved one conflict, but at the same time you may be stressing over another emotional conflict. This can make it seem like you have a headache all the time because it may not be clear that you have resolved one conflict while other conflicts are still active. They become intertwined. Very severe headaches indicate you are in a healing crisis. If you have headaches for more than a few days, the healing is not complete. Often this is because the pain itself is a trigger and you get into a vicious cycle.

Nausea: You may feel nauseous both during times of acute stress and when you are recovering from stress. That is because blood drains from your gastrointestinal tract into your arms and legs (to fight or flee) when your acute stress response kicks in, and that can cause nausea. The blood flows back when your stress response ends, and that can also cause nausea. So nausea can be a common symptom of stress. But there may be more to it. Nausea may also arise if you feel like you have had enough (fed up), feel sick to your stomach about something, or if you want to throw up. Again, such feelings may be experienced literally or figuratively. Consider what irritates you. What do you no longer want to swallow? What do you have to swallow against your will? The saying *I cannot stomach it* points to these types of conflict. This type of irritation is called a Chunk Conflict, which was discussed in section D | Digestive Tract Issues. Nausea may also arise during a Territorial Anger Conflict. It usually involves aggression such as arguing with neighbors, family members, or co-workers. Finally, nausea can be a sign that you are in the conflict-active phase of an Identity Conflict: not knowing where you belong or what choice to make.

Paralysis of muscles: This is a symptom of a Motor Conflict, which may arise if you feel literally or figuratively trapped, not being able, allowed, or daring to move or make a movement, not being fast enough, or not being allowed to grab or push away something or someone. This may occur during the conflict-active phase. In an intense conflict, there may be a sudden paralysis of large muscle groups. In a less intense conflict, there may be muscle weakness (as opposed to paralysis). If your symptoms suddenly worsen, that is a sign that you have moved into the healing phase.

Note: During the healing crisis of a Motor Conflict, you may experience an epileptic seizure. This signifies that the normal control of the muscles is returning. However, this is often interpreted differently by mainstream medicine, namely as a new problem with the associated stress of a diagnosis and the consequences. Muscle paralysis or weakness often causes ongoing stress that prevents healing from being completed, and may even result in a diagnosis of MS (Multiple Sclerosis) or Parkinson's Disease. See section B | Bones, Muscles and Tendons for further information in this regard.

Stomach upset, stomach cramps and intestinal upset: These symptoms may arise when you have 'indigestible' annoyances and anger. We have already discussed these in section D | Digestive Tract Issues.

Tics: See section O | Obsessive-Compulsive Disorder.

EFT Approach

With all symptoms, but especially with medically unexplained symptoms, it is important to address all of your fears about the symptoms themselves. Once you know what your symptoms are, you can use them as pointers to help you identify the underlying emotional cause, which you can then resolve. Let us review how to do this with EFT:

1. **Detective Work:** Begin by asking yourself when the symptom began. Use a timeline. Using the information above, identify which conflicts may be playing a role in your symptom. If it is a symptom in the healing phase or healing crisis, you know you have resolved something. This resolution may have happened a few hours ago or some days ago. If the issue is fairly recent, ask yourself these questions: Did you make

a decision, do something you did not do before or did not dare to do before? Did you say something that you usually do not say, did you finish or achieve something? Did you settle a dispute or forgive someone? Did you keep your job after being threatened with dismissal? Was something resolved? Is the pressure off?

Begin to look for what has changed for the better. It may be something big, or it may be much more subtle. To avoid repetition of going through conflicts and their subsequent healing phases, make a list of all relevant specific events that are related to the conflict you have identified. These are the specific moments when something happens when you experience your conflict and you feel stressed because you have not resolved it yet (typically your symptoms start later when you have resolved them). Neutralize them one by one with EFT. For each event, once the intensity is below 5 but not yet 0, examine what belief or conclusion is involved and then ask yourself when you have felt and thought that way before. Identify a previous specific event and neutralize that event as well. If you have a belief that your symptoms are serious or permanent or a sign that things will never be right again, then over time you will probably discover where that belief comes from. It is important to identify who told you this or where you read, heard, or saw it. You may have learned it from a movie or documentary, from information you read on the internet, from an online forum with personal stories, etc. Who do you know who has had similar symptoms? Also, look to see if you were taught by a parent to be overly cautious about your physical health. Be careful not to stop once you discover the connection to your past experiences. Make a list of all these specific moments and neutralize them with EFT. This is the only way to get out of the vicious cycle.

2. **The WMOMD:** Use this approach to address both the specific unpleasant moments of the day when you experience the symptom (or it gets worse) and also use it to identify any negative inferences and beliefs about your symptom. Once you have identified what type of emotional conflict is underlying your symptom, you can also aim EFT at your WMOMD at those specific moments where this particular conflict is at play.

Start by identifying the specific times of the day when you have the symptom. Look at both what is happening when the symptom is present (or gets worse) and what was going on just before the symptom arose. Often your symptoms are healing symptoms, which means that they occur during the healing phase after you have resolved something. Sometimes they are stress symptoms (arising during the conflict-active phase) so you need to consider what is stressing you out and whether that is still ongoing. Use the information above (including the descriptions of the various conflicts) to better understand what to look for. Address each moment using the WMOMD approach. Once you have reduced the current WMOMD to an intensity below 5, but not yet 0, ask yourself about past experiences:

- When have I felt this kind of emotion before? This helps you to identify specific events in which the conflict occurred in the past.

- How did I learn to think that this is a serious symptom? This identifies specific events in which you learned to think about your symptom in this way.

- Who taught me to be so afraid of what is going on in my body? This again identifies specific events that play a role in the symptom itself, or in perpetuating the symptom.

This approach is similar to the Detective Work Approach, but there is definitely an added value to starting with a present moment in which you feel triggered because you often end up with other specific events that you may not have identified otherwise.

Of course, with Symptom-Focused EFT, you can work on the symptom itself, but that will only get you so far. The symptom may become less intense or even disappear temporarily, but in order to ensure it is completely resolved permanently, it is best to apply EFT to the underlying emotional causes.

3. **Big Cleanup:** Make a list of all the events you have not yet identified with steps 1 and 2. Other events may come up that have nothing to do with your current symptom but use EFT to resolve them anyway. The

more events you resolve, the calmer and more relaxed you will feel. This is always helpful. If you had a stressful childhood (which we all did, to varying degrees), it will continue to have a negative impact on your well-being and health. So, the more you apply EFT, the weaker this impact will be, and the better you will feel.

If you feel anxious or worried about your condition or about a diagnosis you have been given, then neutralize every specific moment in which you felt anxiety or worry, including during conversations with your doctors and therapists, when undergoing medical examinations and awaiting or receiving test results, and when encountering the reactions of others. Include every moment in which you felt startled by what you read, heard or saw related to your diagnosis.

4. **Symptom-Focused EFT:** Use EFT immediately when you experience any intense emotion or physical symptom. If at all possible, make it a specific event and address it completely using the WMOMD approach. You can also use Symptom-Focused EFT on any fear or anxiety you feel about your symptom. You may find this reframe useful: *This is the umpteenth time I have had this, and I have managed to get through it every time.*

N | NEGATIVE LIMITING BELIEFS

In this chapter, we look at how to address negative limiting beliefs with EFT. You cannot work globally on your negative limiting beliefs. This is one of the most frequently made mistakes in EFT. Instead, you need to use the negative limiting belief as a starting point to help you identify the origin of the belief, which is the specific events in which you learned the belief and adopted it as your truth.

If you often think the same negative limiting belief or stressful thought, you are programming yourself every time you think it. Your thoughts have power. Thoughts are not neutral, and there are no idle thoughts. With your thoughts, you plant seeds that can sprout in the future. Your dominant thoughts become your reality. Therefore, it is crucial to be mindful of your thoughts. More importantly, if you notice you are stuck in a pattern of negative thoughts or beliefs, use EFT to weaken and even eliminate them. By now, hopefully, you understand that every problem or issue you are encountering can be formulated as a conclusion or negative limiting belief that you can release with EFT.

For our discussion here, we will use the metaphor of the Table Top and Table Legs, discussed in Part 1. The Table Top is your problem – the conclusion or negative limiting belief. The Table Legs that support the Table Top are the individual specific events that make this conclusion true. Each of these events seems to prove that your conclusion is true. There may be dozens, hundreds, or even thousands of Table Legs, depending on how long a problem with its associated belief (conclusion) has been a part of your life. As explained in Part 1, once you use EFT to resolve a series of related specific events (Table Legs) that are holding up the Table Top, this will weaken the remaining Table Legs (that you have not yet worked on) and destabilize the Table Top, causing it to collapse and the entire issue to resolve completely.

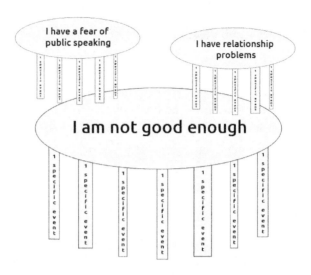

Figure 6. Metaphor of Table Top with Table Legs – Expanded

Negative limiting beliefs are formed because you experience something, interpret it (thus giving it meaning), and draw a conclusion from it or pass judgment on it. The negative belief is true for you and becomes more true every time you repeat the belief in your head. Also, the more you repeat a negative belief over time, the more it generalizes, increasing its influence over more areas of your life. For example, the thought *Pete and Jeff do not like me* may broaden to *My classmates do not like me* and then, with further repetition, it becomes *Nobody likes me* until finally, it becomes a general conclusion that *I am not lovable.* There is always the first moment when you start to form the conclusion, which eventually becomes a belief. While we may not remember the first specific event, we usually understand how we learned most of our beliefs and from whom, often during early childhood from those close to us. You may recall the specific situations involved and often the specific people involved. If you cannot remember the precise details, then you can use your imagination to make up the details, using what you do remember.

The key to resolving a negative limiting belief is to use EFT to neutralize the series of specific events (the thread) that makes the belief true, as explained in detail below. This thread starts with the earliest events, which caused you to draw the conclusion. Then it continues with further events that caused you to draw the same negative conclusion, thus strengthening the belief. Over time, you learned to think this negative limiting belief whenever you encounter certain situations.

EFT Approach

This approach is about addressing the origin of the negative limiting belief, by taking the belief itself as the starting point. We recommend that you use a combination of the WMOMD approach, the Detective Work approach and the Big Cleanup approach:

1. **Negative Limiting Belief (NCB):** Identify the negative limiting belief (the conclusion) on the Table Top. This may be your negative core belief (*I am not good enough* or a variation thereof), or you may choose other more specific beliefs or thoughts, such as *I am a bad father, I will never get a job, I cannot do this, This will never work out, I am ashamed of my mother, Men are scary, I always fall for the wrong guy, I will not survive this, I cannot sing, I will end up in a wheelchair.*

2. **Validity of Cognition (VoC):** The VoC is a useful test to determine the strength of your belief and measure your progress with EFT. Measure the VoC of your belief as follows: Close your eyes and say your belief mindfully and out loud. Then become aware of how true this statement feels emotionally, not how true it is logically. Identify its strength using a scale from 0% (does not feel true at all) to 100% (feels completely true). Write down this number and retest the VoC every 2 to 4 weeks, to determine whether it is decreasing in strength. If necessary, see Chapter 5 of Part 1 for a detailed explanation of the Validity of Cognition (VoC) test.

3. **The WMOMD:** Choose the best example of a relatively recent specific event in which this belief plays a role. The key is to choose a moment when you think the belief. Use the sentence *The moment when X happens and I think Y.* The moment needs to be specific so that you can

point to it in your diary. Make sure you choose a moment in which something is happening because that is easier to work with. You need to visualize exactly where you are, whether you are sitting or standing, who is present and what is happening. The more you can anchor yourself to a concrete moment in which you think the belief, the better.

4. **Detective Work:** Relive the moment in which you think the belief, in an associated way. Do not think about the belief itself or analyze why you are thinking it. When you relive it, identify what you feel about everything that is happening in this particular moment and also what feelings you have while thinking about your belief (i.e. not what you feel when you think about the belief but what you feel while thinking the belief itself). Use EFT to bring down all of the emotions and bodily sensations you experience in this particular moment. When the intensity of all the emotions is lower than 5, but not yet 0, relive the moment again and ask yourself:

- When have I felt and thought this way before?
- How did I learn to think this and who taught me?

If you identify a specific event from the past to work on, use one of the EFT protocols to resolve both the past event and the recent moment you initially identified. Continue to follow this process, ideally every day or a few times a week. By following this process, you can make lists of the specific situations that contributed to the formation of this belief. If all goes well, you will soon discover the period of your life during which you started forming this conclusion and you may even identify the first time you had this thought. Do not worry if you can't remember everything, just work on whatever comes up. Sometimes it can take time. You may need to spend some time neutralizing numerous specific events before the whole series of events that led to the formation of the belief becomes clear to you. Test the VoC of your belief at regular intervals, to measure your progress. Ideally, aim to bring the VoC down to less than 10%, in which case the negative limiting belief will no longer play a significant role in your life.

Additional tips

1. **Getting out of the routine:** If you find yourself in the same daily situation over and over again, thinking the same negative belief, then that moment has become an anchor in itself. For example, you may notice that whenever you sit on the couch in your spot at night or when you wake up in bed in the morning, you think the negative belief and feel the same corresponding emotions. A routine has developed; in that place, you have these kinds of thoughts almost subconsciously. However, the fact that you think your negative belief is not so much related to the place itself. If you really relive the moment properly, you will notice that other thoughts precede the limiting negative belief and the resulting emotions. Notice what are you thinking about right before? If that is a memory, apply EFT to that specific memory in the usual way. It may also be more general, for example, *I feel so alone because I do not have a partner, I do not feel like going to work,* or *I cannot sit on the couch doing nothing.* If that is the case, you still need to figure out which specific situations have given rise to such thoughts:

   - **Regarding the thought of feeling alone:** Identify specific situations from the past in which you feel alone. Also, consider how you learned that you need to have a partner in order to not feel alone. What specific situations does this 'alone feeling' remind you of? Make a note of anything else that is related to feeling alone.

   - **Regarding the thought about your work:** Identify specific situations that make you feel like not going to work. Are there situations in your workplace that cause you stress? Are situations in your personal life involved?

   - **As for the thought about sitting here doing nothing:** Identify specific situations when you learned that you always need to be doing something and consider who taught you to think this way. Then, apply EFT to neutralize any specific events that come up.

2. **Overwhelmed by emotions:** If thinking about a negative belief immediately gives rise to intense emotions (such as sadness, fear or irritation at yourself for thinking it again), then it may be helpful to apply Symptom-Focused EFT to such emotions right away. Rather than neutralizing such emotions completely, we recommend that you apply EFT until the intensity has dropped below 5 but is not yet zero, then ask yourself (while feeling the emotions) when you have had the same thought and feeling before. Apply EFT to whatever moment comes up. If more than one moment comes up, then take time to neutralize those too.

3. **It has yet to happen:** Your belief may also be related to what might happen in the future. You may experience fear because you expect things to happen in a certain way again, or that you will be in pain again. Even in such cases, we still advise you to look back at how you learned this belief. What experiences have caused you to expect this to happen in the future? If you really neutralize those past experiences, the expectation will also disappear. After all, if you do it right, you will clean up the entire stress pattern, which means the link between the trigger and the stress response will no longer work. This takes perseverance because you have to deal with two kinds of specific experiences, both the moments when something stressful happened and you dread re-experiencing it and the moments that taught you to respond in this way.

O | OBSESSIVE-COMPULSIVE DISORDER

Obsessive-Compulsive Disorder (OCD) is a condition where you have unwanted recurring thoughts or fears (obsessions) that lead to repetitive behaviors (compulsions). An obsession creates distress and anxiety, driving you to perform compulsive acts to ease your stress. Your anxiety and fear may subside temporarily, but the bothersome thoughts or urges keep coming back. OCD usually interferes with your ability to perform daily activities and affects your quality of life.

According to mainstream medicine, the cause of OCD is unknown and there is no cure. Some theories and risk factors have been suggested, such as a genetic component (although no specific genes have been identified), that OCD is learned from others, that traumatic experiences may increase the risk of developing OCD, or that it is related to other mental health disorders, such as anxiety disorders. However, no explanation is given as to how OCD develops and no treatment is recommended to address such possible causes. Rather, people with OCD are advised to get treatment to manage their symptoms and prevent OCD from worsening.

In our experience, there is no doubt that OCD is caused by underlying emotional conflicts that develop from specific events that have a negative emotional charge. The symptoms of OCD are often a 'solution' to the underlying conflict, such as nail biting (discussed below). Once you understand the underlying emotional cause of OCD, you can address and resolve it, so that the symptoms disappear.

OCD usually involves two emotional conflicts going on simultaneously. One conflict is related to 'mother or child' and the other conflict is related to 'partner.' See Appendix 5 for an explanation of the 'mother or child' side versus the 'partner' side. The two conflicts usually start at different times in one's life, prior to the onset of the symptoms. Typically, one conflict is running for years, then a second conflict arises, and at that point, the symptoms of OCD arise. While the two simultaneous conflicts are continuing in the conflict-active phase, there are rarely any noticeable physical symptoms but there are usually psychological symptoms. However, once one or both of the underlying conflicts are resolved, the healing phase begins, and that is when noticeable physical symptoms may occur.

In this chapter, we discuss various ways in which people experience OCD and the various emotional conflicts that may have given rise to it. Hopefully, this discussion will help you identify the conflicts and events that are underlying your symptoms so that you can resolve them with EFT.

Obsessive Thoughts

Everyone experiences obsessive thoughts from time to time, but it is usually temporary, such as when you are facing an extremely stressful situation. You may be constantly thinking about the problem as you try to solve it, and you may not be sleeping well, waking up in the middle of the night thinking about it. This is perfectly normal. After a while, once the most intense part of the stressful situation has passed, and you have either solved the problem or enough time has passed so that you are not so worried about it, these types of obsessive thoughts may disappear.

However, when you continue to have these obsessive thoughts and they make you feel so anxious that you are not able to properly function in your daily life, this suggests that they are excessive and may amount to OCD.

Obsessive thoughts may involve fear of contamination or dirt, needing things orderly, the urge to steal or throw things away, fear of harming yourself or others (deliberately or by mistake), fear of shouting obscenities or acting inappropriately, or obsessive thoughts about violent or aggressive sexual behavior.

You need to look for the underlying emotional causes. OCD arises when you are experiencing two conflicts at the same time. Look for negatively charged events where one conflict is related to 'mother or child' issues and the other is related to 'partner' issues.

Many different types of conflicts may be at play, including the following:

- **Fear-Disgust Conflict:** feeling fear and disgust (which may involve dislike, repulsion, or aversion) toward something or someone you perceive as unsanitary, unacceptable, inedible, or otherwise repugnant.
- **Separation Conflict:** wanting or not wanting contact, often skin contact.
- **Territorial Conflict:** fear, loss or annoyance related to your territory (including your possessions, status, time, and body)
- **Shock-Fright or Speechlessness Conflict:** situations that frighten you and often render you speechless.
- **Sexual Conflict:** wanting to have or not to have sex or a relationship.
- **Identity Conflict:** who am I, where do I belong?
- **Territorial Marking Conflict:** being unable (or not daring) to set boundaries.
- **Existential Conflict:** feeling alone, abandoned, isolated, am I allowed to be here?

Compulsive Behavior

Motor Conflicts and Social Conflicts are frequently involved when compulsive behavior is an issue, and they can manifest in different ways. We provide some examples of OCD behaviors below, where the emphasis is on compulsive behavior, as opposed to obsessive thoughts. Often the reason why you behave in a certain way is not conscious, so it can take some perseverance to identify the underlying emotional conflicts at play.

Nail biting: is due to two or more Biting Conflicts going on simultaneously. You may be in a weaker, subordinate position and someone, who is higher in rank, keeps ignoring or overstepping your boundaries. You want to 'bite' this superior or opponent to show them their place but, since that is unacceptable, you start biting your nails instead. Nail biting is very common amongst children and adolescents, who often find themselves in a weaker or lower position in relation to parents, older siblings, teachers, friends or classmates.

Jaw tics: are also rooted in two or more Biting Conflicts - not being able or allowed to bite one's opponent.

Hyperactivity: This is due to Motor Conflicts, which arise when you feel you cannot move or you are stuck in something, either literally or figuratively. The hyperactivity starts when you have two Motor Conflicts running simultaneously. You see this a lot in children. In psychiatry, this is diagnosed as a hyperactive disorder, sometimes as ADHD. The hyperactivity has nothing to do with sugar (which is often claimed to be the cause) but with being stuck. For example, a child may be stuck in a difficult situation either at home (abuse or violence), at school (bullying), in childcare that they do not like or when they are confined to watching TV or even playing computer games for long periods of time. Hyperactivity can occur as early as in utero, when the fetus in the womb feels stuck, especially because of unbearable noises in the immediate vicinity (such as screaming, screeching, sounds of jackhammers, chainsaws, and heavy traffic). As a result, the baby may be born with hyperactivity. A stressful vaccination experience or other medical procedure (being held, not being able to escape) can also lead to hyperactivity in early childhood.

Motor tics: are sudden, brief, repetitive movements that cannot be easily controlled. For example, head jerking, neck pulling, shrugging of shoulders, hand and arm gestures, compulsive touching, or leg movements. These symptoms indicate a Motor Conflict, which is the original conflict situation where a person could not leave and/or felt trapped. The situation may have involved a fight, rape or sexual assault where they wanted to push a perpetrator away, or felt fear because they could not stop someone from hurting them or could not escape. In children, motor tics may stem from being stuck in school or stuck in a difficult family situation (involving abuse or domestic violence). This explains why most children lose their motor tics when they become adults.

Facial tics: may include excessive eye blinking, flaring nostrils, raising eyebrows, opening the mouth or grimacing. They also arise from a Motor Conflict, where one feels stuck and unable to get out of situations accompanied by a loss of face, loss of dignity, shame or being ridiculed.

Obsessive skin picking: is where you cannot stop picking at your skin. It involves a Territorial Anger Conflict (anger towards others at home, school or work) combined with an Identity Conflict (not knowing where you belong or not fitting in).

Stuttering: is the result of a Shock-Fright Conflict or a Speechlessness Conflict in which you are startled (violently) while you are just beginning to talk or say something (so that your voice literally sticks in your throat) in combination with a Territorial Conflict, a (different) Shock-Fright Conflict, a Sexual Conflict or an Identity Conflict. Stuttering is caused by muscle spasms of the larynx. When the stuttering is mild, rhythmic contractions cause the repetition. When the stuttering is severe, there is severe cramping so that no sound can be uttered for a while.

Tourette Syndrome: is a diagnosis given when you have multiple motor and vocal tics. You need to examine the individual symptoms (discussed in this section) to determine the underlying emotional cause.

Vocal tics (or phonic tics): The specific repetitive vocalizations are pointers to the content of the underlying conflict, for example, grunting, squeaking, barking, throat clearing, or complex sounds such as words, phrases or complete sentences. The underlying conflicts are a Shock-Fright or Speechlessness Conflict in combination with a Territorial Anger Conflict.

Combination of Obsessive Thoughts and Compulsive Behavior

Contamination OCD: is an exaggerated fear of dirt and often an obsession with cleaning. You understand very well that your fear is unfounded but you cannot stop yourself because for a moment, it gives you a sense of relief. What is the theme? How does the act keep you safe? This gives clues about the emotionally charged situations that play a role in developing a fear of dirt.

Hoarding: is caused by an Existential Conflict. How and what is collected gives clues as to when it originated and what the theme is.

Checking OCD: is about control anxiety. You doubt whether you did something right and start checking. And then you doubt that again and start checking again, creating a vicious cycle. What is the theme? How does your Checking OCD keep you safe? The content of the thoughts and actions gives clues as to what kind of emotionally charged situations to look for.

Compulsive actions and compulsive thoughts worsen during stress and diminish when you are calmer or distracted. Recurring periods of tics or compulsions with intermittent, symptom-free periods indicate that one or both conflicts have been resolved temporarily.

EFT Approach

When applying EFT to OCD, you need to look for two active conflicts that are running concurrently. Then you need to identify the associated specific events, bearing in mind that one of the conflicts is related to a 'mother or child' issue and the other to a 'partner' issue.

1. **Detective Work:** Create a timeline from the time you were conceived (in the womb) to the present. When did your OCD symptoms start? Make a note of the times when your symptoms are clearly worse (causing you more stress and anxiety). Identify the possible conflicts (using the information above) and then look for the underlying specific events at that time. It may be helpful to ask yourself the following questions:

    • At what point am I experiencing this problem? What is the clearest, best example of a moment when this occurs?

    • When did it start? What stressful issues were at play during that period of my life?

    Identify as many specific events as possible and neutralize them with EFT.

2. **The WMOMD:** Identify a recent moment in which you had the obsessive thought or performed the compulsive behavior (in the last 24-48 hours). While reliving the moment, notice what emotions you feel at that precise moment (not what you think). If these emotions have an intensity above 5, then apply EFT until the intensity is below 5, but not yet 0, and ask yourself when you have felt this way before. The first memory that comes up is relevant. Neutralize it with EFT. Then go back and neutralize the moment you started with. We are not addressing the obsessive thoughts or the compulsive behavior with EFT. Rather, we are neutralizing the emotions and feelings you experience when you have the thoughts or perform the behavior. The more you use the WMOMD approach and apply EFT to both a current moment and an earlier moment, the more you will gain insight into the specific events that are underlying this stress pattern. Each time, you will go further back, until eventually you will be able to identify the original specific events that first gave rise to this stress pattern. The WMOMD approach is an effective way of resolving OCD, as you are neutralizing the origin of your OCD stress pattern (by working on past events), and you are also addressing (and weakening) your daily OCD habits (by working on current events).

3. **Symptom-Focused EFT:** Apply EFT immediately to any intense emotions, such as hopelessness, shame, or sadness you feel when you have an obsessive thought or feel compelled to perform a compulsive behavior. The more you allow yourself time to address these types of emotions thoroughly and neutralize them, the faster you can achieve lasting results.

4. **Big Cleanup:** It is best to be thorough, so we recommend doing a Big Cleanup as well. If you make a list of all of the emotionally charged events in your life and address them with EFT, you will also end up resolving specific events that are underlying your OCD.

If you feel anxious or worried about your diagnosis, neutralize every specific moment in which you feel anxious or worried, including any moments during conversations with your doctors and therapists, when encountering the reactions of others, and in which you felt startled by what you read, heard or saw in relation to your diagnosis.

P | POST-TRAUMATIC STRESS DISORDER

Post-traumatic stress disorder (PTSD) is common and often goes undiagnosed. Many people experience PTSD or PTSD-like symptoms in certain situations but have not been diagnosed as such. Strictly speaking, PTSD is not a disorder because PTSD symptoms can be logically explained by what you have experienced. A disorder is defined as a disturbance of the normal functioning of the mind or body, caused by genetic factors, disease, or trauma. Hamer's insights show us that the mind and body are doing exactly what they should be doing. Your system is intact and PTSD symptoms are learned behavior, a conditioned response to traumatic experiences. However, the symptoms can be very intense and debilitating, disrupting not only your own life but also affecting those around you. Like all consequences of trauma, such symptoms can be resolved with EFT. We always recommend that you seek the help of a well-trained and experienced EFT professional to help you address your PTSD symptoms. Achieving success with EFT requires that you are willing to both cooperate with your EFT therapist and apply EFT by yourself at home on a regular basis, in between sessions.

You may have been struggling with your symptoms for a while and feel that you have tried everything without any significant improvement. We hope this book encourages you to try EFT because it has several important advantages over other treatments. It can be applied gradually so that you are not overwhelmed and re-traumatized by being unnecessarily exposed to intense memories. In addition, you can learn how to apply EFT by yourself, giving you more control over your feelings and ensuring that you do not remain dependent on a therapist. When EFT is applied correctly, it may eventually make medication unnecessary.

Although we always recommend that you seek the help of a well-trained and experienced EFT professional to help you address your PTSD symptoms, this chapter explains how you can apply EFT to your PTSD symptoms by yourself if your symptoms are less severe, provided that you stick to a few basic rules, which we explain below.

Sometimes, PTSD is caused by a single event, like an accident, a complicated birth or an operation. Often, however, there is a series of similar traumatic events, such as child abuse, sexual abuse, bullying at school or violence in a relationship. Certain occupations may pose a greater risk of developing PTSD if there is frequent exposure to life-threatening situations or other trauma, such as military personnel and first responders (paramedics, police officers, firefighters, rescue workers and others).

If you want to apply EFT to a traumatic event on your own, without an EFT practitioner, please ensure you abide by the following rules:

Rule #1: First, learn to apply the WMOMD approach and the Symptom-Focused EFT approach to small everyday triggers, as explained in Steps 1 and 2 below. If you can do that successfully for at least 4 – 6 weeks, then you are ready to move to Step 3.

Rule #2: If it does not feel safe to relive a memory in an associated way as if it is happening right now, then do not do it. EFT, in itself, has no side effects, but when you are working on traumatic events, it is essential to use EFT to take the edge off gradually and keep yourself dissociated until you are able to associate without re-traumatizing yourself and feeling overwhelmed. For that reason, we recommend that you consult an experienced EFT professional to help you process a traumatic event if you have even the slightest suspicion that you may feel overwhelmed by reliving it on your own.

EFT Approach to PTSD Symptoms

You may have various symptoms of PTSD, such as nightmares, flashbacks, high alertness, being easily aroused, mood swings, and so on. We strongly recommend that you do not start applying EFT to your traumatic experiences right away, as noted above. Instead, use EFT to address your daily stress triggers and smaller situations first, as explained below. You can use both forms of EFT and see which one you prefer or alternate between them.

If you feel it is too overwhelming to do the first two steps (WMOMD approach and Symptom Focused EFT) on your own, we recommend that you contact an experienced EFT professional to help you.

1. **The WMOMD:** Every day, apply EFT to the most negatively charged moments of your day. Rather than waiting till the end of the day or even several days later, we strongly encourage you to apply EFT to these moments as soon as possible. Simply excuse yourself and go to a quiet room (or the bathroom, if necessary). Relive the moment and neutralize all negative reactions with EFT, as described in Chapter 2 of Part 1. To start, work only on the daily moments themselves (rather than doing the whole WMOMD approach that includes identifying past events when you felt the same way). If you feel angry, sad, anxious or irritated about the way you react, apply EFT directly to that emotion to bring down the intensity. Take your time. Remember that your reaction is the result of what you experienced and being triggered is beyond your control at this point. This will change and you will soon have more control over your emotional reactions.

   Note: When you apply EFT, you may experience an energy discharge. For example, your legs may shake, or even your whole body. You may also experience an emotional release (causing you to cry) or you may have evoked so much energy that you feel the need to walk or even run. Do whatever feels good. These reactions are perfectly normal and natural. Let them happen. Do not be afraid of your emotional or physical reactions, just keep doing EFT until they subside. When you think you have done enough and you want to stop this release of energy and emotion, then take a break. Just get up and move around, distract yourself and tell yourself you will continue this process at a later time. This is how you turn off the discharge of the stress response. Again, just take your time. You will know that you are done when you are no longer shaking or feeling the compulsion to move and release energy.

2. **Symptom-Focused EFT:** If you are anxious, stressed or angry during the day or night, apply EFT to your emotions immediately until their intensity has subsided sufficiently. Continue doing EFT for up to half an hour at a time. Even if you only reduce the intensity by 1 or 2 points,

you have still made progress. The more often you do it, the greater the effects will be.

Continue to apply Steps 1 and 2 on a daily basis until you feel confident doing it and it is going smoothly. When you notice that you are feeling calmer and your PTSD symptoms and reactions are less severe (or even slightly less), you may choose to start addressing your negative core belief, as described in Step 3 below (in addition to continuing to follow Steps 1 and 2).

3. **Negative Core Belief (NCB):** Identify your negative core belief (if you do not already know what it is). Choose a recent non-traumatic moment in which you are criticized and/or rejected. Relive the moment in an associated way and listen to your inner critic. Is it saying something like *I am not good enough, I do not belong, I should not be here?* If necessary, see Chapter 5 of Part 1 for a detailed explanation of the NCB and the Validity of Cognition (VoC) test. The VoC is a useful test to measure your progress with EFT and determine whether your NCB is losing strength. Measure the VoC of your NCB as follows: Close your eyes and say your NCB mindfully and aloud. Then become aware of how true this statement feels emotionally, not how true it is logically. The scale goes from 0% (not true at all) to 100% (completely true). Write down this number and retest the VoC regularly. Make a habit of applying EFT to everyday situations in which your NCB plays a role. Use the complete WMOMD approach, so that once you have reduced the intensity of your current moment to below 5, but not yet 0, ask yourself when you felt the same way before, and then neutralize the previous experience with EFT. However, as noted above, if you feel that it would be too overwhelming to relive the moment by yourself, then do not do it. Safely park the moment using the Black Box Technique and contact a well-trained EFT practitioner who can help you. If necessary, see Chapter 5 of Part 1 for a detailed explanation of the Black Box Technique.

4. **Big Cleanup for the NCB:** Make lists of specific events with a negative emotional charge from the past that are related to your NCB but NOT to your PTSD. Neutralize them one by one with EFT. Take your time. Address one event every day or several times a week.

Continue applying EFT to your NCB as explained in Steps 3 and 4, for at least a few weeks. Also, keep using EFT as described in Steps 1 and 2. If you apply EFT to all the unpleasant events in which your NCB is activated on a regular basis, then you may start to notice that you are experiencing fewer PTSD symptoms. If that is the case, you can now move on to Step 5 and start working on the underlying causes of your PTSD:

5. **Big Cleanup for the Specific Traumas:** Make a list of the specific traumatic events that may be underlying your PTSD. While making the list, stay as detached as possible. Do not go into (relive) any event as yet. If writing down the title is already triggering you, do Symptom Focused EFT to bring the intensity of your emotions down before continuing with your list. Rule #2 remains in effect: if it does not feel safe, then do not do it. If you feel like you are ready to work on a traumatic event, please follow the specific instructions below. Address one event and finish this one before going to the next. You may not be able to finish this event in one sitting. It may take several days or even weeks to properly neutralize one single event. After working on it for up to approximately one hour, safely park it using the Black Box Technique and continue when you can. Take your time. If you start to feel overwhelmed, safely park the event using the Black Box Technique and contact a well-trained EFT practitioner before proceeding any further.

EFT Approach for a Traumatic Event

Do not start applying EFT to a traumatic event until (I) you have followed Steps 1 through 4 above, (II) your PTSD symptoms have started to decrease in severity and (III) you feel confident and ready. Once you are ready, apply EFT to the event as follows:

1. Decide if you can tackle the event in its entirety or if you have to break it down into parts. For example, you may divide a car accident into smaller moments, such as the actual collision, being stuck in the car and the rescue activities. Each part is a little movie with its own emotional crescendo.

2. Begin by taking the edge off the whole event (as described in Chapters 2 and 5 of Part 1). Notice how you feel when you realize that you are about to go through the event, step by step. If you feel that your stress response is activated, identify the emotions and/or any bodily sensations that come up and apply EFT to each of them, until the intensity is 3 or below, and you feel ready to continue. Whenever you feel any intensity, remind yourself that it is not happening right now, that this is only a memory from the past, and that you are safe now.

3. Keep your eyes open and tell the story aloud (or in your head). Do not relive the moment. Just tell the story, starting at a point in the story when nothing is happening yet. STOP as soon as you feel any intensity or any unsettled feeling, no matter how minor. Again, take the edge off this point in the story: Do EFT with your eyes open until this emotional reaction subsides. If you are using Optimal EFT, you may choose to look with a soft gaze at focus point (rather than close your eyes). If you find Optimal EFT is too difficult, stick to EFT Tapping. Continue working your way through the entire event in this way until you are done. Take your time.

4. Repeat step 3, and start again at the beginning of the story. If the intensity of any emotion is above 3, apply EFT with your eyes open. For anything less than 3, you may close your eyes and watch this one small piece of the story as if looking at yourself in a movie. Do this to stay dissociated. Do NOT relive the moment by stepping into the movie, as if you are in it. Keep your distance and look at yourself, as though you are watching yourself on a screen. Apply EFT until the intensities of all emotions in the moment are 0 and then continue the story. If necessary, repeat this step for the entire event several times until you have neutralized all the moments with your eyes closed while remaining dissociated (looking at yourself in the movie).

5. Repeat step 4, but this time relive each moment of the event in an associated way. Go through the story step by step as you relive each relevant detail in an associated way, as if you were in the movie. Pretend it is happening right NOW. Apply EFT until the intensity of every emotion and bodily sensation in the moment is 0, before continuing to the next

moment. Repeat this process until every moment of the event remains at a 0, as you relive each moment in an associated way.

6. Test the result by really trying your best to stir up any remaining emotional intensity. Test all the different moments in the event by reliving each moment, trying to get any negative emotional reaction, and ask yourself if you can feel any emotional intensity at all. If not, you are finished. If you still feel something, repeat step 5 until every emotion has been completely neutralized, down to 0. Then test once more. Remember that it could take quite a while (days, weeks) to neutralize each moment. Do not be in a hurry, take your time.

R | RECOVERY FROM ADDICTIONS

In this chapter, we discuss addictions, not only to substances but also to habits or behaviors. A person is addicted when they are mentally and/or physically dependent on a substance or behavior and unable to stop using or engaging in it, even though it may be causing psychological and/or physical harm. The person is thus focused on obtaining the substance or partaking in the behavior, at the expense of other activities. Letting go of the addiction is almost always accompanied by severe physical or psychological withdrawal symptoms. Examples of substance addictions include addictions to drugs, alcohol, food, smoking and medication. Examples of behavioral addictions include addictions to gambling, gaming, cell phone, the Internet, sex, relationships and work (workaholic).

Substance addiction usually affects the user's brain as a result of ingredients within the substance which may have stimulating, narcotic, or mind-altering effects. Many addictive substances (such as nicotine, opium and heroin) have a generic effect; in other words, they almost always lead to addiction when used for a long period of time. This is partly due to the change the substance brings about in the dopamine system – the reward system in the brain. Therefore, if such substances are stopped abruptly, this can contribute to the occurrence of withdrawal symptoms. In other cases, a person may also become psychologically addicted to a substance or habit, thinking they need it, even though there is actually no physical dependence.

Sugar can also be addictive. Almost everyone has experienced the sugar high brought about by eating sweets, which can make you feel happy and provide a sense of comfort. As an active substance, sugar is no different from alcohol or amphetamines, in the sense that the effect travels along the same nerve channels and also results in a dopamine rush. The difference, however, is that sugar does not cause physical withdrawal symptoms when abruptly stopped. In any event, there is no doubt that sugar and food addictions can cause major health issues, affecting individuals and society at large.

Root Cause

The root cause of any addiction lies in the negative core belief (NCB) and the negative emotional experiences and feelings that arise from such beliefs. Underlying this, there may be trauma or unmet needs. If there is trauma, the addiction is often used to numb or mask the emotional pain and stress of the trauma. In this case, the NCB may be related to a belief that one cannot cope with life without the addictive substance or behavior. Accordingly, you need to address and resolve the underlying trauma to resolve such an addiction. In the case of unmet needs, the NCB plays a lead role: you believe you are not good enough, lovable enough, worthy enough of attention, a relationship or fulfillment in life. Again, the addiction serves to numb the emotional stress, which in this case arises directly from your NCB. So, if the NCB is the root cause of the addiction, recovering from an addiction entails identifying and resolving any Self-Devaluation Conflicts. It goes without saying that you may also have to address any underlying traumas and other stressful life events, particularly those giving rise to your NCB (in the first 6-7 years of life).

An addiction may also develop because you discover that it (the substance or the habit) relieves your stress. Quite often, you are introduced to the addiction because you see others using or doing it. Or they might even actively promote it as a successful way to feel better and persuade you to try it. It may start quite inconspicuously as a necessary or pleasant distraction from stress, but then you start doing it more and more often and for longer periods of time, until eventually you find that you cannot stop. Sometimes, an addiction may arise in connection with a compulsive disorder, where you feel driven to repeat the habit (your addiction). See section O | Obsessive-Compulsive Disorder for more information on OCD, or section E | Eating Disorders.

Even though you may feel better while you are using the substance or partaking in the behavior, the underlying emotional conflicts have not gone away. They are festering beneath the surface of your consciousness and continue to produce intense emotions, even though you may not consciously experience them. Over time, they may also manifest as 'disease' symptoms within the physical body. You may discover that the rush of adrenaline or euphoric high of the substance or behavior causes you to feel better temporarily and so you want more of it. Unfortunately, the use of the substance or the behavior itself also activates your negative core belief. This becomes a vicious cycle, as giving in to the addiction makes you feel better on the one hand, but on the other, it generates negative feelings about yourself, which drives you to give into the addiction even more.

It can sometimes take a while for your negative core belief, and the role it plays, to become clear. It may be hidden from view by conclusions you have drawn about yourself such as *I am weak, I am a loser,* or *I am a coward* and negative limiting beliefs about the addiction itself, such as *I will never get rid of this* or *Quitting always fails.* Or perhaps your fears run even deeper, as you may subconsciously fear that you will fall into a deep black hole and become overwhelmed by your negative feelings if you stop indulging in your addiction. Whatever the case may be, if you dig deep enough you will eventually arrive at your foundational negative core belief. Everyone has one, as we explained in Chapter 5 of Part 1, but in the case of addictions, your negative core belief has taken on a major role in your life, as has the solution you have resorted to (your addiction). We, therefore, encourage you to use the approaches below to overcome your addiction and regain your freedom.

EFT Approach

The more you use all of the approaches provided here, the faster you will get a hold of your addiction, instead of being controlled by it.

1. **Acceptance:** A successful approach starts with accepting your addiction and accepting yourself. By this, we do not mean giving yourself permission to indulge in the addiction, but acknowledging that the addiction is simply learned behavior that has developed as a result of past negative emotional experiences. If you have taught yourself to behave in a certain way, then you can also unlearn this behavior. If you find yourself resistant to accepting yourself and / or your addiction,

identify exactly what that resistance is. What emotions are coming up? Apply EFT directly to these emotions as they arise. What are your thoughts or beliefs that block this acceptance? More often than not, your negative core belief (NCB) is playing a significant role. Use the strategies explained in section N | Negative Limiting Beliefs to weaken any beliefs that may be blocking you from accepting yourself or your addiction, paying particular attention to your NCB.

NCB: Identify what your negative core belief is if you do not already know it. Choose a moment when you feel completely rejected or criticized, or when someone is upset with you for doing something wrong. Relive the moment in an associated way and listen to your inner critic. Are you saying to yourself, for example, *I am not good enough, I do not belong, I should not be here?* If necessary, see Chapter 5 of Part 1 for a more detailed explanation of negative core beliefs and the Validity of Cognition (VoC) test. Establish the VoC of your NCB. The VoC is a useful test to measure your progress. Measure the VoC as follows: Close your eyes, mindfully repeat your NCB out loud and become aware of how true this statement feels emotionally, not how true it is logically, right now. Assess how true it feels using a scale of 0% (not true at all) to 100% (completely true). Write down this number then start working on your NCB with EFT, using the action plan set out in section N | Negative Limiting Beliefs. Retest the VoC of your NCB with some regularity.

2. **VoC of Your Addiction:** Do a VoC test of your addiction so that you can assess your progress. Close your eyes and mindfully repeat *I am addicted to ...* out loud and become aware of how true this statement feels emotionally, not rationally, right now. The scale goes from 0% (not true at all) to 100% (completely true), as explained above. Write down this number and retest the VoC with some regularity.

3. **Addressing the Immediate Craving With EFT:** As soon as you notice that you want to use it, eat it, smoke it or do it, stop and do EFT first. This takes some willpower but it is essential! The more often you do this, the more effective you will be. Proceed as follows:

a) **Gold Standard EFT:** Score the craving for the addictive substance or behavior between 0 and 10. Tap for one round. Start with the Setup phrase: *Even though I have the craving/ urge to..., I still accept myself.* As you tap around the points, repeat: *This craving/this urge.* Score the craving again. Repeat the Setup phrase and keep tapping until the craving is 0 or so low that you can at least postpone giving in to your addiction for some time.

b) **Optimal EFT:** Score the craving for the addictive substance or behavior between 0 and 10. Meditate and ask The Unseen Therapist to dissolve this craving or urge for you. You may wish to use a metaphor and suggest, for example, how the craving dissolves into light or love. After the meditation, score the craving again and repeat until the craving is 0 or so low that you can at least postpone giving in to your addiction for some time.

The more often you apply one or both of these protocols to your immediate need to satisfy your craving, the weaker and less frequent this urge will become, giving you more control over the vicious cycle of your addiction.

4. **EFT When Things Have Gone Wrong:** To break the vicious cycle of addiction, it is essential to use EFT immediately whenever you fall off the wagon (by indulging in the addiction) and neutralize all the negative feelings and emotions that arise as a result. This is crucial and requires more explanation. If you get angry at yourself or feel like a failure because you gave in to your craving again, you keep yourself trapped in a vicious cycle and achieve the opposite of what you want. Beating up on yourself makes things worse, not better. When you process and release your emotions (anger, sadness, powerlessness, etc.), you are not letting yourself off the hook. You are just neutralizing the negative emotions and that will make you feel better. Holding onto guilt, shame and other negative emotions will only make you feel worse, which means you will be more likely to indulge in your addiction, in order to make yourself feel better.

5. **The WMOMD:** Identify any moment during your day when you feel the craving. Note the role of your NCB and any social triggers. Apply

EFT to this moment and, once the intensity drops below 5, but not yet 0, ask yourself when you felt like this before, then apply EFT to that earlier specific moment. Neutralize that moment, then return to the worst moment of your day and completely neutralize that as well.

6. **Subconscious Resistance to Quitting:** Pay attention to any resistance to quit the addiction, which may be subconscious. After all, the addiction solves a problem, as it helps relieve feelings of intense tension caused by triggers that activate your negative core belief. The following questions can help you identify the nature of your resistance. What is the downside of quitting?

    - What will I lose if I do not have my addiction anymore?
    - What am I afraid of?
    - What will I miss?

    If specific situations come up, work on them with one of the EFT protocols, to release their emotional charge.

7. **Symptom-Focused EFT:** Apply EFT to any withdrawal symptoms (abstinence symptoms). Withdrawal symptoms are symptoms that can occur after discontinuing or not taking a substance you are psychologically and/or physically addicted to. Sometimes an out-of-control habit, such as gambling or using the Internet, can also lead to withdrawal symptoms. Even if there are no withdrawal symptoms per se, there may be an almost uncontrollable urge to give in to the addiction. Address this urge with EFT, as described above in point 3.

8. **Detective Work:** Create a timeline. When did the addiction start? What was going on in your life at that time? Use these questions to uncover the origin of your addiction. Make lists of specific events from each answer. If there are many events during a particular time in your life, make a list of the top 10 or 20 events. Ask yourself:

    - How did I learn this habit? Who did I learn this from?
    - When was the first time I indulged in this addictive substance / behavior?
    - When did the addiction start? What was going on in that period of my life?

- Did I develop the addiction as a substitute for an unmet need, such as a need for intimacy, connection or healing? Did I undergo traumas in my past that cut me off from intimate relationships, causing me to turn to food or alcohol or some other substance to help me feel better? If so, what are those events?
- What beliefs play a role? When and from whom did I learn them?
- Are there times when I tried to quit but failed? If so, why?
- Who has a negative influence on my addiction?

9. **Big Cleanup:** This is important. Go through your past with a fine-toothed comb, identify all negative experiences and neutralize them with EFT. If there are many experiences of the same type on your list, make a list of the top 10 or 20 events. This will undoubtedly include many situations in which your NCB played a significant role. The more you use the Big Cleanup approach to release the negative emotional charge of your past experiences, the better you will feel, and the less likely you will feel the urge to indulge in your addiction.

Finally, overcoming an addiction begins with the decision to be free (rather than simply an attempt to quit). So focus on the feeling of liberation and the power you will enjoy, by gaining control over your mind and your actions.

S | SLEEP DISORDERS

In this chapter, we will explain how to apply EFT to the emotional causes of insomnia. Needless to say, the underlying cause of all sleep disorders, including insomnia, is stress. When your nervous system is in balance, your sympathetic stress response is slightly more activated during the day, because you are active, physically and/or mentally. During the night while you rest and sleep, your parasympathetic (or relaxation) response is more activated to enable you to recover from the stress of the day. Sleep is thus essential to keep your nervous system balanced. However, contrary to what you may think, it is normal to wake up several times a night and then go back to sleep. No one remains asleep all through the night, although it may seem that way if you do not remember waking up for short periods of time. The amount of sleep you need is unique to you – there is no optimal sleep duration. The key is to simply be aware of how you feel during the day. If you are sleepy or feel tired, then you need more sleep. If you use EFT to address your daily stress triggers and let go of any stress that you have about sleeping (or not sleeping), then a balanced sleep pattern will naturally emerge.

You may sleep poorly when you are in the middle of an acute conflict situation. All types of emotional conflicts mentioned in this book can cause stress during the conflict-active phase, while you are trying to resolve a conflict. In this sense, poor sleep is a general symptom of the stress phase. When you are dealing with an extremely stressful situation, you may constantly be thinking about the problem and trying to solve it. You may feel as if you cannot stop thinking about it, night and day. As a result, you may find it hard to fall asleep, your sleep may be shallow, you may wake up in the middle of the night thinking about your problem(s), and you may wake up earlier than normal. This is a natural biological response to conflict, which is designed to keep you awake so you can resolve the conflict. In other words, there is a good reason why we experience these symptoms – the extra waking hours and the total focus on the problem increase the chance that we will find a resolution to the conflict, sooner rather than later. Once you have resolved the problem or enough time has passed, your regular sleep pattern will return.

You may also be sleeping poorly due to stressful situations that have continued for such a long time that you have developed a belief that you will never sleep well again. The longer the period of stress and poor sleep, the stronger this belief becomes. It is no wonder that you then start to worry about your ability to get a good night's sleep, thinking at night *If only I can sleep* and in the morning *If only I can get through the day.* Thus, the experience of sleeping poorly perpetuates poor sleeping patterns by creating a negative thought pattern, just as any series of experiences can feed a stress pattern. In addition, the long-term use of sleep medication may give rise to the belief that you cannot sleep without it. After all, once you stop using it, the sleep problems return, because you have not yet addressed the underlying causes of the poor sleeping patterns.

You may also have problems sleeping if your nervous system is on high alert, even though you are not currently facing any particularly stressful problems. This may occur when recent situations subconsciously remind you of stressful past events, in which you needed the stress response and ended up sleeping poorly. This may occur even though the recent situations do not seem to have anything to do with the past. For example, you may sleep poorly now because a current situation subconsciously reminds you of your parents fighting when you were a child (while you were in your bed, feeling upset and therefore unable to sleep). You may also sleep poorly following a stressful period in your life, during which you were required to stay on constant alert. That subconscious instinct to stay alert may not go away because you are constantly triggered by new, similar situations that remind you of that past stress. Examples include: sleeping poorly since the birth of a child (because you felt the need to stay alert at night, to tend to your child's needs) or following a period of illness that activated a fear of sleeping (as falling asleep may remind you of losing consciousness or going under general anesthesia or it may activate your fear of dying).

Another reason for sleeping poorly is that you may be going through an intense healing phase. During the day, you may feel tired and long for your bed, but once you finally get to bed, you may find that you cannot fall asleep until the early hours of the morning, causing you to feel tired again the next day. This is a natural reaction of the body and it is designed to ensure that you do not go too deeply into the parasympathetic phase (of rest and recovery) at night so that your healing symptoms are not too intense. If you are encountering this problem, the best thing to do is to take a nap during the day or try this seemingly paradoxical approach: drink a small cup of coffee about an hour before going to bed(!). The caffeine will activate the sympathetic nervous system (stress response) for a while and, by doing so, you will fool your system because it will seem like it is still daytime. This removes the sleep impediment.

EFT Approach

Below are the key approaches we recommend to address insomnia:

1. **The WMOMD:** Identify your worst moments of the day (in which you feel stressed) and address them with EFT during the day, well before you go to bed. Once you reduce the intensity of an event to below 5, but not yet 0, look for previous experiences in which you experienced similar emotions. By taking the time to identify your daily stressful moments, you will become more aware of what is stressing you during the day so you can then take steps to resolve such stresses, both with EFT and other practical means. If you can resolve your stresses and be in a reasonably relaxed state during the day, you will usually sleep better at night. Often you may not be aware that you are stressed, in which case we recommend that you become more mindful about how you feel during the day and check whether you have felt any stress (even mild stress) that you had not noticed previously. The day itself may feel relatively peaceful, but if you look carefully at your WMOMD moments (however mild), you may discover that old stress patterns in the background play a more significant role in your insomnia than you realized. By becoming more aware of these stress patterns and addressing them with EFT, you may notice these stress patterns weaken and your sleep improves.

2. **Symptom-Focused EFT:** Pay close attention to the moments in which you experience any emotions about your sleep issues. As soon as you feel any sense of agitation or anxiety, address the emotion with EFT. If you wake up at night, immediately note your first thoughts. What are they about? If they relate to a problem, identify which specific moments need to be addressed. Is it a problem at work or with another person? Did you have a nightmare? Or is your first thought about sleeping itself? Use EFT to address any fear that you will not be able to fall asleep again, that you will wake up too early or cannot sleep through the night, or that you will be very tired the next day and will not be able to do what you need to do. You may feel powerless because you cannot fix your sleep problem, afraid that it will never go away or that too little sleep is unhealthy, or angry that it is happening again now that it is the weekend. Think the thought and feel what emotion comes up, then work on that emotion with EFT. If previous memories come up, be sure to work on them too. You may want to keep it simple at night and gently use EFT to address your feelings until you get sleepy again. If anything comes up that needs more attention, either commit it to memory or write it down and make time to work on it the next day.

Tip: We recommend that you do not apply EFT to your problems (and past specific events) during the night while in bed. Keep your bed a safe place to sleep. If you need to work on a problem during the night, it is best to get out of bed and work on it somewhere else.

3. **Detective Work:** It is essential to identify not only the origin of your sleep problem but also the origin of any beliefs and expectations you may have about sleeping. Use questions, such as:

- When did this sleep problem start? What was going on in my life at that time?
- From whom or from what experience did I learn that I need to stay alert at night?
- How did I learn to sleep so lightly?
- Did I have a previous stressful period during which I had a disrupted sleep pattern? What was going on at that time? What beliefs did I

retain from that period? Is there anything in my current life that (subconsciously) reminds me of that period?

- What beliefs do I have about sleep that do not serve me (by simply adding to my anxiety)?

Make a list of any related specific events and address them with EFT.

4. **Big Cleanup:** Apply EFT to any emotional events from your past that come to mind. Unresolved emotions about past events affect your daily stress levels more than you realize. The calmer you feel during the day, the better you will sleep at night!

T | TINNITUS

Tinnitus is a symptom of an auditory conflict that occurs when you hear something you do not want to hear. The conflict may be triggered by annoying or upsetting words, giving rise to thoughts such as *I cannot believe what I am hearing* or *What I am hearing cannot be true, it must be a lie.* Or it may be triggered by aggravating noises such as a screaming child, barking dog, construction noise, traffic noise, noisy neighbors, a nagging voice, or loud or annoying music. Also, keep in mind that such conflicts may arise during a phone conversation.

Tinnitus is characterized by a loss of function of the inner ear, resulting either in deafness and/or perceiving a noise, such as ringing, whistling, buzzing, hissing or humming. The biological purpose of tinnitus is to block out the undesired sound or noise by distracting you, so you do not hear it. Tinnitus occurs during the conflict-active phase, which means that you are under active stress, and thus the cause is still present. Once the conflict is resolved, there may be sudden short-term deafness, as though your ear suddenly closes and then opens again. With hanging healing or many relapses, your hearing may deteriorate. Phrases or songs that get stuck in your head have the same goal as tinnitus, to distract you from having to hear something.

Tinnitus is a clear example of a symptom becoming a trigger for the same type of conflict. Tinnitus is originally triggered by hearing something externally that you did not want to hear. It then gives rise to a sound inside your head that you also do not want to hear and that gives you a lot of stress. The internal sound results in another auditory conflict about the tinnitus itself, making the tinnitus worse and thus creating a vicious cycle.

Whether your left or your right ear is affected is meaningful. For those who are right-clapping, tinnitus in the left ear means that the conflict has to do with 'mother or child,' and tinnitus in the right ear indicates a conflict with other social 'partners.' In left-clapping people, it is the other way around.

See Appendix 5 for an explanation of conflicts that are related to 'mother or child' versus 'partner' and how to determine whether you are biologically left or right-handed (which can usually be determined by the clapping test). If you have tinnitus in both ears, there are multiple conflicts at play related to 'mother or child' as well as other 'partners.' Often, but not always, there is a difference in the intensity of the tinnitus between the two ears.

Note: You may notice some internal sounds in your head when you are in an extremely quiet place. It is normal to hear some sounds such as the beating of your heart, the movement of your blood and other sounds. Thus, not all sounds are indications of tinnitus.

EFT Approach

First and foremost, your beliefs about tinnitus are a key consideration. If you believe that the tinnitus will not go away, or that it will take a long time to heal, then you need to weaken (and ideally eliminate) those beliefs with EFT, otherwise, they will hinder your ability to resolve it. It is our experience that focusing entirely on the symptom (that is, the internal noise) is not the best way to resolve tinnitus. We do recommend that you apply EFT to the symptom, but it is essential to move beyond the belief that nothing can be done about it. Again, information from the Internet, doctors and others plays a negative role, as it instills self-limiting beliefs about your prognosis, which then become additional blocks that you need to address with EFT.

To resolve tinnitus, you need to neutralize any negative emotions that arise when you hear the irritating sound in your head, as well as any emotional reaction to the original sound that triggered the tinnitus to begin with.

1. **Detective Work:** When did the tinnitus start? What did you hear immediately before you noticed any internal sound? Look for any possible hearing conflicts as mentioned above and identify the specific moments in which you heard a sound that you found irritating or stressful. Also, take note of any situations where you hear something again, for example, the repetition of sentences or words or a song. If

you are afraid that you may have damaged your hearing (for example, by standing too close to loudspeakers at a concert), such fear can perpetuate tinnitus, because every time you subconsciously think back to that event, you start to worry. Your thoughts and memories of the event can then become a trigger, keeping you in a conflict active state. In addition, use EFT to neutralize any stressful moments when you hear, see or read information about tinnitus so that you address any unhelpful beliefs as well. Also, work on all the specific moments that contribute to any fearful thoughts or beliefs about tinnitus.

2. **Symptom-Focused EFT:** Do EFT on all your emotional reactions to the tinnitus noise itself. Become aware of any fear, panic, irritation, frustration, hopelessness or anxiety. Remind yourself that this is a temporary symptom, but in order to break the vicious cycle, you need to resolve your emotional response to the internal sound that you are hearing. So, as often as possible, work on your emotions about the tinnitus as soon as you become aware of them. Also, several times a day, sit down in a quiet place, listen to the noise in your head and resolve any emotions that come up in relation to it. Also, if you practice Optimal EFT, meditate with The Unseen Therapist and ask Her to help you step out of this cycle. The moment you can truly say *I do not mind, I am completely neutral about the sound I hear in my head,* that is the moment it will go away.

3. **The WMOMD:** Identify any specific moments during your day in which you notice the tinnitus getting louder and, if possible, apply EFT to them immediately. Aim EFT at your emotions about what is happening in the specific moment. Look for any possible auditory conflicts as mentioned above. If possible, also identify any specific moments in which the tinnitus noise decreases or goes away and ask yourself whether you just resolved an auditory conflict. If so, make a note of that conflict, identify any specific events related to it and work on them with EFT, to ensure that the conflict is completely resolved. As often as possible, search for earlier specific moments once you have reduced the intensity of your WMOMD to less than 5, but not yet 0. Neutralize such moments, then return to your WMOMD and neutralize that as well.

4. **Big Cleanup:** Use this approach as a final sweep to neutralize any other emotionally charged memories.

If you have any fears or worries about having tinnitus, neutralize any specific moments related to it such as any conversations with doctors or therapists, hearing tests and discussions about your hearing, the reactions of others to your symptoms, and any moment when you were or are startled by what you read, heard, or saw in relation to the diagnosis.

V | VERY FORGETFUL (DEMENTIA)

In this chapter, we want to look at the emotional causes of dementia and Alzheimer's disease, as well as lighter forms of forgetfulness. Several conflicts are involved in these types of symptoms.

Separation Conflict

Extreme forgetfulness (which may lead to a diagnosis of dementia or Alzheimer's disease) arises because of multiple Separation Conflicts that are both chronic and active.

A Separation Conflict usually involves skin contact, feeling like you want contact (often skin contact) but you are not getting it, or that you do not want such contact but you are getting it. It concerns all forms of contact and touch by people, animals and things.

Many elderly people in our society are faced with multiple Separation Conflicts. They may lose their life-long spouse, family members and/or friends, they may have little or no contact with immediate family (children or grandchildren) and/or they may have no choice but to move into a senior care or nursing home.

A Separation Conflict produces short-term memory loss during the conflict-active phase. The biological purpose of short-term memory loss is to block out the emotional distress caused by the Separation Conflict, so the person is better able to cope with the separation. This forgetfulness continues until the healing crisis (the peak of the healing phase, illustrated in the graph in Figure 7, Chapter 5 of Part 1). In humans, short-term memory loss is almost imperceptible if there is only one Separation Conflict. In animals, however, there is pronounced memory loss that can quickly result in the animal forgetting about the conflict. Thus, they may no longer recognize their young after being separated from them for a few days, or sometimes after only a few hours.

291

Separation Conflicts may also produce symptoms in the skin and, again, the symptoms often go unnoticed during the conflict-active phase. The skin at the affected site may feel cold, rough, or pale due to a lack of blood supply to the area, and there may be reduced sensitivity (which mainstream medicine calls neurodermatitis). In the healing phase, there may be a rash and the reduced sensitivity may continue during the first half of the healing phase. Quite often, there is itching in the healing phase, as the skin 'cries out' to be touched. See section Z | Zits and Other Skin Problems.

When multiple, intense Separation Conflicts related to both 'mother or child' and other 'partners' are involved, the short-term memory loss may become more pronounced and may give rise to severe memory loss (which is diagnosed by mainstream medicine as dementia). See Appendix 5 for an explanation of the 'mother or child' side versus the 'partner' side.

Existential Conflict

With dementia or Alzheimer's disease, several Existential Conflicts and Separation Conflicts are active at the same time. The Existential Conflicts are the cause of the confusion and disorientation in time, space, place and person and, as stated above, the Separation Conflicts are the cause of forgetfulness. In addition, one or more of the following physical symptoms may be present: reduced urination, puffy eyes and swelling in the hands, feet and/or lower legs.

An Existential Conflict may arise when you fear for your life, feeling like your physical existence is threatened and you may not survive. It may also arise when you are driven from your home (like a refugee) or when you do not feel at home, as though you do not belong. You may feel abandoned, isolated and alone, or like a fish out of water because you have been separated from the pack. For instance, you may experience an Existential Conflict after receiving a diagnosis shock where you feel *I will not survive this*. Or this conflict may arise when you are hospitalized, because you may fear for your life and feel alone and separated from your loved ones. You may feel your physical existence is threatened if you lose your home, your job or a loved one who has taken care of you. You may also experience such a conflict if you have to leave your home or your country, like a refugee.

Again, these types of conflicts are commonly encountered by elderly people in Western societies, and more recently in the East as well. A well-known phenomenon is sudden confusion that can occur during hospitalization, which usually disappears after being discharged.

Milder Forms of Separation and Existential Conflicts

You may also experience Separation and Existential Conflicts in milder forms. The symptoms tend to be more transient, as the underlying stress is less severe, so the conflicts do not lead to a permanent condition. When you experience such milder forms, it is more difficult to distinguish between mild memory impairment (which is caused by a Separation Conflict) and a sense of disorientation in time, place and person (which is a sign of an Existential Conflict). Examples of mild symptoms include: lacking a clear sense of what you want, lacking direction and purpose, difficulty making decisions, not having an opinion of your own, not being able to think about something (feeling blocked, not knowing what line of thought to follow), not being able to find your way around in an unfamiliar environment (like a new city), confusion about left and right, mixing up c and s or other letters, confusing certain numbers (for example 67 and 76), and struggling to find the right word.

EFT Approach

If the short-term memory loss and the level of disorientation are severe (resulting in dementia or Alzheimer's), it may not be possible for the person suffering from such symptoms to do EFT themselves. Also, it will not always be realistic to resolve the Separation Conflicts and Existential Conflicts in a practical manner that would aid the recovery process.

However, if you are reading this because someone close to you is experiencing the early stages of these types of symptoms, you can do EFT surrogately for them. See Chapter 5 of Part 1 for an explanation of how to do that. In addition to doing EFT, it would be extremely beneficial to do practical things to alleviate their sense of loneliness and abandonment. We highly recommend that you take all steps possible to help them not feel so alone and abandoned.

In the case of early-stage symptoms, address the underlying emotional conflicts with EFT and take specific steps to alleviate the loneliness to try to stop the process of forgetfulness from continuing and clear up the symptoms. If you experience mild symptoms of forgetfulness yourself, you can follow the same approach outlined below.

1. **Detective Work:** Look for any situations that involve a Separation Conflict or Existential Conflict, as described above. Make a list of the specific events and use EFT to neutralize each event.

2. **The WMOMD:** Identify any situations where you become aware that the forgetfulness or confusion is getting worse and identify whether a Separation or Existential Conflict is playing a role. Address these specific moments with EFT. As often as possible, once you have reduced the intensity of a specific moment to below 5 but not yet zero, ask yourself whether you have felt like this before. Apply EFT to any earlier specific events that come up. This process will help to reveal any related specific events (including early childhood experiences) that may play a role in this stress pattern.

3. **Big Cleanup:** Use this as a final sweep to neutralize anything you have not identified yet using the above two approaches. If there are many similar experiences with a particular person or thing, then make a list of the top 10 or 20 specific moments and address those with EFT first. Once you have done that, consider whether any similar specific events still have an emotional charge and neutralize those as well.

4. **Symptom-Focused EFT:** Use either EFT protocol to address any acute anxiety, sadness, or anger you may feel. By applying EFT in this way, you are reducing your stress load, so it will help you feel better, even if you are not resolving the entire stress pattern. You can also do this surrogately for another person.

W | WHIPLASH

In this chapter, we explain how to apply EFT to whiplash. Whiplash is a neck injury that may occur when a sudden, forceful back-and-forth movement strains your neck, potentially causing damage to bones, muscles, ligaments and nerves. Symptoms may include a stiff and painful neck and headaches. There may also be temporary concussion symptoms, including dizziness and problems with memory, concentration, balance and coordination. Whiplash is usually caused by car accidents, but it may also result from falls where the neck violently jerks backward, contact sports (such as football or boxing), horseback riding accidents, motorcycle crashes and physical abuse. The symptoms are usually short lived, lasting only a couple of days or a few weeks. However, some people experience chronic neck pain and/or headaches that continue for months or even years after the event that caused the initial injury. People who suffer from chronic pain may also experience poor sleep, emotional instability, hypersensitivity to light and sound, difficulty concentrating, memory problems and dizziness, which are also attributed to the whiplash. It is striking that the severity of the symptoms is often disproportionate to the impact of the initial incident.

Typically, conventional medicine cannot offer any explanation for chronic symptoms following a whiplash injury. Many publications report that no (permanent) brain damage is found. In our experience, negative limiting beliefs play a major role when whiplash symptoms become chronic.

Below is a structured approach you can use to apply EFT to your whiplash that addresses all aspects of the initial incident, any diagnosis or prognosis shock, consequences following the incident, your negative core belief and any underlying stress patterns. If you resolve these with EFT, there is a high likelihood that your whiplash symptoms may disappear.

EFT Approach

1. **Addressing the Traumatic Incident Itself:** Go through the entire incident that caused the initial injury step by step and neutralize each moment with EFT. If it is a very intense traumatic event, follow the instructions given in section P | Post Traumatic Stress Disorder. In addition to the emotional shock of the incident itself, it is essential to address all of the emotions you feel about your role (such as anger or guilt) and any emotions you feel toward others, including anyone who you consider caused the incident, other road users, the emergency responders, or any other relevant person. Neutralize any specific moments that have an emotional charge with EFT.

2. **Addressing the Consequences:** Neutralize any specific events surrounding the consequences of the incident that caused the initial injury. Make a list of every charged moment, including conversations with doctors, therapists and other medical personnel, visits to the hospital, dealings with insurance companies and attorneys, and so on. Pay particular attention to any diagnosis and prognosis shocks you may have experienced during conversations with doctors or while doing research on the Internet or elsewhere. Also, consider the emotional impact of any stories you heard from others with similar complaints that may have shocked or worried you. Neutralize the emotional charge of all of these moments with EFT.

3. **The WMOMD:** Identify the most stressful moments of your day, both those related to your symptoms as well as other moments. Address each moment with EFT and, as often as possible, take the time to search for earlier experiences. Do this once you have reduced the intensity of the WMOMD to lower than 5 but not yet 0. Then relive the moment again and ask yourself when you have felt the same way before. The more you do this, the easier you will be able to identify whether other stress patterns have been triggered either by the incident or by the symptoms themselves. Apply EFT to any past events that come up, and if you identify a stress pattern, take the time to break it down into specific moments and address them with EFT one by one. Then return to the

WMOMD and continue to work on it with EFT, until the emotional charge is completely neutralized.

4. **Addressing your Negative Core Belief (NCB):** As explained in section B | Bones, musculoskeletal symptoms may be related to Self-Devaluation Conflicts. Even though your neck problems may have arisen after a whiplash injury, there may be underlying Self Devaluation Conflicts at play if the symptoms persist for more than 4-6 weeks. Your neck may be weakened by these underlying conflicts, and therefore the residual symptoms may be more intense than the incident itself warrants. The types of Self-Devaluation Conflicts that show up in the neck area are moral-intellectual Self-Devaluation Conflicts. Such conflicts may involve a perceived injustice, dissatisfaction, lack of freedom, dishonesty, ingratitude, indecency, intolerance or disloyalty. They may also arise if you feel stupid or not intelligent enough, if you are never happy with what you have achieved, or if you are overly ambitious, causing you to set the bar too high. The Self-Devaluation Conflicts may also be related to the incident itself, particularly if you blame yourself for contributing to the incident. In fact, your self-blame may play a bigger role in your injury than the impact of the whiplash itself. The incident may also trigger a stress pattern. Do your best to identify as many specific moments as possible that involve these types of conflicts and neutralize them with EFT.

5. **Other Considerations:** If you have long-term symptoms attributed to whiplash, we recommend that you take stock of what is going on in your life right now. What are you stressed about in your personal life, your work, your education or any other area? Is anything holding you back from healing? What would happen if you no longer had any symptoms? Are the symptoms helping you in any way by giving you an excuse for not doing something (like going back to work) or not confronting a problem, or by ensuring that others give you care and attention that you may otherwise not receive? Resistance to healing is often subconscious, so do your best to let go of any feelings of self-blame or guilt that you are somehow responsible for your condition. Do a thorough, honest inventory, as this may reveal other emotional

causes (which you have not previously considered or even been aware of) that may be contributing to your persistent symptoms. Neutralize any specific events that come up with EFT.

X | XEROPHTHALMIA (DRY EYES) AND OTHER EYE SYMPTOMS

In this chapter, we discuss various symptoms which can affect the eyes and how to address them with EFT, starting with xerophthalmia, a medical term to describe dry eyes. Dry eyes are a general symptom of the stress response. We also discuss conjunctivitis, keratoconus, gray cataracts, glaucoma, and macular degeneration.

Xerophthalmia (also known as keratoconjunctivitis sicca): The most common cause of dry eyes is chronic stress. When the sympathetic stress response is activated, tear fluid production (like saliva production) decreases because tears (and saliva) are not immediately required to save the body in a life-threatening situation. The production of tear fluid returns to normal when you enter the parasympathetic recovery phase, but you may experience a period of watery eyes at the beginning of this phase. When you are in a balanced state, meaning a normal day-night rhythm of sympathetic and parasympathetic activity, the tear glands produce the right amount of fluid to keep your eyes moist and to clean and nourish the conjunctiva (a thin membrane that protects your eye).

In addition to being a general symptom of the stress response (in which any conflict may be at play), there is also a specific underlying conflict that gives rise to dry eyes, namely a Chunk Conflict. You may experience a visual Chunk Conflict (that is, a Chunk Conflict relating to your eyes and vision) when you cannot see something that you want to see (which would manifest in the right eye) or when you see something unpleasant that you do not want to see (which would manifest in your left eye). This type of conflict is also the underlying cause of dry eyes experienced by those diagnosed with either Sjögren's syndrome (characterized by dry eyes and a dry mouth) or cystic fibrosis of the tear glands. If you experience dry eyes for more than 2 to 4 weeks, this suggests that there are either recurring visual Chunk Conflicts or you are in a hanging healing phase of such a conflict. If this continues, it will cause more and more scar tissue in the tear glands, resulting in less tear fluid production over time. This effect is permanent, so it is important to address these conflicts as soon as possible.

Conjunctivitis: If the whites of your eyes are red and inflamed, you are in the healing phase of a visual Separation Conflict. You may suffer such a conflict when you lose sight of (or lose 'eye contact' with) a loved one or a pet. Even though this symptom indicates that you are in the healing phase of such a conflict, you still need to apply EFT to the conflict (by neutralizing the emotional charge of the specific events giving rise to it), to make sure that the conflict is completely resolved and does not recur. As with other conflicts, you usually do not experience any noticeable symptoms during the conflict-active phase.

Keratoconus (cone-shaped bulging of the cornea): Keratoconus occurs as a result of prolonged or intense and/or frequently recurring visual Separation Conflicts. During the conflict active phase of such conflicts, there is thinning of the cornea. Keratoconus develops during the healing phase. Due to the recurrent conflicts, the healing phase is constantly interrupted and thus the cornea is not able to fully recover.

Gray cataracts: Gray cataracts develop due to repetitive healing phases of intense visual Separation Conflicts (which involve many visual triggers and relapses). They commonly occur in older people who see more and more of their loved ones pass away, and often tend to see their extended family less frequently. Either (or both) of these situations can give rise to ongoing Separation Conflicts.

Glaucoma: This may arise during the conflict-active phase of a visual Chunk Conflict (described above) or the healing phase of a Fear of Rear Attack Conflict (where you are afraid of being attacked from behind, by someone or something, or by some invisible danger that cannot be avoided). Identify which conflict is at play and then identify and resolve the specific events giving rise to the conflict with EFT, so that you either resolve the Chunk Conflict or avoid a recurrence of the Fear of Rear Attack Conflict.

Macular degeneration: This may arise during the conflict-active phase of a Fear of Rear Attack Conflict (described above), but it is usually specifically related to negative expectations about the future and may also involve self-devaluation, guilt, shame or disgrace. Identify the underlying emotional causes as soon as possible and resolve them with EFT, to avoid any further degeneration.

EFT Approach

With respect to symptoms that arise during the healing phase, there is no need to do anything immediately other than get through this phase as best you can, so your body can heal. However, once you have sufficiently recovered, then you need to make sure that the underlying conflict is completely resolved (to prevent a recurrence) and also address your emotional response to any vision problems that have developed. With regard to the underlying conflict, remember that you have most likely only resolved a recent conflict, and you may be triggered again by the same person or thing, resulting in another conflict. If your vision is impaired or blurred, this in itself can give rise to a visual Chunk Conflict and may result in you getting stuck in a hanging healing phase or relapsing into the conflict-active phase. It is therefore important to address any feelings of fear or anxiety that you may have about your impaired vision and any pain or discomfort you are experiencing, as these can be triggers in and of themselves.

1. **Big Cleanup Focusing on the Diagnosis:** Address all your fears and worries about the diagnosis with EFT. Make a list of all the specific events related to the diagnosis, any medical examinations or treatments, and any diagnosis shocks and prognosis shocks. Also, pay attention to your emotional reaction to other people's stories, information you found on the Internet, and so on. Neutralize any negative emotional reactions that come up.

2. **The WMOMD:** Use this approach to address all the stressful moments of your day with EFT, so that you can bring yourself into a state of peace as often as possible. Wait until your eye symptoms have improved significantly before you start working on past specific events.

   • Identify any specific moment that triggers you into worrying about the symptoms. These would typically be moments when you notice your impaired vision. Other moments could be when you worry about the information you have received from doctors or others. Do be aware of the stressful effect of information found on the internet. Neutralize any such moments with EFT.

- After you have completed the healing phase and your symptoms are gone, continue to use the WMOMD approach to keep resolving your daily stressful moments, paying particular attention to any visual conflicts and triggers. When searching for related past events (after reducing the intensity of the current event to below 5, but not yet 0), also consider whether your negative core belief plays a role, and if so, take the time to weaken this important stress pattern with EFT.

3. **Detective Work:** Create a timeline. When did the symptoms start? Once you have identified the relevant underlying conflict (using the descriptions above), use the following questions to help you identify the specific stressful events that need to be resolved with EFT:

- When do I experience this conflict? What is the clearest, best example of a moment when this conflict is at play? When was the first time?

- What does it remind me of? What similar emotions and situations did I experience during my childhood?

4. **Big Cleanup:** Make a list of any negatively charged memories and events from the past. The Big Cleanup approach helps you to let go of the past, allowing you to feel a sense of inner peace. Aim to clear as many events as possible, not only those involving visual conflicts.

Z | ZITS AND OTHER SKIN PROBLEMS

In this chapter, we will look at the underlying causes of skin problems and how to resolve them with EFT. The skin is our largest organ. It is the physical boundary between ourselves and our environment and through it, we make contact with the outside world. In an adult human, the total surface area of the skin is between 16 and 22 square feet (1.5-2 square meters). The skin consists of three layers, the epidermis, the dermis and the subcutaneous connective tissue or fat. Any skin issues may also affect our hair, sebaceous and sweat glands as well as our toenails and fingernails, which are all found in the layers of our skin.

Right or Left?

Whether skin issues manifest on the right or left side of the body is meaningful. For those who are right-clapping, the left side of the body is the 'mother or child' side and the right side is the 'partner' side. For left-clapping people, it is the other way around. Please see Appendix 3 for an explanation of the significance of the 'mother or child' side versus 'partner' side, as well as the tests to determine whether you are right or left-clapping.

Types of Conflicts The underlying conflicts associated with skin problems include:

- Separation Conflicts
- Attack or Disfigurement Conflicts
- Self-Devaluation Conflicts

Location and Meaning

The location of any skin problem is meaningful and can help you determine the nature of the underlying conflict. It is, therefore, important to consider the relevance of the location and whether anything happened there, for example, something unpleasant (and thus unwanted), something you liked (that you miss) or an attack on that part of the body (either physical or verbal). Or maybe you are self-conscious about that area of your body. For instance, you may get cellulite in an area of the body where you feel unattractive and thus lack self-esteem. If a Separation Conflict is at play, the location of the skin condition determines whether the conflict involves wanting to have contact (and missing it) or not wanting contact, as illustrated in the table below. In addition, metaphors and common expressions can help you to understand what the underlying conflict may entail. For instance, if you have a skin condition, consider whether the conflict involves feeling irritated by someone who is 'getting under your skin.' If you experience a rash on the outside of your arm, consider whether you want someone to stay away and 'keep them at arm's length.' If you miss 'giving someone a hand,' because they have moved away or no longer need you, this may manifest as a skin condition on the palms of your hands.

Table 5: Different locations for wanting contact or not wanting contact[1]

Wanting contact Loss of skin contact Loss of contact with a loved one or animal	Abdomen, chest, inside of arms and legs, palms of hands
Not wanting contact Someone gets too close, not enough personal space	Back, buttocks, backs of hands, soles of feet, outside of arms, legs, elbows, wrists and knees
Missing being caressed (typical parent-child contact 'pat on the head'); conflict regarding 'being seen' or one's reputation, stress in connection with facing an issue	Head or face

---

1 *The Psychic Roots of Disease.* Eybl, B., Thirty-Three and 1 Publishing ISBN -13: 9781948909-00-6.

Epidermis - Separation Conflicts

Skin problems in the epidermis, the outermost layer of the skin, indicate that there is a Separation Conflict at play, either in the conflict-active phase or the healing phase. Perhaps you want contact with someone or something but you have lost contact (due to moving house, changing jobs, the death of a loved one or an unexpected divorce etc.) or maybe you do not want contact with or to be touched by someone or something. The conflict could also involve a fear of separation if you fear that you may lose someone you love. It usually involves skin contact and may include contact with people, animals or things. During the conflict-active phase, the skin may become a little thinner, cold, rough, less sensitive, pale or poorly supplied with blood. Often these kinds of symptoms go unnoticed. In the healing phase, the skin is usually red, warm, inflamed and swollen. There may be itching and (burning) pain. It may seem like the skin is sick at this point, but in reality, it is recovering. The phase during which you were 'sick' (conflict-active) has already passed.

Examples of symptoms that manifest in the skin during the healing phase after resolving a Separation Conflict: All types of rashes (including contact dermatitis, rosacea, heat rashes, exanthem), inflammation of the epidermis (neurodermatitis), eczema, red skin (erythema), hives (urticaria), nodules (lichen planus), pemphigus or other skin conditions with blisters (vesicles), autoimmune disease of the skin (lupus erythematosus), measles, rubella, chicken pox (varicella), allergic contact eczema, scarlet fever. Note: If there is a pronounced healing crisis, you may feel cold and have chills, pain and absences (see also section J | Juvenile Myoclonus Epilepsy).

EFT Approach: All of the above symptoms indicate that you are in the healing phase. Use EFT to neutralize any triggers to prevent a recurrence of the conflict. Consider the location of the symptoms, as it may help you identify the precise nature of the conflict and then look for emotionally charged specific events related to it. Neutralize them with EFT. If you are experiencing any itching or pain, apply Symptom-Focused EFT directly to the symptoms. If you have emotions associated with the symptoms themselves, address those with EFT as well. Also, be aware of your emotional reaction when you see the skin abnormality (in the mirror) and when you received any diagnosis, as well as any emotions you feel about how others will react.

Examples of symptoms that manifest in the skin after resolving a Separation Conflict, but in which healing is hanging: Warts (verrucae), plantar warts (on soles of feet), genital warts, age warts (seborrheic keratoses), erysipelas, basal cell carcinoma (basalioma), squamous cell carcinoma.

EFT Approach: Identify the Separation Conflicts at play and any triggers. Usually, the Big Cleanup approach works best here. Make lists of all relevant specific events that involve a Separation Conflict and resolve them one by one with EFT. Do Symptom-Focused EFT if any symptoms need attention. Apply EFT to any emotions that arise when you see or are confronted with warts or other skin issues, or when you encounter any reactions or comments from others. Also, pay attention to any feeling of shock you may have experienced when you received a diagnosis or underwent treatment.

Examples of symptoms where two conflicts are in different phases: Psoriasis arises when two Separation Conflicts affect the same area of skin. One is in the healing phase (resulting in red skin) and the other is in the conflict-active phase (resulting in dry, scaly skin).

EFT Approach: Identify all specific moments related to any Separation Conflicts involving both wanting contact and not wanting contact and address them with EFT. The location of the symptoms provides a clue as to the underlying conflicts. Use a combination of the Big Cleanup approach and Symptom-Focused EFT.

Examples of symptoms that manifest in the skin during the conflict-active phase of a Separation Conflict: Pigment disorders (vitiligo), baldness or hair loss (alopecia totalis and alopecia areata), dandruff, and gray hair.

EFT Approach: These symptoms indicate that you are in the conflict-active phase of a Separation Conflict that feels intense or brutal, very painful, difficult, overwhelming or unfair, such as a bitter divorce. Use the location of the symptoms to help you identify any Separation Conflicts, then use the Big Cleanup approach, which involves making a list of all the relevant specific events related to such conflicts. Also, make sure you apply EFT to your emotions regarding the symptoms themselves and the reactions of others.

Dermis – Attack or Disfigurement Conflict

A skin problem that affects the dermis, the middle layer of the skin, indicates that an Attack or Disfigurement Conflict is at play. Such a conflict may arise if you are attacked or you feel violated (literally or figuratively) or dirty in some way. It could be a physical or verbal attack, such as being slapped in the face or sworn at. A surgery or a biopsy may be subconsciously perceived as an attack on the body, and even a medical diagnosis or announcement that you need an operation can trigger such a conflict. You may feel dirty if you come into contact with something you perceive as disgusting (such as vomit, urine or feces) or if you are touched or embraced by someone you perceive as repulsive or who you believe has an infectious disease. During the conflict-active phase, cell growth takes place to strengthen the dermis to provide better protection against further attacks. Such cell growth usually occurs at the site where you experienced the attack. For instance, melanoma may develop on the face if you were attacked verbally, or on the breast following a biopsy or surgery related to breast cancer. If the skin problem only manifests on one side of the body, you need to determine whether you are left or right-clapping, as this will reveal whether the Desfigurement or Attack Conflict relates to 'mother or child' or 'partner.'

Examples of symptoms that manifest in the skin in the healing phase after resolving an Attack or Disfigurement Conflict: shingles (herpes zoster), acne (zits), panaritium (inflammation of the nail bed), all fungal (yeast) infections of the skin, including tinea pedis (foot fungus or athlete's foot), onychomycosis (nail fungus).

EFT Approach: Allow the healing phase to take its natural course. If there is a recurrence of the symptoms, then take the time to identify any previous Attack or Disfigurement Conflicts that are part of this stress pattern and also look for any potential triggers. Make a note of the location of the symptoms because it may provide a clue about the nature of the underlying conflict. Create a list of any specific events and neutralize them with EFT. If you are experiencing itching or pain, do Symptom-Focused EFT directly on those symptoms. If you have any emotions regarding the symptoms themselves (such as annoyance or fear), address those with EFT. Also, use EFT to address any emotions you feel when you look at your skin issues (in the mirror), any emotions you felt when you received a diagnosis and any emotions you feel when you encounter (or think about) the reactions of others. Often, the symptom itself may be a trigger if you find it gross or very unattractive, such as acne or nail fungus. Negative beliefs about your condition, such as *This will never go away,* may also play a role in these symptoms becoming chronic, so it is important to identify and address these beliefs with EFT.

Example of symptoms that manifest in the skin during the conflict-active phase of an Attack or Disfigurement Conflict: Skin cancer (melanoma).

EFT Approach: You are in an active ongoing conflict, so it is important to identify and resolve the underlying Attack or Disfigurement Conflicts. Use the Big Cleanup approach and make a list of all the specific events that may be related to such a conflict, as well as any diagnosis shock and other emotions you feel in connection with your skin problem and how others will react.

Subcutaneous Connective Tissue / Fat – Self-Devaluation Conflicts

A skin problem that involves the subcutaneous connective tissue or fat, the deepest layer of the skin, indicates that there is an underlying Self De-valuation Conflict. Your negative core belief plays a significant role here. You may feel inadequate and lack self-esteem, particularly with respect to the area of the body in which the symptom manifests. Again, if the skin problem only manifests on one side of the body, you need to determine whether you are left or right-clapping, as this will reveal whether the Self Devaluation Conflict relates to 'mother or child' or 'partner.'

Examples of symptoms that manifest themselves in the skin in the healing phase after resolving a Self-Devaluation Conflict: Keloid (thick raised scar tissue).

EFT Approach: A keloid scar usually arises when you feel self-conscious or inferior about an area of your skin that has been injured or operated on. The scar formation (which is permanent) occurs after the conflict has been resolved. To prevent a recurrence and more keloid from forming, identify how your negative core belief plays a role in this conflict. Identify and resolve as many specific events as possible using the Big Cleanup approach, and also take the time to address your beliefs with EFT.

Examples of symptoms that manifest in the skin after resolving a Self-Devaluation Conflict, but where the healing phase remains hanging: Fatty tumors (lipoma), cellulite, and lipedema.

EFT Approach: Identify the underlying conflicts and triggers and resolve them with EFT. The issue is a Self-Devaluation Conflict: feeling unattractive or inferior in that area of your body. If you have cellulite or lipedema, this means there is also an active Existential Conflict (not feeling at home, feeling like you are not in the right environment, being out of your element). Usually, the Big Cleanup approach works best here. Make lists of all relevant Self Devaluation Conflicts and Existential Conflicts. Resolve them with EFT, one by one. Do Symptom-Focused EFT on any symptoms you experience. Also, pay attention to any emotions you experience when you see or are confronted with the symptoms (like when you look in the mirror), as well as any emotions regarding other people's reactions or comments.

Examples of symptoms that manifest in the skin in the event of a recurrent or conflict-active Self-Devaluation Conflict: Scleroderma (buildup of tissue and hardening of the skin).

EFT Approach: Identify and resolve the underlying conflicts and triggers so the skin condition does not get worse. Do Symptom-Focused EFT on any emotions as well as any bodily symptoms. Consider whether the skin on the right or left side of the body is affected, which will indicate whether the conflict relates to 'mother or child' or 'partner.' Mainstream medicine classifies scleroderma as an autoimmune disease (where your body's defenses supposedly attack connective tissue for no reason). However, there is a reason for this condition, very intense Self-Devaluation Conflicts are at play. The sooner you resolve these underlying conflicts, the sooner the process will come to a halt.

Use EFT to Resolve Anxiety About Your Diagnosis

If you have received a diagnosis you are anxious about or worried about, take the time to neutralize every specific moment related to it in which you experienced stress, including all conversations with doctors or therapists, all medical examinations and moments when you received any test results, the reactions of those around you and every moment when you felt startled by what you read, heard or saw regarding the diagnosis.

Appendix 1
BACKGROUND OF EFT

EFT (Emotional Freedom Techniques) was developed in the early 1990s by Gary Craig, a Stanford University engineer, ordained minister, personal performance coach and Master Practitioner of NLP (Neuro-Linguistic Programming). After studying the work of Roger Callahan (a clinical psychologist) in Thought Field Therapy (TFT), Gary developed the basic protocol of EFT (Tapping) and incorporated many elements of NLP.

To put the origins of EFT into context, it is helpful to know more about the genesis of TFT. Key to the development of TFT was an incident in 1979 in the clinical practice of Roger Callahan, who specialized in treating anxiety disorders. One of his patients, Mary, suffered from a severe water phobia. Despite using all of the traditional psychotherapy techniques in his tool belt, Mary showed minimal improvement after a year of treatment. Callahan was deeply frustrated by the lack of results. One day during a consultation, Mary said she would get a terrible feeling in the pit of her stomach whenever she thought about water. Callahan, who had been studying Traditional Chinese Medicine and had some knowledge of the meridians, instructed Mary to tap under her eyes (on the stomach meridian). To his astonishment, after just a few minutes of tapping, Mary reported that both the terrible feeling in her stomach and her water phobia were gone. She was permanently cured of her water phobia.

Callahan realized that he may have discovered a new strategy for treating anxiety and started experimenting. He used his knowledge of applied kinesiology (movement therapy) and developed TFT, which involved a series of complex tapping algorithms. After studying with Callahan, Gary realized the potential of this approach and worked to refine and simplify the techniques. He ultimately developed a simple yet profound set of techniques with a fixed tapping protocol, which he called Emotional Freedom Techniques (EFT). In 1995, Gary released an EFT manual and made it available as a free download on his website. As a result, EFT became known worldwide.

It is significant to note that both TFT and EFT are also based on even earlier insights and techniques developed in the West, which we will now explain.

Muscle testing was first developed by Swedish physical therapists around 1860–1880. In 1910, Robert Lovett, an orthopedic surgeon, introduced the concept of muscle testing when diagnosing nerve damage in the spine. Henry and Florence Kendall, physical therapists, modified and systematized Lovett's approach and documented it in a 1949 publication *Muscle: Testing and Function.*

Frank Chapman, an osteopath, developed the concept of the 'Chapman Reflex Points.' He discovered that massaging these points reduced the symptoms of certain complaints. Around the same time, Dr. Terrence J. Bennett, a chiropractor, developed his own set of reflex points, which he called neurovascular points. Whereas Chapman attributed the reduction of symptoms to the improved flow of lymph, Bennet took the view that it was due to the improved flow of blood.

In 1960, George J. Goodheart, a chiropractor, discovered that muscles test weak when affected by a particular disease and linked this result to Chapman's work. Thus, he discovered a connection between symptoms, muscle tests and reflex points: a muscle is strengthened when you massage the associated reflex point. He called this approach 'applied kinesiology.'

In 1966, Goodheart defined the concept of tonification points: by holding meridian points, weak muscles test strong again. He also discovered that muscle strength varied depending on one's thought processes. One of Goodheart's students, Dr. John Thie, developed Touch for Health (TfH) based on this discovery. One of the best-known techniques from TfH is Emotional Stress Release.

Several people who followed Goodheart continued to build on the concept of applied kinesiology. One of the best-known is Paul Dennison, who developed Educational Kinesiology (Edu-K) and Brain Gym, concepts designed specifically for children with learning and behavioral problems.

John Diamond, a psychiatrist, built on Goodheart's work, shifting the focus of applied kinesiology from physical problems to psychological and emotional problems. He is considered the father of a large number of healing approaches aimed at identifying and treating psychological problems using muscle testing. For the treatment of various problems, he defined test points and emotion-oriented affirmations for each meridian. He also observed the tendency of energy in meridians to become unbalanced as a result of emotional problems and experiences. In retrospect, it is clear that John Diamond's work was a direct precursor to TFT.

Various students of Roger Callahan subsequently developed their own techniques and approaches based on his work. Some of his well-known students include Patricia Carrington (who abandoned her own approach, learned EFT from Gary Craig and then developed the Choice Method within EFT), Lary Nims (Be Set Free Fast (BSFF)), and Fred Gallo, clinical psychologist (NAEM, EDxTM). Gallo is credited with introducing the term Energy Psychology as an umbrella term for these different approaches.

Since 1995, Gary has continued to refine EFT. In 2014, Gary started teaching Optimal EFT, which is the latest advancement. Optimal EFT uses the professional methods of EFT Tapping for identifying the issue but replaces the tapping with the unlimited healing power of unconditional spiritual love. It is based on the principles of *A Course in Miracles,* a spiritual text which is non-denominational. However, in the same way that it is not necessary to study Traditional Chinese Medicine, NLP or other techniques to use EFT Tapping, there is no need to study *A Course in Miracles* to use Optimal EFT. Both techniques can be learned and used effectively without resorting to these foundational materials.

Appendix 2
CONFLICT DEFINITIONS

Attack or Disfigurement Conflict: Feeling attacked, disfigured, tarnished or that your integrity is violated (literally or figuratively) or feeling 'soiled' or dirty in some way. It may be a physical or verbal attack, such as being slapped in the face or sworn at. A surgery or a biopsy may be subconsciously perceived as an attack on, or disfigurement of, the body, and even a medical diagnosis or being told that you need an operation can trigger such a conflict. You may feel soiled or dirty if you come into contact with something you perceive as disgusting (such as vomit, urine, blood or feces) or if you are touched or embraced by someone whom you perceive as repulsive or who you believe has an infectious disease.

Biting Conflict: Feeling like you want to defend yourself or attack another (by biting or snapping at them or talking back to them) but not doing so because you feel like you are in a weaker position than them, physically, socially, intellectually and/or culturally. For example, child vs parent, child vs older child, colleague vs boss, woman vs man, and minority vs those in control. It also includes conflicts related to not being able to or allowed to bite something physically.

Chunk Conflict: Feeling like you cannot get something ('chunk') that you want or you cannot get rid of something that you do not want. It may be literal, where you cannot grab or catch, swallow, digest or eliminate food. Or, more frequently, this conflict may be experienced figuratively, where you are unable to get what you want, to let go of what you do not want or to emotionally digest and process something difficult that has happened. For example, not being able to get a partner, a job or promotion, or money from an inheritance or investment; not being able to swallow or process an insult or betrayal; or not being able to digest an unexpected loss of a relationship or job. The small intestine may be affected if there is a fear of starvation or poverty, such as fearing the loss of income or benefits. The

315

colon or large intestine may be affected if the conflict is experienced as ugly, mean or despicable, or involves deceit or fraud.

Existential Conflict: Fear for one's life, feeling like your physical existence is threatened and that you may not survive. Feeling abandoned, isolated and alone. Feeling like a fish out of water because you have been separated from the pack. For example, a diagnosis shock where you feel *I am not going to survive this*, being alone in the hospital, losing your home because of a divorce, losing your job or feeling like your livelihood is at stake, losing a loved one who has taken care of you, or leaving your home or country like a refugee.

Fear of Death Conflict: Fear of death. Fear of dying.

Fear of Rear Attack Conflict: Feeling afraid of being attacked from behind, either by a known threat (your colleagues, classmates, boss, tax authorities, or criminals) or by an unknown danger that you cannot see but which you fear is going to overtake you and cannot be avoided.

Fear-Disgust Conflict: Feeling both fear and disgust towards something or someone you perceive as repugnant, unhygienic or unacceptable, or being in a situation where you are experiencing something shocking, disgusting and/or scary and reacting in a passive way (withdrawing or turning away).

Frontal Fear Conflict: Fear of a danger that is coming toward you, a danger that you cannot avoid or escape (real or imagined).

Identity Conflict: Not knowing where you belong (in which group). 'Who am I?' 'What am I?' Feeling distressed about not being able to establish your place within a relationship or a society or culture. Not knowing what decision to make. For example, not knowing which career path to follow or which partner to choose.

Motor Conflict: Literally or figuratively feeling stuck, being unable to move or not wanting or daring to move, feeling like you are not fast enough, not being able to push away or grab something or someone.

> **Visual Motor Conflict:** Not being able to open or close your eyes, or not daring to do so.

Powerlessness Conflict: Feeling like you cannot or dare not take action. Feeling at the mercy of others. This may be real or perceived.

Resistance Conflict: Feeling compelled to fight or defend yourself against someone or something that feels like a threat or that is trying to force you to do something you don't want to do. For example, teens standing up for themselves against parents or school teachers, resisting medical treatment or sexual advances or even food that a person does not want to eat.

Self-Devaluation Conflict: Feeling rejected, not good enough, unworthy, useless or a failure. This type of conflict involves self-blame. It arises when you judge yourself as not being good enough in some way. Thus, the way we perceive ourselves and our self-talk can give rise to this conflict.

Such a conflict may concern the person as a whole (a generalized Self-Devaluation Conflict) or a specific part of the body (a localized Self-Devaluation Conflict). For the latter, symptoms may manifest in the area of the body that is perceived as not being good enough.

Examples of situations that may give rise to a generalized Self-Devaluation Conflict include feeling humiliated (by accusations, scoldings, derogatory remarks), being abused (physically, sexually or verbally), feeling like a failure (at work, at school, in sports, in a relationship, as a parent or partner), a poor performance, feelings of shame and guilt, loss of status or a job, illness or injuries (causing one to feel less than), and aging (*I have no value anymore, I am old and useless*).

Examples of situations that may give rise to a localized Self-Devaluation Conflict include poor performance (artistic, athletic or at work) which involves a specific part of the body (such as the arms or legs), a cancer diagnosis (such as breast cancer which results in lack of self-esteem in that area), a negative prognosis *(You will not be able to walk again)*, or the removal of an organ (mastectomy).

Separation Conflict: Feeling like you want something but you are not able to get it or feeling like you do not want something, but you are getting it:

> **Touch:** Feeling like you want (skin) contact, but you are not getting it, or that you do not want (skin) contact but you are getting it – either from a person or thing. It concerns all forms of contact and touch by people, animals and things.
>
> **Visual:** Wanting to see someone or something but not being able to or seeing someone or something that you do not want to see.
>
> **Auditory:** Wanting to hear something and not being able to hear it, or not wanting to hear something but hearing it.

Sexual Frustration Conflict: Wanting to have sexual relations with someone but not being able or allowed to do so, or not wanting to have sexual contact but being forced to do so. For example, not having a sexual partner, losing a sexual partner or sexual abuse.

Shock-Fright or Speechlessness Conflict: Being startled by a sudden threat or noise and reacting passively to it. Not being able to speak loud enough or scream, feeling like you have lost your voice or not daring to express yourself. *I am speechless, The words stuck in my throat.*

Social Conflict: Any conflict that relates to the pack or group. This includes Separation Conflicts, Territorial Conflicts and Biting Conflicts.

Stink-Smell Conflict: Not wanting to smell something or not being able to smell something, either literally or figuratively. Literally: not wanting to smell something (for example, a bad odor). Figuratively: not wanting to smell something (for example, *This situation stinks*), or not being able to pick up the scent, so you cannot sense what or when something dangerous is going to happen or come at you; suspecting that something is wrong but not being able to work out what it is.

Territorial Conflict: Territory includes your home, workplace, school, playground, community center and the village, city and country where you live. It includes 'pack' members in the territory, such as your parents, spouse or partner, child, relatives, friends, colleagues, clients, neighbors and pets, as well as assets in your territory, for example, your car, jewelry, money, stocks, investments, licenses, immigration status or club membership. Territory can also be your body or your time. There are several types of Territorial Conflicts:

Territorial Anger Conflict: Feeling angry, irritated or annoyed by people or situations in your territory. Annoyed about remarks (accusations, criticism, insults) or information. Aggression may be involved, either your own anger or someone else's anger. For example, literal or figurative boundary disputes with neighbors, family members or colleagues.

Territorial Fear Conflict: Feeling fearful about a threat to the Territory, a fear within the Territory or a fear regarding one's own safety as well as the safety of the 'pack.' For example, domestic violence, physical or emotional abuse, bullying, a frightening diagnosis or prognosis, hospitalization, an accident, fire or flood or a natural disaster. Children feel this conflict when they are yelled at or punished, when they are scared or when they have nightmares. This conflict may be experienced by a large number of people in certain areas who share the same fear, such as during a natural disaster or wartime, or through reports of potential terrorist attacks or pandemic fearmongering (AIDS, SARS, swine flu, and the like) by the media.

Territorial Loss Conflict: Feeling fearful because you are losing all or part of your territory, or fear that you will lose it. For example, the loss of a member of the territory (because of an argument or separation), the loss of your home (due to an unexpected move, bankruptcy, natural disaster or divorce), the loss of a job, business, position or confidential information, forced early retirement, not being able to continue a hobby, or the loss of abilities (as a result of an accident that leaves you unable to do something).

Territorial Marking Conflict: Being unable or not daring to set boundaries around your territory. For example, others crossing your boundaries.

Wrong Path Conflict: Feeling like you are on the wrong track, that you have made the wrong decision, that you have gone 'off course' or that you are on a slippery slope. Feeling like you or something has fallen into the wrong hands. For example, you have chosen the wrong partner, the wrong job, the wrong house or place to live.

Vicarious Conflict: You suffer a conflict for a loved one (person or pet). Examples include: developing a liver tumor because your pet refuses to eat and is threatened by starvation, getting pneumonia after resolving a Fear of Death Conflict in relation to a loved one, or suffering from heart palpitations because you are worried there is something wrong with somebody else's heart.

Appendix 3
WHICH SIDE OF THE BODY?

Left or Right

Certain emotional conflicts may manifest on a particular side of the body, depending on the nature of the conflict and whether you are right or left-handed. For such conflicts, it is important to determine whether you are naturally (biologically) right or left-handed. If the biological handedness is relevant to any of the symptoms listed in Sections A to Z of this book, it will be indicated within the text.

Many left-handed people were taught (or forced) to write with their right hand in early childhood, so the hand you write with may not necessarily be your dominant hand. The most useful test to determine whether you are naturally right or left-handed is the clap test. When you clap, the hand that leads and is naturally on top is the dominant hand. However, if a person claps by bringing the lower hand up to clap the upper hand, then the lower hand is the dominant hand. If this test is inconclusive, check which hand you use to open a bottle with a screw cap.

Right-handed: If you are right-handed, the left side of your body is the 'mother or child' side and the right side of your body is the 'partner' side, which includes anyone other than your mother or child.

Left-handed: If you are left-handed, the right side of your body is the 'mother or child' side and the left side of your body is the 'partner' side, which includes anyone other than mother or child.

'Mother or child' side: If symptoms manifest on the 'mother or child' side, the underlying conflict relates to issues with or about your mother, you in a mother role, your child, or you as a child. Someone other than your mother may feel like a mother to you, and someone other than your child may feel like a child to you. Your partner may sometimes feel like a child to you (in certain situations or in general). Pets may also feel like your child or even a mother. Also, your business, a project or a product may feel like your child. In all these situations, a related conflict may show up on your 'mother or child side.'

'Partner' side: If symptoms manifest on the partner side, the underlying conflict is related to anyone other than your mother or child. In other words, this side concerns conflicts with all other social partners, including your spouse or partner, father, siblings, all other relatives, friends, colleagues, classmates, teammates, neighbors and the public at large. If your mother or your child plays the role of a partner, then conflicts related to them may show up on the partner side. Pets may also feel like your friend (partner).

Appendix 4
DISEASES AND SYMPTOMS COVERED IN PART 2

Appendix 5
THREE CASE STUDIES

These case studies are provided to illustrate the following key points:

- How important it is to do EFT on a daily basis;
- Why testing is essential to your success;
- The importance of making a plan of action, which includes identifying the underlying emotional causes of your specific symptoms or problems;
- You may not get immediate results, but success is possible if you take the time to practice;
- Physical problems are (often) caused by emotional issues.

During sessions, I work with my clients to identify the underlying emotional issues and make a plan of action, which you can do using the information provided in this book. In addition to applying EFT in our sessions, I also use the sessions to test what the client has worked on by themselves, which is a crucial part of the process so that they know what has been resolved and what they need to work on next. This is also something you can do by yourself, to measure your progress and maintain your focus.

We hope that these case studies will show you the importance of practicing on your own and help you understand that the process requires time and perseverance. Almost no one can precisely follow every part of the EFT approach from the outset and achieve immediate success. Expect some internal resistance to using EFT, but then use EFT to overcome it. If you start to gradually incorporate EFT as a part of your daily routine, we are confident that the results that you achieve will be more than worth your efforts!

Case 1: Optimal EFT for Fear of Pain Attacks

John, a 47-year-old married man with 3 children, sought my help because he was experiencing recurring attacks of pain in his left upper abdomen that felt like a stabbing sensation. The pain was so intense that he did not dare to move during an attack. He was in a state of constant fear and panic that the pain would return. The first time it happened, the pain was so severe that he went to the emergency department, but they could not find anything. He continued to experience pain attacks during the night, about once or twice a month, for over a year. He had not been to the emergency department again, but he had consulted his family doctor, who thought the pain was most likely due to diaphragmatic cramps. His doctor was unable to identify the cause of such cramps, simply concluding that the cause for such pain attacks is often unknown. He recommended physical therapy but that did not help with the pain.

The pain attacks always happened at night, so John did not sleep well because he was afraid of having another attack. Even though he had only experienced the pain attacks during the night, he remained fearful of a pain attack, day and night. Whenever he felt the slightest strange feeling or pain in his abdomen, he would get extremely anxious and would not dare to move because he was afraid it would turn into a severe pain attack. He did not understand what was happening or why, and he felt like his body was failing him. He had just started his own business and felt frustrated that he could not give it his full attention.

As he was so fed up with the pain, anxiety and fear, John was highly motivated to do whatever it took to solve the problem once and for all. He was familiar with EFT Tapping, but he was curious about Optimal EFT. When I explained that, in my experience, Optimal EFT often works faster than EFT Tapping, he was eager to give it a go.

First Session

I asked John when he experienced the first pain attack and what was going on in his life at that time. He recalled that it happened when things were going well, which surprised him. It occurred after he decided to resign from his job and set up his own business with a friend. Upon further questioning, it turned out that he had been very unhappy at his previous job because there had been a lot of changes after a corporate reorganization, which meant an increased workload with fewer people and lots of new rules that he found irritating. He also said that his manager was breathing down his neck. He was under immense pressure and felt as though he could not move or breathe. Once he decided to start his own business, he used his accrued vacation days to resign immediately and started working on his own business. Shortly thereafter, he had his first pain attack at night, after he had been out for dinner with his new business partner and their respective wives to celebrate the start of their new business.

I explained that diaphragmatic cramps usually occur in the healing phase after resolving a Motor Conflict. A Motor Conflict means that you are feeling stuck like you cannot, will not, or should not move. (See Section B | Bones, Muscles and Tendons for a more detailed explanation). The diaphragm is especially affected by the feeling of being stuck and not having enough room or air. John recognized this feeling immediately and knew it was related to his previous job. I asked him to identify specific events at his previous job in which he felt *I am stuck and I cannot breathe* and to describe them using the present tense. John identified the following two moments:

- The moment when my supervisor says, *I do not care, this has to be finished first,* and I feel trapped and angry.
- The moment when colleague X makes a comment in a meeting and my breathing feels obstructed and I just want to get out of there.

We worked on these two events with the Unseen Therapist. John found it easy to connect to a loving feeling by recalling a loving moment with his family. During the meditation with The Unseen Therapist, he did not see any images or hear any messages. Whenever his mind wandered, he brought his attention back to the loving feeling. After doing 4 rounds of meditation, the emotional charge of the first event went down to zero. The charge of the second event was neutralized after only 3 rounds of meditation. Each meditation lasted about 1.5 to 2 minutes. For each event, we did a lot of testing, which involved reliving the moment. I encouraged John to really make an effort to get upset while reliving the moment, to make sure that any remaining emotional charge was activated and then released with EFT. By the time we finished, he was able to relive both events while remaining completely calm.

Then we started to work on the feeling of anxiety John was experiencing during the day, whenever he felt any sort of twinge in his stomach, which caused him to fear an attack. I taught him the WMOMD approach, which involves applying EFT to a recent moment when he felt anxious, bringing the intensity down to below 5 but not yet 0, then asking *When have I felt this way before?* John identified a moment that happened 3 days before our session when he was dealing with his emails in his office. When he was reliving the moment, he noticed a vaguely unpleasant feeling in his upper abdomen with an intensity of 3, his anxiety was at a 7 and he could feel the anxiety in his chest. We started by focusing on his symptoms first. After the first meditation with the Unseen Therapist, the unpleasant feeling disappeared, and the anxiety went down to a 5. I asked him to relive the moment again, and then I asked him when he had felt the same way in the past. That brought him back to his first pain attack, so we started working on that moment instead. I asked him to relive it and tell me how he was feeling, reminding him to use the present tense. He said: *I feel pain at a 10, panic at a 9. I think I am going to die of a heart attack. I am short of breath. I can hardly breathe.* I reassured him that he was fine, nothing was wrong now, and that these were just feelings that belonged to that moment in the past. He managed to recall a loving moment and start the meditation, asking The Unseen Therapist to help resolve these feelings. After one meditation, the intensity of the pain reduced to 3 and the panic went down to 4.

During the next meditation, I suggested that he ask The Unseen Therapist to explain to him that these feelings are symptoms of a healing phase and therefore harmless. After the second meditation, the pain and panic had disappeared and he felt peaceful. Then, we returned to the moment that we originally started working on, when he was in his office dealing with his emails. After another meditation, the charge of that moment went down to zero. I did a final test, asking him to relive the moment once more, but he felt nothing – the emotional charge had been neutralized.

I then taught John how to address the anxiety and pain that he felt when he woke up at night with a pain attack. John identified a moment two months earlier, which he recalled clearly because it was the night after his birthday. When reliving the moment, he reported feeling pain at a 6 and anxiety at an 8. After one meditation, the pain went down to 2 and the fear down to 4. I asked him to relive the moment again and then asked if he could recall feeling this way in the past. He told me that he had never felt like this before, but it reminded him of the time when his father had had a heart attack and almost died. This happened when John was 42 years old. I asked him to identify the specific moment that had the most charge related to his father's heart attack, reminding him again to use the present tense. John recalled the moment as follows: "I am in the hospital visiting my father, sitting by his bed. He looks very weak. He says to me, *I have never been in such pain. I have never been so afraid.*" We neutralized this moment completely by doing 3 meditations with The Unseen Therapist. We then switched back to the first moment he identified, on the night after his birthday, and applied EFT until that moment was also completely neutral.

During one of the meditations with The Unseen Therapist, John remembered that his father had visited him on his birthday and mentioned that he had not been doing well. That may have subconsciously triggered John's fear about his own health, in particular regarding his heart. As John started to understand how his physical issues were related to his emotions, and that he did not have to fear that his body would suddenly fail him for no reason, he began to feel more reassured. As the first session drew to a close, I gave him a homework assignment, which involved applying EFT to 3 specific events where he recalls feeling *I am stuck and I cannot breathe* in his previous job. I instructed him to bring the intensity down to below 5 but not yet 0, and then while remaining in that feeling, to ask himself when he felt this way before (and if he identified a past event, to neutralize that event as well). I also recommended that he apply Symptom-Focused EFT to any moment in which he feels anxious during the day or night, as well as any pain that arises (which involves simply meditating with The Unseen Therapist until he feels calm).

Second Session

We met for a second session a month later. John appeared to be less anxious. He had experienced one pain attack during the night since our first session, but it was less painful and passed more quickly because he had managed to apply EFT, doing several meditations with the Unseen Therapist until he felt calm and the pain subsided. Whenever he felt anxious during the day, he managed to release the anxiety by doing a meditation with The Unseen Therapist. He had also applied EFT to 3 work situations until the charge went down to 0, and he had identified a few earlier specific events in which he felt the same way.

First, we tested the emotional charge of the work-related specific events that he had worked on by himself, to make sure they had been neutralized. One of the events was neutral, but the other two required further meditations with The Unseen Therapist before they were neutralized. Upon further questioning, he disclosed that he had identified related earlier events from his childhood, but he had not yet worked on them. He explained that he had a strict upbringing, and his mother, in particular, had been extremely demanding. She always gave him lots of tasks and assignments that he had to finish before he was allowed to play.

We started working on one of the earlier events, and once we brought the intensity down to below 5, I asked him: What conclusion do you draw about yourself in this moment? What negative thoughts do you have about yourself? He said: "I am thinking *I am not worth it.*" I explained that this belief is more than likely his negative core belief about himself and that we all have a predominant negative core belief (NCB). He said he used to feel like he had to earn his mother's approval but even when he tried really hard, he usually did not succeed. Nothing was ever good enough, and once he finished something, his mother always had another assignment for him to do. She often commented that he had a lousy attitude and did not try hard enough. Thus, it was very clear how he learned this NCB that he was not worthy.

John began to understand how comments from others in the past cause us to judge ourselves and to form beliefs about ourselves and the world.

We also discussed how the work situations he had identified and worked on were the root cause of his stress at work. Even though he had managed to resolve his stress at work by resigning, I explained that it was still important to neutralize any remaining emotional charge in his subconscious regarding these events to ensure that a similar issue does not arise in the future. For homework after the second session, I asked John to identify 5-10 situations from his childhood, in which both his mother and his NCB played a role, and to apply EFT to each of those situations. I also encouraged him to continue to use the WMOMD approach to neutralize any anxiety he feels during the day and to take note of any specific things that may have triggered that anxiety. While we had identified the emotional cause of the intense cramping pain that he experienced during a pain attack, we had not yet identified the emotional cause of the unpleasant feeling in his stomach that he experienced during the day. An unpleasant feeling in the abdomen may have several causes, so I was curious to see if he could identify any triggers that might help us identify the root cause. I asked him to make a note of any moment when he feels that unpleasant feeling and what he was doing leading up to that moment.

Third Session

When we met a month later, John reported that he was sleeping normally again. He told me that after hearing my explanations in the previous sessions as to why we experience anxiety and pain, he was feeling a lot less fear and anxiety. He realized he can handle a pain attack himself using EFT and now understands that his pain attack does not mean that there is something wrong with his heart. Since the last session, he had not had another pain attack at night and had only felt a slight fear of a pain attack on 4 occasions during the day. He noted that he did not experience any real fear anymore, just a little anxiety.

John explained how he had applied the WMOMD approach to a feeling of mild anxiety he experienced one day when he was doing something on his computer that he did not feel like doing. To his surprise, when he asked himself when he had felt this way before, an early childhood memory came up in which he was doing an assignment for his mother that he did not want to do. He ended up identifying and neutralizing 6 other specific events with his mother from his childhood, with the help of The Unseen Therapist.

During our session together, we tested to make sure that all the events he had worked on by himself had been completely neutralized. I explained that the stress at his previous job was probably mostly fueled by the fact that he was subconsciously reminded of the past experiences with his mother, and probably other experiences in which his NCB (*I am not worth it*) had played a role. For homework, I asked John to make a comprehensive list of moments in which he felt *I am not worth it*, not only with his mother, but also with others (using the Detective Work questions we had discussed in our second session), and then to use this list to create a top 30 list of moments which he could then work on with The Unseen Therapist. In addition, I asked him to continue with the WMOMD approach and also apply Symptom Focused EFT if he experienced any fear or anxiety.

Fourth Session

Two months later, we met for our final session. John had not experienced any more pain attacks and no longer felt any fear or anxiety about having one. He reported feeling more relaxed and he was enjoying building his business. The collaboration with his friend was going well. He had read the free ebook on The Unseen Therapist from Gary Craig's website, and he had completed his list of the top 30 events related to his NCB. He was continuing to add to his list (as earlier events came up when using the WMOMD approach), and he had not yet resolved them all. He had discovered that the moments he usually identified as the WMOMD were, more often than not, related to his NCB, *I am not worth it* and that these moments arose in both work and social situations involving his family and friends. He noticed how much more relaxed he now felt after using the WMOMD approach for the last few months, and he felt very motivated to continue using it. We neutralized 3 more events together in this session from his top 30 list and also tested the emotional intensity of a few of the more significant ones he had worked on by himself, to make sure they had been neutralized. Given that John's issues had been resolved and he now had the skills to continue applying EFT on his own when needed, the counseling was done and we said our goodbyes.

Case 2: Fibromyalgia

Rianne, a 39-year-old divorced mother with 12-year-old twins, came to me because she wanted to resolve her fibromyalgia (a chronic condition characterized by widespread musculoskeletal pain all over the body, accompanied by fatigue and sleep, memory and mood issues, which according to mainstream medicine has no cure). She had read in an online forum that EFT could help. She had been suffering from fibromyalgia for five years and her symptoms had worsened over the previous 2 months. She was exhausted and worried that she would not be able to continue her work and her studies. Upon questioning, I discovered that her symptoms began around the time of her divorce after being married for 14 years. Her marriage had been extremely stressful and the relationship with her ex-husband (M) was still problematic. She had a good relationship with her two daughters, but she found it difficult when M came to pick them up for visits. He refused to come in, insisting on waiting outside in his car. She found this stressful and it reminded her of the problems they had experienced during their relationship. She was working part-time as a counter clerk in a large company, but she was not really enjoying it, even though her colleagues were friendly. She did not get along well with her supervisor, who was difficult to please and always had something critical to say. Rianne was aware that she was overly sensitive to criticism, but she still found it difficult to let go. She was also training to become a coach in her spare time and was hoping to make it a full-time job and work from home. Rianne was taking ibuprofen and acetaminophen almost daily.

First Session

First, I took inventory of all of Rianne's symptoms. She reported pain and stiffness in her neck and upper back at an intensity of 5, pain in both upper legs (intensity of 7 in the left and 4 in the right), pain in both upper arms (8 in the left and 5 in the right). She rated her fatigue at an 8.

I began by explaining Hamer's theory of fibromyalgia and showed her his chart of the autonomic nervous system (see Figure 7 in Chapter 5 of Part 1). I explained that the symptoms are minimal in the conflict active phase and that pain and fatigue occur in the healing phase. No one had ever explained her condition to her in this way – not her family doctor, or her physical therapist or her rheumatologist. Visits to her rheumatologist left her feeling despondent because he told her that the cause of fibromyalgia is unknown and that there is no cure. I explained that the cause of fibromyalgia is serious Self-Devaluation Conflicts manifesting in the musculoskeletal system and that these conflicts can be addressed and resolved with EFT if she was diligent. For the first time, she felt a glimmer of hope. She did not necessarily believe me, but she was open to the possibility, which is totally fine. EFT does not require any belief for it to work. The key is to simply do EFT and see for yourself how it works. I then explained that we all have a predominant negative core belief (NCB), which is our own negative conclusion about ourselves, and how it plays a major role in all Self Devaluation Conflicts. I gave her examples of the wording of the most common NCBs and asked her whether any of them felt true to her. She quickly identified her own NCB, which was *I am not good enough*. She felt that this was her dominant belief about herself in all situations, at home, as a mother, towards her family, towards M and at work. She also recognized identifying with it throughout her childhood, from a young age. I asked her to say out loud *I am not good enough* and tell me how true it felt, emotionally. She said it felt 90% true (see the explanation of the Validity of Cognition test in Chapter 5 in Part 1).

It became clear that her Self-Devaluation Conflicts were rather intense during her marriage but less so after the divorce. Indeed, she felt relieved to be separated from M and more settled living with her children without

M. I explained that it was no coincidence that the fibromyalgia symptoms arose after her divorce. As her Self-Devaluation Conflicts were mostly resolved at that time, she had entered the healing phase and therefore experienced pain and fatigue, which are labeled as fibromyalgia by mainstream medicine.

I noted that her symptoms had worsened in the last two months. When I asked when she had started the training to become a coach, Rianne started smiling - it was two months ago. She was starting to understand the connection between the events in her life and her bodily symptoms. She explained that the decision to do the coaching training had felt like a breakthrough and that she really enjoyed the training and was doing very well. She had been receiving compliments from the trainers and her self-confidence was increasing. Finally, she felt like her life was on track and she was excited about starting to work as a coach from home. This development in her life had resolved further self-esteem issues, causing her to enter the healing phase with respect to those issues, which explained the increase in pain and fatigue.

Now that we had a good understanding of the emotional issues underlying her physical symptoms, it was time to start applying EFT. I explained the two forms of EFT and Rianne chose to start with Gold Standard EFT Tapping. I asked her to identify a good example of a moment in her marriage when she really felt like she was not good enough, and to describe it using the present tense. Rianne identified the following:

• The moment when M says, *I have not loved you for a long time and I am in love with someone else,* and I am in shock. This takes place in the kitchen.

When reliving this moment, she reported feeling sadness at a 9, shock at an 8 and fear at an 8. We created a Setup phrase, then started tapping and reliving the moment until the emotions dropped below 5. Then I instructed her to relive the moment again and asked *Do you feel rejected and not good enough?* She felt both were true, with an intensity of 10. We did another round of tapping. I asked her to relive the moment again and then asked if she had felt that way earlier in her life, noting that the earlier the memory she could identify, the better. The first memory that came up was:

- The moment when I am 6 years old and my friend says, *I do not want to play with you because you are not nice* and I feel sad. This takes place in the schoolyard.

We tapped on all aspects of this moment until it was completely neutralized and then tested the moment with M in the kitchen, which we had been working on earlier. I guided Rianne to work on different aspects of this one moment, using the present tense to encourage her to really feel her emotions: the way he looks, the impatient tone of voice he uses and his body posture (which is very distant). By the end of this session, Rianne understood how to apply the basic EFT Tapping protocol, so I gave her homework to do before our next session. I asked her to identify at least one WMOMD in which her NCB was activated and to tap on that specific moment the way we had just done it. I also asked her to create a list of past events with a negative emotional charge and to add these events to the list with the proper wording, *The moment when X happens and I feel Y.*

Second Session

Rianne told me that she could not believe how often her negative core belief came up in her daily life. In the two weeks since our last session, she had written down at least 5-6 moments a day when she caught herself identifying emotions triggered by her NCB. She had tapped on only one WMOMD each day, rather than all of them. I explained that the more often she took the time to address all of the worst moments of her day, on a daily basis, the faster she would progress. In this session, I wanted her to learn the entire WMOMD approach, explaining to her that this means bringing the emotions of her WMOMD down to an intensity of 5 but not yet zero, and then while reliving the moment and feeling the emotion, asking herself when she felt like that before, to identify related events from her past. I also wanted to clarify the whole EFT approach for working on her NCB. I explained that we would target her NCB in the following way:

1. We are going to look at the origins of your NCB by going through a series of questions related to the first 7 years of your life. We will then continue to identify events in the following years of your life, until your whole life is mapped out, up to the time when your relationship with M began.

2. You will need to make a list of the challenging moments in your marriage and in the relationships before you got married (a Big Cleanup List) and narrow this down to the top 30 events.

3. Your daily homework will include doing the whole WMOMD approach.

4. Apply Symptom-Focused EFT on pain symptoms, as needed. Understanding that there are indeed causes for your symptoms (Self-Devaluation Conflicts) and that pain and fatigue mean that you are in the healing phase helps to shed a whole new light on what is the cause and what is the effect. Symptom-Focused EFT does not solve the underlying problem, but it is still useful to bring relief.

To help Rianne get started on this EFT approach, we practiced each part of the plan of action together in this session:

Re: Point 1: Who taught me to think that I am not good enough? This came from both parents. She had an older brother (L) who received all her parents' attention. He had special needs and his behavior was very problematic for her parents, but she did not realize that as a child. She usually felt unimportant and alone. She identified the following specific moments:

* Age 7: The moment when my parents are not at my report card ceremony because they are in the hospital with L and I feel lonely and sad.

* Age 6: The moment when L receives a really big present from Grandma and I get a small package and I start crying. Daddy is angry at me for being *so childish.*

* Age 4: The moment when L slaps me and I start screaming, and Daddy says, *Stop screaming, it was not that hard.*

Re: Point 2: Rianne then identified the following specific moments relating to her relationship with M (as part of her Big Cleanup list).

- The moment when M smells like perfume I do not use and I panic and become intensely sad.
- The moment when M turns his back on me at the party at K and A's house and I feel totally rejected and lonely.
- The moment when M texts me, saying *I will be much later, I have to work overtime* and I know he is lying and I feel angry and powerless.

Re: Point 3: Rianne chooses the following moment from the WMOMD list from the previous two weeks:

- The moment when my child says, *Daddy would never do that,* and I feel upset, like a totally worthless mother.

Re: Point 4: Rianne chose to apply Symptom-Focused EFT to the pain and stiffness in her neck and upper back.

We began by applying Symptom-Focused EFT, focusing on the pain and stiffness in Rianne's neck and upper back which had an intensity of 6. We reduced it to 4 in 5 rounds of tapping and left it at that for the time being. I explained to Rianne that whenever she does a few rounds of tapping on her symptoms, she turns on the parasympathetic relaxation response, which accelerates the healing phase.

Then we tapped on the moment when her brother slapped her at the age of 4 and her father got angry at her. We tapped on the emotions of terror, fear and sadness that came up. She reported feeling rejected by her father and thinking she is not good enough. We completely neutralized all her emotions and then tested the whole event to make sure that it was neutral, which it was.

At the end of the session, Rianne committed to continuing with the plan of action and had already decided to focus on it in the evenings, after her daughters went to bed. We agreed to meet a month later, to give her time to make progress on her own.

Third Session

Rianne reported feeling disappointed that she had not done as much EFT as she was hoping to do. Some days she only worked on one WMOMD, which she knew was not enough. Also, she often did not bring the intensity of a specific event down to zero. As a result, she again concluded that she was not good enough, so we tapped on her sadness (which was at a 7) and her anger (which was at a 6) until they went down to a 1-2. We left it at that because we were merely using Symptom-Focused EFT to bring the immediate emotions down enough to work on other things.

I certainly understood how challenging it was for Rianne to do this intensive EFT project in addition to her work commitments, her responsibilities as a mother and her coaching training. I told her that and did my best to reassure her that she was doing enough, in the circumstances. I also pointed out that there was no rush and that the EFT project did not have to be completed within any deadline. After all, she had been walking around with her NCB all her life and she had also been dealing with fibromyalgia symptoms for five years. The key was to work steadily on her issues with EFT, which would create the best results over time. We agreed that she would aim to do the entire WMOMD approach every day at a specific time and that she would also apply Symptom-Focused EFT as needed. In addition, she would set aside 30 minutes to an hour, 3 days per week, to work on the rest of the plan. This plan felt feasible to her.

For the rest of the session, I suggested that Rianne try Optimal EFT to see if it would work for her. I pointed out that this form of EFT is often faster and deeper than tapping and the generalization effect is usually greater. Rianne had meditated before and understood that Optimal EFT works slightly differently than regular meditation because it involves an intention to resolve the emotional charge of a specific event, just like tapping, and to continue until the charge is neutral. I asked her if she had a 'spiritual' view of life and death. She informed me that she believed in an organizing principle, a connecting, loving energy. She was not religious and did not have a relationship or connection with God. She was happy to use the term Unseen Therapist and with the idea of The Unseen Therapist having a female identity.

We started by applying Optimal EFT to an event that she had worked on but had not completely neutralized:

- The moment when M says, *I do not know if I want to continue in this relationship* and I feel anxious and lonely.

When Rianne relived this moment in an associated way, she reported feeling anxiety at a 7 and loneliness at an 8. When she had previously worked on this moment by herself, they had started at a 9 and 10, respectively, and she had gotten stuck at this level, unable to bring them down. However, after one meditation together with The Unseen Therapist, the intensities dropped to 4 and 6, respectively. I asked her to relive the moment again and then asked her when she had felt this way before. Rianne identified the following:

- The moment when I am 7 years old and my brother L pushes me from the climbing frame in the playground because he does not want me to climb up with him and I feel sad.

We switched to this particular moment and did 3 meditations with The Unseen Therapist to neutralize the emotional charge (which began with sadness at an 8 and shock at a 7). Another moment came up during the last meditation:

- The moment when I see that my parents realize what L is doing but say nothing and I feel intensely lonely.

When she relived the moment, Rianne initially felt upset and lonely at a 9. We applied Optimal EFT to that moment, meditating with The Unseen Therapist. When the intensity dropped to 5, I asked Rianne to relive the moment again and notice whether she is thinking *I am not good enough*. Rianne began to understand that in moments like this, she had come to believe she was not good enough. Thus, her NCB had become more and more true for her. We finished this particular moment and tested it properly to ensure it was completely neutralized. Then we returned to the moment we had started with, in which M said he did not know whether he wanted to continue with the relationship. When Rianne relived that moment, her fear had dropped from 4 to 1 and her loneliness had dropped from 6 to 2. We did one more meditation and managed to bring both emotions down to zero.

Rianne started to understand that when the intensity of an event lingers and plateaus, it is necessary to look for earlier specific events and neutralize those first. I asked her to continue doing homework on a daily basis as we had agreed, applying the WMOMD approach daily and Symptom-Focused EFT for pain and stiffness whenever necessary, and to dig deeper three times a week and work on all parts of the plan of action. We decided to schedule the next session a month later.

Sessions 4 through 8 (every other month)

Rianne continued to meet with me every other month. In between sessions, she used both forms of EFT. She preferred to tap when applying Symptom-Focused EFT and to use Optimal EFT when resolving the emotional charge of specific events. When she experienced something at work that made her feel really stressed, she would go to the bathroom and then tap until she felt calm (talking to herself but not out loud). By applying EFT at work, it had become much clearer to her that her stress was mainly caused by her NCB and she noticed that it had weakened. I pointed out that it would be even more effective if she chose a work-related moment as a WMOMD and applied Optimal EFT to it at home (to address the underlying cause, as opposed to only addressing the feeling of stress at work).

During our sessions together, we discussed what she had worked on herself with EFT since the last session and tested as many specific events as possible to make sure they had been neutralized. Together, we would usually work on two more specific events that she had not yet worked on by herself. In the eighth session, we did an inventory of all her issues and found that:

- The VoC of her NCB (I am not good enough) was reduced to 40-50% (it had felt 90% true in our first session);
- Pain and stiffness in her upper back and neck had dropped to 2 (from 5) and were no longer present every day;
- Pain in her upper legs was gone (initial intensity was 7 in left, 4 in right);

- Pain in her upper arms had reduced (from 7 to 4 in the left, and from 4 to 1 in the right) and was no longer present every day;
- Fatigue had reduced from 8 to 4. There were also days when she did not feel tired at all.

Rianne was pleased with these improvements and had definitely noticed that her NCB was not playing such a prominent role anymore. She was more energetic and felt less tired. She had received feedback from several colleagues that she seemed much more relaxed and a lot less anxious. She had noticed that her supervisor seemed to be less critical, but then smiled and pointed out that it could also be that she no longer felt as triggered and stressed as she used to. Her interaction with M had improved and it no longer bothered her when he was distant and insisted on staying in the car when he picked up their daughters.

She had discovered, by doing EFT on all the specific events of her marriage, what a huge impact they had had on her self-esteem. Of course, she had realized that she was unhappy about it and that the relationship had not gone well, but she completely underestimated the impact of all that stress. She could now clearly see that they had both played a role in the breakdown of their relationship. It felt good not to blame M and no longer see him as the major culprit. She now recognized that he was (and is) responsible for his choices, and she is responsible for hers. She was now much more at peace with the divorce, ready to move on with her life and determined to do her best to get along with M as much as possible for the sake of their children. The coaching training was still going well. She felt inspired and motivated to continue applying EFT on her own because she had not yet finished working on all the events in her Big Cleanup list. She was experiencing 1-2 stressful moments a day, which she addressed with the WMOMD approach. That was a significant improvement (as she previously had 5 or 6 moments), and she was hopeful that it could be even lower.

We decided to finish the counseling at that point. Rianne said she would come back if she needed to. That was two years ago now and I have not heard from her again, which I see as a good sign!

Case 3: Sleeping problems

This is Simon's story, age 57, where he explains how he was able to use EFT to resolve his insomnia, which he had suffered from for over 30 years.

"I suffered from insomnia from the age of 20. Usually, I would fall asleep quickly, but I would wake up a few hours later and not be able to fall asleep again. For years, I tried everything to sleep better, including psychotherapy, hypnotherapy, breathing exercises, neurofeedback, yoga, sports, abstaining from coffee in the evenings and other things, but nothing really helped. What bothered me the most was the deep fatigue I felt during the day. I was not just a little tired, I felt completely dead and exhausted, actually more tired than was warranted given the number of hours of sleep I did get. As a result, I got into bed every night thinking *As long as I am rested by tomorrow, I will be ok.* And the first thing I thought in the morning as I woke up feeling exhausted was *How on earth am I going to get through today, I am dead tired.* The poor sleep, the stress and the fatigue irritated me enormously, especially given that, in my opinion, I led a happy life, had a good relationship with my spouse, good friends and meaningful work. I did have the feeling that it might have something to do with my youth.

"During my childhood, our family did not have much money. I always felt afraid of my father, who would get extremely angry with my mother and us children. Sometimes, he would be violent. There were also many other challenging times, including two sudden moves (at age 11 and again at age 12), an emergency hospitalization with acute appendicitis at age 16, and a rather abrupt departure from home at age 18, without telling my father. A year and a half after this stressful period, I moved to a big city to study. Seven months later, my sleeping problems began.

"When I was 53 years old, I read an article by Gabriëlle Rutten about EFT, ordered the Dutch version of 'EFT From A to Z,' co-authored by Gabriëlle and Henk van der Veen, and started working with it. During the tapping process, to my amazement, five incidents from my early childhood spontaneously came to mind, even from my year at kindergarten. I decided to tap on the feelings surrounding these events because I noticed that I still felt a lot of fear and anger. That same night, I slept better than usual and, more importantly, I woke up feeling more refreshed than usual. Since then, I have been tapping on everything that bothers me and any emotional events that come to mind. I now also use Optimal EFT, the meditative version of EFT. I sleep a lot better, and if I lie awake at night now and cannot get back to sleep, I get up and tap on the tension in my body for fifteen minutes, sometimes longer. Then I get back into bed and usually fall asleep quickly and wake up rested. I am extremely happy with EFT. Not only do I rarely suffer from fatigue, but I no longer feel stressed about sleeping anymore. Whereas I used to feel incredibly angry and powerless when I would lie awake at night again and count the hours I had left to sleep, I now just tap for 15 minutes and then say to myself, *I am going to lie down for a while,* and I do not worry at all anymore about whether I can fall asleep or how long I sleep. In short, thanks to EFT, I have a totally different mindset, and I also feel much better and more balanced during the day."

Appendix 6
GLOSSARY

Amygdalae: Two small almond-shaped nuclei in the midbrain that help us process and regulate our emotions, form and consolidate emotional memories and make decisions. They keep track of all your body sensations (sight, smell, touch, taste, sound) and assign a positive or negative value to stimuli in your environment. They decide whether something poses a danger and, if so, initiate the fight, flight or freeze response.

Association: Being fully present and aware in the moment. Reliving a past experience associatedly means stepping into the moment and fully reliving it by being in the memory, looking through your own eyes and engaging all of your senses, as though it is happening right now, so that you see what you saw, hear what you heard, feel what you felt and so on.

Big Cleanup: Making a list of all emotionally charged memories and resolving them with EFT.

Conflict: An event that you find emotionally stressful that may involve your identity, territory, self-worth, integrity, or other types of issues. See Appendix 2 which lists the various types of conflicts.

Detective Work: Looking for the origin of your stress pattern by asking yourself various questions.

Dissociation: Dissociation is a mental process of disconnecting from your thoughts, feelings, memories, surroundings or sense of identity. When you think about a past event you remain detached from the experience. Rather than imagining yourself in the situation, looking through your own eyes, you observe yourself in the situation from a distance, as though you are watching yourself in a movie. You may still feel emotions or feelings about the situation but you are not fully connected to it.

EFT: Emotional Freedom Techniques, which include both Gold Standard EFT (Tapping) and Optimal EFT.

Gold Standard EFT: EFT Tapping, the form of EFT in which acupressure is used.

Hamer: R. G. Hamer (1935-2017), a German doctor of internal medicine who developed the 'Five Biological Laws of Nature' and discovered the connection between various types of emotional conflicts and physical and mental symptoms (see Appendix 2).

NCB (Negative Core Belief): The main negative conclusion you draw about yourself that starts with I am ... It is a judgment that describes how you feel about yourself when you feel criticized or rejected by others or by your own inner critic. Examples include *I am not good enough, I am worthless, I am not allowed to be here, I am not lovable.* This belief is formed in the first 6-7 years of your life, including the 9 months in the womb before birth.

Optimal EFT: The form of EFT that involves the spiritual dimension, in which you meditate with The Unseen Therapist (your inner healer and guide) to resolve your issues.

Parasympathetic Nervous System: One of the two parts of the autonomic nervous system (the involuntary nervous system governed by our subconscious) that regulates the body's relaxation response. When activated, it facilitates rest, digestion, reproduction, repair and recovery.

Taking the Edge Off: Applying EFT to your emotions about a specific event as a whole, before you start reliving the event and applying EFT to the details of the event. Use this strategy when you suspect that the emotional intensity of a specific event is likely to be high to avoid getting overwhelmed by your emotions. You can repeat this when working through an event with each subsequent crescendo that feels overwhelming, in other words apply EFT to this new crescendo as a whole before reliving it.

Surrogate EFT: Doing EFT for the benefit of another, which does not require the other person to be physically present.

Sympathetic Nervous System: One of the two parts of the autonomic nervous system (the involuntary nervous system governed by our subconscious). When activated, it initiates the fight, flight or freeze response.

Unseen Therapist: The Unseen Therapist is our inner guide or healer. Gary Craig uses the pronoun "she" in reference to her. You are welcome to call this powerful force any name that works for you. For instance, you might use Love, Source, Peace, Higher Power, Intelligence, Guide, Wisdom, Universe or any of the names you have learned from your religious tradition.

VoC (Validity of Cognition) Test: A test to determine how true an idea or belief feels, on a scale of 0% (not feeling true at all) to 100% (feeling completely true).

WMOMD (The Worst Moment of My Day): The moments of your day which give rise to a negative emotional reaction, triggering the stress response.

ABOUT THE AUTHORS

Gary Craig

Father of 3 children and founder of Emotional Freedom Techniques (EFT). He is a Stanford engineering graduate, a Master Practitioner in NLP (Neuro-Linguistic Programming) and an ordained minister. Since the age of 13, he has had a keen interest in personal development, recognizing at that early age that the quality of his thoughts was reflected in the quality of his life. He was self-taught in this field, studying only methods which, in his view, produced real results. After studying with Dr. Roger Callahan (founder of TFT, Thought Field Therapy), he developed the basic EFT protocol (Tapping) in 1995. He released an EFT manual at that time, making it available as a free download on his website. It is estimated that this manual, including 23 translations, has been downloaded over one million times. Over the years, EFT has been continually refined, in collaboration with his daughter Tina Craig. In 2011, this culminated in the Gold Standard EFT Tapping Tutorial, which has been in use since then. Gary further developed a major innovation in the field of EFT which involves the spiritual dimension called Optimal EFT and working with The Unseen Therapist. He has been using and teaching this latest advancement in EFT since 2014. Gary's website is emofree.com.

Gabriëlle Rutten

Worked as a doctor for many years until she discovered EFT over 20 years ago, at which time she started her EFT practice. Gabriëlle uses EFT exclusively to resolve stress-related psychological and physical issues. She is a Gary Craig Certified Official EFT™ Master and has been conducting training in EFT since 2009. In 2016, she was appointed director of one of the Gary Craig Official EFT Training Centers, offering workshops, courses and training in Gold Standard EFT and Optimal EFT for both professional applications and personal (self-help) use. During her medical studies, Gabriëlle was surprised that mainstream medical science focused exclusively on treating symptoms, as opposed to treating the underlying causes of symptoms. After working as an MD for 15 years, she decided there must be a better way to help people solve their problems. This set her on a quest to discover better alternatives. After certifying in EFT, she decided to deregister as an MD so she could dedicate herself to healing clients based on this new paradigm, with an emphasis on resolving the cause as opposed to treating the effects. She uses both Gold Standard EFT and Optimal EFT in her practice. Gabriëlle's websites in Dutch are eftpraktijkactrom.nl and official-eft.nl. Her English page is www.eftpraktijkactrom.nl/home-english/.

ABOUT THE TRANSLATORS

Alison Brock

Alison is a Gary Craig Certified Official EFT™ Master as well as an integrative health coach, a meditation teacher, a yoga teacher and a mother of 3 children. She trained initially in law and worked as an attorney in Australia, Hong Kong and England for over 10 years. Following a cancer diagnosis, she made a lifestyle change to focus her efforts on learning to heal herself. She learned from experience how detrimental the effects of stress can be. Alison is passionate about helping others use EFT to relieve their stress and anxiety and let go of negative thought patterns and beliefs, so they can optimize their health and well-being and avoid (or better deal with) any diagnosis of a seemingly life-threatening illness. She helps her clients identify and resolve the emotional root cause of their physical and emotional issues and teaches them how to use EFT by themselves, empowering them to take their healing into their own hands. Alison's website is alisonbrock.com.

Helle Gylling

Has worked with personal and spiritual growth since 1985 using many different techniques and healing modalities. As a young child, she had a near-death experience that opened her up to many spiritual experiences and she has a deep, personal relationship with Jesus. She discovered EFT in 2006, which later became her full-time work as a Gary Craig Certified Official EFT™ Master. She uses Gold Standard EFT and Optimal EFT to resolve a wide range of emotional issues ranging from childhood abuse, trauma and emotional pain to grief and family conflicts. She has a Master's degree in Geochemistry and worked as an environmental scientist and a translator/editor for a number of years. She is also an Evolutionary Astrologer. Helle is passionate about helping people who carry deep wounding that has never been healed through other techniques and more conventional therapies. Helle's website is PeaceWithEFT.com.

Index

Tables

Figures

Appendices

About the Authors   357

About the Translators   359

Any somewhat important book should be read twice in a row.

Arthur Schopenhauer, German philosopher, 1788 – 1860

Printed in Great Britain
by Amazon

23275278R00215